Man
and
The Animal World

By B. R. WEIMER

Man and the Animal World

By B. R. WEIMER and E. L. CORE

A New Manual for the Biology Laboratory

By P. D. STRAUSBAUGH and B. R. WEIMER

General Biology, *Second Edition*

Elements of Biology

Man
and
The Animal World

BERNAL R. WEIMER, Ph.D.
Professor of Biology, Bethany College

NEW YORK · JOHN WILEY & SONS, INC.

LONDON · CHAPMAN & HALL, LTD.

Second Printing, August, 1953

Preface

This book attempts to treat the organisms of the animal world as dynamic living entities, manifesting in various ways the fundamental life phenomena common to all living animals. The road charted for the student follows the sound pedagogical principle of approaching the unknown from the known. Man is the one living animal that the student knows best; hence the study of man affords a logical approach to the study of those life principles and processes manifested in other animals. The author is of the opinion that there should be a balance between the emphasis placed on the teaching of the principles of zoology and that given to the practical aspects of the animal kingdom. Hence interesting information concerning economic zoology, the ways in which animal organisms influence our health, and aesthetic appreciation are introduced without apology or the slightest hesitation.

An effort is made to acquaint the student with the methods of science. This is attempted somewhat intensively in the first chapter where the attention of the student is directed to the working of scientific investigation and generalization which have led to important biological discoveries. In various strategic places in connection with important biological discoveries the working of scientific investigation and the method of generalization are introduced. Such treatment necessitates the logical inclusion of historical material in the discussion of specific biological processes rather than the mere recital of the names of biologists, facts, and dates in some place remote from the context.

The author has tried to avoid writing down to the student. Most college freshmen have already studied biology in high school, and, keeping this in mind, the writer has attempted to prepare a book that presents not a "re-hash" of the high school course, but, at a more adult level, a more comprehensive study of animals and their life processes. The book is written primarily for undergraduate students and not for contemporary scientific colleagues. There is no assumption that the

v

reader has any particular technical background. Each technical term is defined, and the derivation of the word is given when it is first introduced.

Today there seems to be an aversion to the presentation of facts. Principles are important but can be understood only when they are seen in the full perspective of fundamental facts of structure, physiology, and animal relations. The game cannot be played without knowing the cards. Any understanding of the animal as a dynamic, functioning organism demands some knowledge of the fundamental facts of chemistry and physics, but only such essentials as are adequate for the appreciation and understanding of the living animal.

In any survey of the animal kingdom, the student must acquire some knowledge of animal relationships which serve to demonstrate the universality of life functions even when manifested in many diverse forms. Too often the study of classification involves a long recital of difficult names, wholly foreign to the student and requiring laborious memorization. An attempt has been made to bring life to the rather dead, dry nomenclature of taxonomy by stressing the relation of the groups to man from the standpoint of economics, health, and disease. The natural history of the various animals is introduced within the framework of taxonomy.

The author is especially indebted to Dr. P. D. Strausbaugh and certain "unknown readers" who have read the text critically and have made many helpful suggestions. He is deeply appreciative of the assistance given him by his colleagues Lowell Binkley and Harold Kesselring of Bethany College, and by Philip Hall of Western Reserve University. The author acknowledges with gratitude the encouragement and assistance of Dr. Wilbur H. Cramblet, President of Bethany College, and the trustees of this institution.

The author is indebted to the artists who prepared the illustrations for the two textbooks, *General Biology* and *Elements of Biology,* of which the undersigned was the co-author with Dr. P. D. Strausbaugh. New illustrations have been drawn by Rose Eleanor Bentley, Marjorie Huntsberger Fuller, and Webb Higinbotham, and certain original photographs have been furnished by Dana Garner. Wherever illustrations have been borrowed from other publications, the source has been acknowledged in the legend.

Some teachers feel that as good or better results can be obtained by presenting only one of the life kingdoms as a unit instead of a course in general biology. Such an approach is often made necessary by curricular programs and departmental organization. The author has been urged by a number of college teachers of zoology to undertake the preparation of this book. It is hoped that the outcome of his efforts may not prove disappointing but that the book may serve as a useful tool in our program of higher education.

B. R. WEIMER

Bethany, W. Va.
May, 1951

Contents

Biology and the Scientific Method

We are so accustomed to see around us every day various living things, such as flowers, grass, trees, birds, flies, dogs, cats, and people, that we seldom pause to think about the nature of their existence. What do they do and why? What makes them alive? What is life? If we wish to obtain some understanding of these living things we must study biology (*bios*—life; *logos*—study), the science of life, or the study of all living things, both plants and animals. Biology seeks to give understanding and explanation of those complex and fascinating processes that collectively constitute this peculiar phenomenon called life, which is manifested in ourselves and in every living plant and animal. A living entity, regardless of structure, size, or behavior, is called an **organism**. Organisms exist in a wide variety of forms that inhabit the earth's soil, its waters, and its atmosphere. This broad field of biology is made up of two subdivisions: botany, which is the biology of plants; and zoology, which is the biology or science of animals.

Why study biology? Like the dog, the horse, the bird, and the fly, we too are animals. Since all must live together we need to acquire a better understanding not only of ourselves but also of the other living creatures about us, both animal and plant. We should learn something about the structure of our bodies, the workings of the different parts, and the conditions that may either increase or decrease their efficiency. In other words, we should learn to take better care of ourselves. The person who has the best understanding of his physical machinery should know best how to use it.

Man is a social animal with a tendency more and more to live in groups. New towns and cities are being created, and older communities are growing in size and complexity. Life in communities has created new health problems, such as epidemics which are caused not only by bacteria but often by tiny animals. Bacterial and animal diseases are carried by such animals as rodents and insects. To com-

1

bat these scourges requires certain public-health measures such as health regulations, proper sewage disposal, and a pure water supply. These problems are biological.

Unlike primitive man, we do not depend in these modern days on hunting and fishing, but we cultivate plants and rear animals to supply our needs. To do this requires a better understanding of and more accurate information about other living creatures. Biology furnishes us with information about the requirements of domestic animals, about diseases and methods of controlling them, and about the way to obtain better varieties and larger yields. It also provides knowledge necessary for successful animal husbandry. In this science we learn the fundamental principles of proper utilization and conservation of our natural resources.

The study of the science of biology should afford us some understanding of the method of science. Working through the years, scientists have accumulated a tremendous body of knowledge. The psychologists and neurologists have learned much about the workings of the mind and the influence of emotions. They tell us "how to make friends and influence people." Numerous discoveries of the scientists have been put to good use in improving living conditions, in increasing the food supply, in alleviating suffering, in the better control of disease, in the general betterment of mankind, thus making the world a better place in which to live. The achievements of the scientists have been accomplished by certain procedures that collectively constitute what is called the **scientific method,** and the continued application of this method results in the development of **scientific attitudes.**

THE FIELD OF BIOLOGY

As an introduction to animal biology, we shall look first at the science of biology as a unit, which includes all living forms, both plant and animal. For more intensive and critical studies it is desirable to subdivide this unit into a number of highly specialized areas each of which is concerned with some particular phase of plant and animal life. These subdivisions of biology are now generally recognized as follows:

Animal behavior and animal psychology—The study of adjustments and reactions of the organism as a whole.
Ecology—The study of the environmental relations of organisms.
Embryology—The study of the development of organisms.

Heredity or genetics—The study of the inheritance of organisms.

Morphology—The study of the form and structures of animals and plants.

    Anatomy—The study of gross structures.

    Cytology—The study of cells.

    Histology—The study of tissues.

Paleontology—The study of the fossils of pre-existing plants and animals.

Philosophical biology—The study of the origin of life and living forms (evolution).

Physiology—The study of the working or functioning of organisms.

Taxonomy—The grouping and naming of organisms.

These fields are so integrated and so interrelated that the sum of these parts makes the total of the "pure" science of biology. Other recognized divisions which have grown out of "pure biology" may be considered collectively as "applied biology." Progress in applied biology naturally depends on the advancements made as a result of investigations concerned with the fundamental principles of biology or "pure biology." A list of the fields of "applied biology" may be arranged as follows:

Agriculture.

    Horticulture—Culture of trees, shrubs, and vegetables.

    Agronomy—Culture of such field crops as grains and other grasses, cotton, and legumes.

    Silviculture or forestry.

    Animal husbandry, or the care of animals.

    Applied entomology—The study of insects and their control.

    Fur farming and fish culture.

Homoculture, or the culture of man as an individual.

    Dentistry.

    Medicine.

    Nursing.

    Sanitation and public health.

Sociology—Human group relationships.

    Eugenics and euthenics—Human betterment through inheritance and improvement of the environment.

    National policies—Immigration.

Psychology—Human behavior.

This brief outline indicating the scope of biological study should serve to broaden our perspective and give us a keener appreciation of the many phases of this life science.

BIOLOGY AND OTHER SCIENCES

In the development of the program of formal education, biology has only comparatively recently joined the aristocracy of the sciences comprising mathematics, astronomy, physics, geology, and chemistry. In many respects, the science of biology has been developed by aid of the contributions of the other sciences, and any advancement made in the future must depend on contributions from these same fields. A complete understanding of biological science necessarily involves a knowledge of all the kindred sciences.

Chemistry. No adequate concept of the living organism and the organic world can be formed without some understanding of chemistry. Any attempt to study the functioning (physiology) of a plant or animal, ignoring completely such items as matter, elements, ions, atoms, compounds, synthesis, and decomposition, would be utterly absurd. A knowledge of the nature of the basic substance of life itself, protoplasm, and also of the structure and function of the organism, rests on the foundations of chemistry.

Physics. A knowledge of certain physical processes helps us to understand how food is absorbed and distributed, and how wastes are eliminated. The ultimate source of energy for both animals and plants is explained in the analysis of the sunbeam. The modern theory of nervous conduction involves a knowledge of electricity. No one could possibly attempt to study the eye and vision without having some knowledge of optics and light. It was a physicist, Helmholtz, who explained the basis of hearing and the functioning of the human ear.

Geology. One of the greatest contributions to philosophical biology —in fact to the entire field of philosophy—namely, the theory of evolution, is rooted in and grew from evidence revealed by the rock strata of the earth. On the other hand, it is by the aid of animal and plant remains entombed in the rocks (biology) that the geologist studies widely separated areas of land and shows the extent of the land covered by the waters not of one deluge but of many. He makes assertions quite astonishing to the layman that a present mountain top was once sea bottom and that an old rock quarry, sometime in the past, may have been a treacherous quicksand along a river bank where strange huge beasts came to slake their thirst. Adequate comprehension of animal and plant distribution, a phase of animal and plant ecology, is possible only by the aid of geology.

Astronomy. The earth, a planet and member of the solar system, is a home for living things. This fact naturally invites speculation and theorizing about the origin of the earth and its place in the heavens. The influence of the sun and the changing seasons on the life of animals and plants gives to biology a definite interest in the solar system. We shall also see that the moon has an apparent influence on various physiological rhythms in animals.

Mathematics. The average biologist may give mathematics little credit for the development of his science. Indeed, it is often stated that biology is one science that makes use of little if any mathematics. Nevertheless, it is quite clear that mathematics has played a very significant part in the past, and there can be no doubt that its role in the future development of biology will become increasingly important. The modern theory of heredity was born when Mendel subjected his breeding experiments to mathematical analysis. Not only the student of heredity, but also the physiologist, believes that the hope of the future of biology as a science rests in making quantitative studies of various life phenomena which can be expressed in mathematical formulas and equations. It seems hardly necessary to call attention to the fact that any experiment involving measurements must employ mathematics.

Almost every biological process involves principles and laws developed in one or more of the other sciences. When we eat we are interested in the source of our food, which is manufactured by a green plant in which certain elements in water and carbon dioxide have combined to form sugar and starches (chemistry). The energy for this process as well as the energy trapped in the food had its ultimate source in the sun (astronomy). The process by which foods are digested is dependent on chemical principles. The absorption and transportation of food in our bodies involve the phenomena of osmosis and diffusion (physics). Absorption of the gas, oxygen, and the elimination of the gas, carbon dioxide, in the lungs is a physical process. Whether or not iodized salt may be a necessary requirement in the diet depends on the former presence or absence of glaciers in the specific area in times past (geology). The estimate of the amount of food necessary for the individual involves measurements of the intake, the amount of wastes produced, and the energy requirements of the individual (mathematics). Thus, mathematics and four other sciences are involved in solving the energy needs for the everyday processes of living. If the answer to the riddle of life is ever ascertained, the discovery will be made by biologists who are thoroughly trained not only in biology but also in chemistry, physics, and mathematics.

THE SCIENTIFIC METHOD AND THE SCIENTIFIC ATTITUDE

Sifting the true from the false. Never before in his history has man been subjected to the impact of so many devices designed to influence his thinking and his behavior. Scientific discovery and invention have greatly improved our means of communication by giving us more books, a greater number of magazines and newspapers replete with advertisements, the radio, television, flashing neon signs, the sound film, and the amplifier. Today, man is being subjected to persistent assault by various individuals and organizations trying to "sell him something." Unfortunately, there are in almost every community men who are willing to take advantage of and exploit other men and discoveries for their own pleasure and selfish ends. Extravagant claims are made concerning the superior qualities of certain motor oils, face powders, tooth pastes, hand lotions, cigarettes, and patent medicines. The advertisements of many modern drugstore concoctions claim such marvelous remedial properties that one can readily expect them to cure all ills from colds to cancer. We are urged to stock the pantry with special brands of bread, breakfast foods, and other eatables, specially treated and enriched with certain essential vitamins. Men can be made more handsome and women more attractive by consuming patent hormone tablets. Man is bombarded by the radio, television, magazines, and newspapers, with all types of social and political nostrums. With all this advertising propaganda impinging on them our senses are apt to become fatigued, and we cease to think clearly and to evaluate critically. The problem confronting us then is to acquire a technique for sifting the wheat from the chaff; the true from the false. Suggested aids for the acquiring of this technique are the development of the **scientific attitude** and the use of the **scientific method.**

The scientific method. The quest for knowledge or truth by means of the scientific method consists essentially of several steps. First, the problem which is to be investigated must be clearly thought through and well defined. It is necessary to know just what question is to be answered. It is possible that one may have a good guess as to the correct answer or solution. This may be based solely on a "hunch," inference, or on some actions that have been observed. This proposed tentative solution or explanation is known as a **hypothesis.** For example, it may have been observed that insects or mice confined in an air-tight jar, have smothered. Newspapers may have reported that a child, trapped and confined in a tight closet, has been suffocated. The tentative conclusion (hypothesis) is that air is necessary for animal life. Interest may cease at this point, or it may lead to testing the truth or falsity of the hypothesis by experimentation. Various other animals may be confined so that they are deprived of air, and a group of similar animals, known as **controls,** are subjected to the same conditions with this one difference—they have access to air. The records of the observations may be accumulated in notes called **data.** Numerous experiments may be tried yielding more data, and, after careful analysis and evaluation of all these data, **conclusions** are drawn. If all the results of numerous experiments support the same conclusion, the hypothesis will seem to be confirmed. This apparently correct hypothesis may be subjected to further experimentation and observation, and if the results of this additional testing continue to square with the hypothesis it then becomes a **theory.** Finally, when this theory emerges from subsequent testing, substantiated by all the facts available, it becomes a **law.** The facts supporting theories are widely disseminated so that they are made known to all who may be interested in them. Others may repeat the experiments, and, should additional facts be uncovered that show the theory to be false, it will have to be modified or even abandoned altogether.

The scientific attitude. Not only is the application of the scientific method important in solving problems but it must be accompanied by certain attitudes of mind as well. These attitudes collectively have been designated the **scientific attitude.**

The first of these attitudes is the possession of an inquiring mind, that is, a mind that asks questions and seeks to find the true cause for everything that happens. The scientist insists on having factual evidence to support every conclusion, either tentative or final. He cannot accept hearsay evidence, and he pays absolutely no attention to Dame Rumor. He takes nothing for granted. Tradition has no meaning for him unless it squares with the facts. He must accept the truth arrived at by his method of working even though it is the direct opposite of what he would like to believe. In other words, he must have an open mind. He must be intellectually honest. If all the data concerning a certain process lead to a conclusion contrary to all those previously accepted, he must have the courage to announce his findings and conclusions, although doing so may mean ridicule and even abuse. Thus we see how the scientific mind works and what is meant by the scientific attitude, that is, this certain way of looking at things, and insisting on accurate observation and unmistakable, tangible evidence for the solution of any given problem.

We have attempted to say that the scientific method is the utilization of a certain procedure to discover truth; that all statements must be supported by objective evidence (data) obtained through observation alone or accompanied by experimentation, rather than by argument, appeal to authority, and armchair speculation. Not only must data be accumulated; they must also be analyzed and evaluated by an unprejudiced mind.

Application of the scientific method and the scientific attitude. It would seem that a scientific attitude and the application of the scientific method would go a long way toward solving the problem of

Reproduced by permission. Copr. 1950 The New Yorker Magazine, **Inc.**

"Please pardon the intrusion, Mr. Watson. We're from the R. J. Reynolds Tobacco Company, and we understand you have been complaining of a case of throat irritation due to smoking Camels."

FIG. 1.   The cartoon is a potent weapon against unscientific statements.

arriving at the truth. One example must suffice. Some years ago *The Reader's Digest* * sponsored a series of experiments by a research laboratory to determine the validity of the advertising claims of cigarette manufacturers as to the smoking time and the nicotine and tar content of seven leading brands of cigarettes. "Twenty-four cigarettes of each brand, taken from packages bought in the open market, were 'smoked' in a robot made of glass tubes and flasks, which permitted

* *The Reader's Digest*, Volume 41, 1942, pp. 5–8.

complete collection, for accurate analysis, of the nicotine and tars contained in the smoke of each brand. Other precise data were noted such as the amount of nicotine in the tobacco and the length of time required by the robot to smoke each cigarette down to a butt two centimeters long—slightly over three-quarters of an inch."

The results of the experiment are summarized in the following table.

WHAT THE ROBOT FOUND

Brand (the first five are the so-called "Big Five")	Smoking Time per cigarette		Nicotine in Smoke, average milligrams per cigarette	Tars in Smoke, per cent
	min.	sec.		
Lucky Strike	9	6	2.22	2.19
Camel	10	0	2.20	2.13
Chesterfield	9	6	2.27	2.37
Philip Morris	9	36	2.46	2.24
Old Gold	9	54	2.04	1.98
Avalon	7	54	2.20	2.14
Pall Mall	12	24	3.02	2.23
Average	9	32	2.24	2.18

Note that the differences between the various brands of cigarettes are infinitesimal ("pin point") and quite negligible so that they are practically unnoticed by the smoker. But cigarette advertising copy writers would have little to write about if they ignored "pin point" differences. To woo smokers, most United States cigarette tobacco-men puff up advertising campaigns with testimonials from athletes and movie stars and plug slogans such as "less nicotine," "soothes the nerves," "aids digestion," "relieves fatigue," "never irritates the throat," and "it's important to the T-zone." After six years of hearings and investigations, the Federal Trade Commission labeled such claims false and misleading. For example, said F.T.C., tests made by the Food and Drug Administration had proved that "the only physiological effect cigarette smoking can have upon digestion, if it has any at all, is harmful" (*Time*, 1950). The Federal Government under the provisions of the Pure Food and Drug Act has made real contributions not only to the citizen's health but also to his pocketbook by insisting upon truth in advertising and labeling products.

Programs set up by the American Medical Association and The Pure Food and Drug Acts of the government have served to "debunk" various so-called cures. The medicine or preparation is subjected to scientific laboratory testing and analysis by competent chemists and

FIG. 2.   The government rules on cigarette advertising.   Advertisements from various magazines.   *Courtesy of* Time, *Copyright Time, Inc., 1950.*

physicians.   The manufacturer is then compelled to print the truth concerning his product, as revealed by the experimental tests.

The hope of man and democracy, in fact of civilization, rests upon man's ability to analyze propaganda, to detect sham, and to discriminate between truth and falsehood.   Not only has science contributed much to our comfort and physical welfare, but it has given us the technique of straight thinking as well.

2

Life and Living Things
Protoplasm

As we live in this world of ours we constantly encounter such things as trees, dogs, rocks, water, minerals, birds, and cats. Through the years man has learned that some of them are "alive" and some are not. However, it is doubtful if we have ever in our thinking set up certain standards or criteria which would aid us in distinguishing between the living and the non-living. In biology we study living plants and animals (**organisms**) and attempt to discover what peculiar fundamental structural and functional features mark them off from the non-living or lifeless bodies.

MATTER AND ENERGY

We live in a world of substance (**matter**) and forces (**energy**). Matter is defined as anything that occupies space and has mass and weight. For a long time the material, or matter, involved in the structure of living organisms, as well as their life processes, was called **organic matter** as distinct from the so-called lifeless material or **inorganic matter.** But chemical analysis of living matter which, unfortunately, is killed in the process of analysis, reveals only certain substances found also in inorganic matter. Further, a study of the chemistry of living matter shows no essential difference in the nature of the energy processes involved. It seems necessary, then, if we are to understand the fundamental processes of the living organism, to consider certain elementary concepts of matter and energy.

Atoms and molecules. Matter, organic or inorganic, that is, whether a man, a tree or a rock, is made up of submicroscopic particles called **molecules.** **Molecules** are the smallest particles into which any particular kind of matter can be divided without losing its identity. These molecules are in turn made up of smaller particles called **atoms,** usually two or more of which are always present in definite proportion or fixed numbers for each kind of molecule. Thus

12

a molecule of water has two atoms of a substance called hydrogen and one atom of another substance called oxygen (Fig. 3).

Substances which cannot be decomposed into anything simpler by ordinary chemical means are called **elements.** An element retains

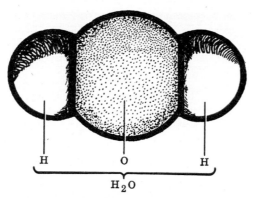

H   O   H

H_2O

Fig. 3. Diagram of molecule of water.

its identity, however finely divided. Over ninety different elements are known to science, but only thirty-four of them are usually found in animals and plants. The elements most commonly found in protoplasm, together with their symbols, are as follows:

Element	Symbol	Element	Symbol
Oxygen	O	Potassium	K
Carbon	C	Iron	Fe
Hydrogen	H	Magnesium	Mg
Nitrogen	N	Calcium	Ca
Phosphorus	P	Sodium	Na
Sulphur	S	Chlorine	Cl

One atom of oxygen would be designated O; two atoms as O_2 or $2O$. If two or more atoms of two or more elements unite in *definite proportion*, a molecule of a substance called a **chemical compound** is formed; e.g., CO_2 (carbon dioxide); H_2O (water). In living organisms the elements just listed usually occur as chemical compounds.

It is possible to prepare from either elements or compounds, or from both, material that is not a compound but a **mixture.** Ordinary concrete is a good example of a mixture, for it is easy to identify the stone, sand, and cement of which it is composed. These materials retain for the most part their original characteristics or properties and may be present in varying proportions. But as water (H_2O), hydrogen and oxygen both lose their own peculiar properties and unite in definite proportion to form a chemical compound that has very different properties (Fig. 3).

Ions and ionization. In the preceding discussion it was pointed out that molecules are the smallest particles of substances, but in

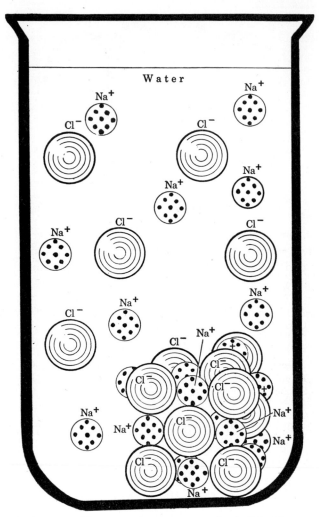

Fɪɢ. 4.   Diagram illustrating the ionization of salt (NaCl) in water.

inorganic material electrically charged particles, smaller than molecules, may be capable of more or less independent motion. Such particles are called **ions** (*ion*-going). They are much more active than molecules. An ion is defined as an atom or group of atoms bearing an electric charge. Some may carry a positive (+) charge, and others a negative (−) charge. When ordinary table salt, NaCl, is dissolved in water the molecule splits or dissociates into the sodium ion which is positively charged (Na^+) and into the chloride ion which is negatively charged (Cl^-)

$$NaCl \rightarrow Na^+ + Cl^-$$
in water

Hydrochloric acid, which occurs in the human stomach during digestion, is composed of hydrogen and chlorine (HCl). When dissolved in water this molecule dissociates into H^+ and Cl^- ions. Inorganic compounds have a much greater tendency to ionize than organic. In fact, very few organic compounds undergo ionization. In addition to hydrochloric acid other acids occur in the life processes not only of men but of other animals as well. Carbonic acid is produced in respiration, and uric acid is produced when certain foods break down.

One characteristic of an acid is a sour taste. When we examine the chemical composition of any acid we find that there is always hydrogen present which appears in solution as H^+ ions. Life is impossible when the body substance of an organism is acid. Maintenance of life depends on the neutralization of acids as they are formed. This neutralization is brought about by substances known as alkalis or bases. A **base** is a compound that on ionization can produce hydroxyl ions (OH^-). When a solution of a base is added to an acid solution in proper proportions the resulting solution is neither acidic or basic but is neutral.

$$HCl + NaOH \rightleftharpoons NaCl + H_2O$$

or to illustrate the ionization

$$H^+ + Cl^- + Na^+ + OH^- \rightarrow Na^+ + Cl^- + H_2O$$
in water

Neutralization of acidic conditions in an organism is necessary for life.

Energy. Matter may exist in three forms or states—solids, liquids, and gases. Since the molecules making up matter are in continuous motion the states or forms of any particular kind of matter depend on the freedom and range of motion of the component molecules (Fig. 5). Thus, the speed and route of a molecule may be changed every time it collides with another molecule. These molecules are traveling in paths restricted by the number of other molecules present in a given space and by their attraction for each other. Thus the molecules of any substance in the gaseous state have longer paths, more space in which to move, and less attraction for each other than molecules of the same matter in the liquid state. Water, for example, may exist as a solid (ice), a liquid, or steam (gas). To change water into steam requires heat, a form of energy. When water, as steam, changes from the gaseous to the liquid state, heat is given off, or, in other words, energy is released. Heat, light, electricity, and movement are all forms of energy.

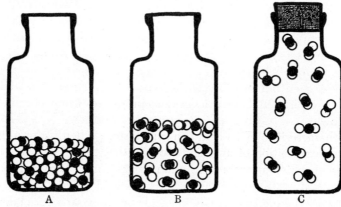

Fig. 5. Diagram illustrating relative position and arrangement of molecules of a substance in the three different states: (A) solid, (B) liquid, and (C) gas.

Every change in the form, composition, and motion of a body of matter involves a transfer or transformation of energy. Thus the power released by heat from coal to make gaseous steam from water to drive a steam locomotive is energy. The power released by the exploding gasoline that drives the automobile is energy. Likewise the swimming of fish, the flight of a butterfly, and the maintenance of heat in the body involve energy changes. Scientists have learned how, by splitting the atom, to release atomic energy, and the magnitude of this force or energy has been demonstrated in the almost incredible destruction wrought by the atomic bomb.

Energy, then, is the capacity for doing work. Energy capable of doing work, such as that stored in coal or gasoline, is called **potential energy.** Energy which is manifesting itself, that is, which is at work, is **kinetic energy.** We shall see that the organism, in order to live, must continually convert potential energy to kinetic energy.

In both the organic and the inorganic bodies chemical compounds are being formed constantly by the union of atoms of different elements, a process known as **synthesis** or building up. At the same time other chemical compounds are being broken down by a process of **decomposition**. The chemist indicates such syntheses and decompositions by a form of shorthand called **equations**. For example:

Synthesis: $\quad\quad 6CO_2 + 6H_2O + Energy \rightarrow C_6H_{12}O_6 + 6O_2$

$\quad\quad\quad\quad\quad\quad$ Carbon $\quad$ Water $\quad\quad\quad\quad\quad\quad$ Glucose $\quad\quad$ Oxygen
$\quad\quad\quad\quad\quad\quad$ dioxide

Decomposition: $\quad\quad C_6H_{12}O_6 + 6O_2 \rightarrow 6CO_2 + 6H_2O + Energy$

$\quad\quad\quad\quad\quad\quad\quad\quad$ Glucose $\quad\quad$ Oxygen $\quad\quad$ Carbon $\quad$ Water
$\quad\quad\quad\quad\quad\quad\quad\quad\quad\quad\quad\quad\quad\quad\quad\quad$ dioxide

Thus all chemical changes involve some form of energy (heat, light, electricity). In synthesis, energy is absorbed. Later this energy may be released by decomposition of the compound.

PROTOPLASM

The basic building material of all living organisms is called **protoplasm** (*protos*—first; *plasma*—form or mold). This peculiar substance was first named in 1840 by Purkinje, who observed it in animals. In 1846, Von Mohl applied the same term to the living substance in plants. Only as we come to know something of the peculiar characteristics and activities of protoplasm as manifested in living plants and animals are we able to catch some glimpses of what life is and what constitutes a living organism.

Protoplasm exists as such only in living organisms, of which it forms the essential material, whether the organism is a microscopic bacterium, a man, a tree, or a whale. Whatever the organisms may be, protoplasm is readily recognized by certain unique attributes or properties; yet it may differ somewhat in the different species of animals or plants. Through the microscope the protoplasm of any particular cell or of different cells may vary in its appearance. When examined ultramicroscopically, protoplasm is found to be full of small suspended particles giving it a homogeneous appearance. When the particles are large enough to be seen by the microscope, protoplasm has a granular appearance; that is, it is made up of rather large liquid particles suspended within a liquid. When specially prepared for microscopic study, protoplasm is killed and coagulated. In its coagulated state it seems to be made up of a network or reticulum, but we must remember that this is now "dead protoplasm."

Physically, protoplasm is a clear, grayish, somewhat transparent liquid with varying degrees of viscosity or ability to flow. The viscosity varies from time to time from a **sol** state where protoplasm is almost as fluid as water to that of a somewhat sticky or jellylike **gel** state. But even in this jellylike state droplets of liquid are present. This characteristic of fluidity of varying degrees as well as certain other peculiarities of structure indicates that protoplasm is a **colloidal** (*kolla*–glue) system.

Colloidal systems are characterized structurally by the presence of innumerable ultramicroscopic particles dispersed or scattered through

Fɪɢ. 6. Illustration showing the difference between the sol state (cream) in which water is the continuous phase containing dispersed droplets of oil, and the gel state (butter) in which oil is the continuous medium containing dispersed water droplets.

a continuous medium. These suspended particles do not settle out. The solid particles and droplets of the different fluids found in protoplasm vary greatly in size. Some substances, like inorganic salts, sugars, and amino acids, in a liquid break up into very small particles which will pass through a filter or a membrane. Such substances are called **crystalloids**, and they form true **solutions**. Proteins, starches, and fats in a solvent break up into much larger particles, forming what are known as colloidal systems. If solid particles are dispersed in a liquid a **suspension** is formed, for example, starch in water. If liquid particles are suspended or dispersed through a liquid an **emulsion** is produced. For example, when oil is shaken up in water an emulsion is formed of small oil droplets dispersed and suspended in the water.

Milk is a good example of an emulsion. Many of the substances found in protoplasm are components of either suspensions or emulsions.

In a colloidal system the substance in which the particles are scattered is called the **dispersion medium** or **continuous phase,** and the scattered particles, whether solids or liquid droplets, form the **dispersed** or **discontinuous phase.** For example, in a cloud in the sky, the air is the continuous phase and the droplets of water (moisture) are the dispersed phase. In cream, water is the continuous phase and droplets of fat the dispersed phase. The phases are reversed in butter, where oil is the continuous phase and water the dispersed phase (Fig. 6). There is also a marked difference in the fluidity of cream and butter.

In protoplasm the continuous medium is a watery solution. In addition to the ultramicroscopic particles of the dispersed phase, pro-

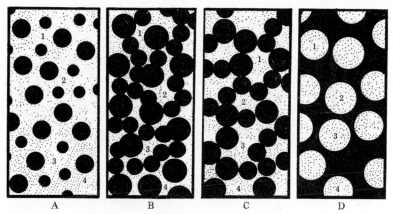

| A | B | C | D |

FIG. 7.   Stages in the formation of a gel.   *A,* a fluid sol consisting of droplets (black) scattered through a dilute solution (stippled).   *B,* the droplets (black) take up water (stippled), enlarge, and come into contact.   *C,* the coalescence of droplets (black) forms a spongelike structure or gel.   *D,* the droplets (black) here form a continuous medium enclosing globules (stippled) of the original (*A*) dispersion medium.   *Adapted from Deming "General Chemistry." By permission of the author and of the publisher, John Wiley & Sons.*

toplasm usually contains visible structures such as crystals, droplets of oil and fats, and bits of various other materials. Collectively these materials are mostly either wastes or stored food.

Thus we see that physically protoplasm is a rather heterogeneous mixture of solids within liquids, liquids within liquids, and liquids within solids. Some of these liquids or droplets are in themselves mixtures or colloidal suspensions. Surrounding these liquid regions, or **phases,** and solid regions (also phases) there are so-called **surface films,** adsorbed on which may be other substances.

The structure of protoplasm varies in different cells and different animals. It likewise varies with the parts of the cell, according to the conditions in and around the cell. Sometimes the entire cell seems to be liquid **(sol)**; at other times it is somewhat gelatinlike **(gel)**. In the living cell the protoplasm may shift from sol to gel and from gel to sol, for the two states are readily reversible.

Protoplasm has been chemically analyzed many times. Some have been inclined to regard it as a "single complex chemical compound," but the modern view is that protoplasm is a complex organization of chemical compounds, proteins, carbohydrates, fats, water, salts, and other materials. Thus it follows that the peculiar properties of protoplasm are determined by the organization of the chemical substances that enter into its composition.

Carbohydrates (*carbo*—coal; *hydor*—water). It is probable that all living protoplasm contains some carbohydrates, familiar examples

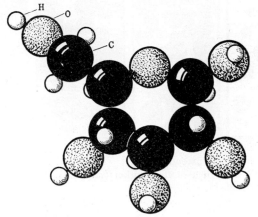

Fɪɢ. 8.   Model of a molecule of a simple carbohydrate, glucose ($C_6H_{12}O_6$). *Redrawn from Amberson and Smith, "Outline of Physiology." By permission of the artist, Norris Jones, and the Williams and Wilkins Co.*

of which are sugars and starches. They are made up of the elements carbon, hydrogen, and oxygen—the hydrogen and oxygen usually in the same proportion as in water (H_2O) (Fig. 8). Carbohydrates most often found in living organisms may be generally classified as:

Monosaccharides (*monos*—single; *saccharon*—sugar)	Ex. $C_6H_{12}O_6$	Examples are grape sugar (glucose); sugar in honey (fructose).
Disaccharides (*di*—two)	Ex. $C_{12}H_{22}O_{11}$	Examples are cane sugar (sucrose); milk sugar (lactose).

Polysaccharides   Ex. $(C_6H_{10}O_5)_n$ These sugars are made up of some multiple of
(*poly*—many) $C_6H_{10}O_5$, which in starch is around 20 or
                                      $(C_6H_{10}O_5)_{20}$. Examples are starches of various
                                      kinds, glycogen, and cellulose.

The monosaccharides and the disaccharides are very soluble in water, but the polysaccharides are relatively insoluble. Disaccharides can readily be changed to monosaccharides by the addition of a molecule of water, a process called **hydrolysis** (*hydor*—water; *lysis*—loosening). Molecules of monosaccharides can be built into (synthesized) disaccharides by the elimination of a molecule of water. Similarly, polysaccharides may be synthesized or hydrolyzed.

Carbohydrates are used mostly as fuel or energy reserves in the organism. The cell walls forming the skeletal framework of plants are composed mainly of carbohydrates. Carbohydrates are stored in plants in the form of various sugars but mostly as the more stable starches and cellulose. In animals they are stored as animal starch or glycogen.

Fats. These compounds contain carbon, hydrogen, and oxygen; but the oxygen is present in much smaller quantities, and the hydro-

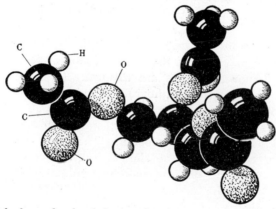

FIG. 9. Model of a molecule of the simplest fat, triacetin ($C_9H_{14}O_6$, *Redrawn from Amberson and Smith, "Outline of Physiology." By permission of the artist, Norris Jones, and the Williams and Wilkins Co.*

gen and oxygen are not present in the same proportion as in carbohydrates, as will be seen from the formula of a typical fat, $C_{51}H_{104}O_9$. **True fats** are familiar to us as butter, lard, tallow, and olive oil (Fig. 9).

When fats are analyzed, they are found to be made up of **glycerol,** commonly called glycerine, and **fatty acids.** In fact, each molecule of a fat is a combination of one molecule of glycerol and three molecules of the same or different fatty acids.

In plants and animals the close relation between carbohydrates and fats seems to indicate that carbohydrates can be transformed into fats. Fats are energy producers, and they are used by animals as a convenient form in which to store reserve energy. By weight fats contain twice as much energy as carbohydrates. The fat deposited under the skin not only serves for effective insulation against heat loss but also affords in man some protection against mechanical injury to more vital mechanisms.

The **compound lipids** are closely related to the true fats. Like the fats, they are insoluble in water. In addition to C, H, and O, some of these compounds called **phospholipids** may contain N and P. A good example of a phospholipid is a substance called **lecithin,** found in practically all living cells. In the eggs of all species of animals it is the major foodstuff used by the developing embryo.

A physiologically important group of lipids is the sterol group. There are a considerable number of sterols, and originally it was thought that they were synthesized by plants alone. It is now known that certain animals, at least, can synthesize cholesterol, the only sterol that can be readily absorbed from the intestinal tract. This sterol is present in large amounts in the brain and nerve tissues of higher animals. It is also the most common constituent of human gallstones. Ergosterol when irradiated with ultraviolet light has the same properties as vitamin D.

Proteins. Proteins are extremely complex chemical compounds whose molecules may contain thousands of atoms. Some rather common and well-known proteins are **albumin** (egg white), **myosin** (lean meat), and **glutenin** (in flour). Proteins are composed chiefly of the elements carbon (C), hydrogen (H), oxygen (O), and nitrogen (N). Sulphur (S) usually is present, and often phosphorus (P). Sometimes other elements may occur. The large complex protein molecules are combinations of simpler organic compounds called **amino acids**—so called because each molecule contains the **amino group** (NH_2) and the **carboxyl group** (**COOH**). The simplest amino acid is glycine, and its molecular structure may be indicated thus:

$$
\begin{array}{c}
H \\
| \\
H\!-\!C\!-\!NH_2 \\
| \\
O\!=\!C\!-\!O\!-\!H
\end{array}
$$

See Fig. 10. As many glucose molecules may be joined to form a starch molecule, so numbers of amino acid molecules may join to form a molecule of protein. It is believed that some protein molecules are formed by the union of a hundred or more amino acid molecules.

Proteins are essential to the structure and life of protoplasm. They constitute the basic material making up all organisms. The biochemist, when he attempts an explanation of life, usually thinks in terms of proteins. Their large molecules and complex chemical make-up enable proteins to react with a large number of other substances. This makes for a complex system of chemical interactions, that is, a series

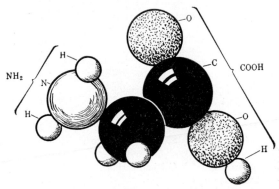

Fig. 10. Model of a molecule of an amino acid, glycine ($C_2H_5NO_2$). *Redrawn from Amberson and Smith, "Outline of Physiology." By permission of the artist, Norris Jones, and the Williams and Wilkins Co.*

of syntheses, decompositions, resyntheses, and further decompositions—in other words, a constant complex series of changes that involve release, transformation, and storage of energy. Proteins have a variety of functions in the living protoplasm. Some, for example hemoglobin, aid in respiration; others furnish energy; still others may form protective structures, such as the outer covering of insects, nails, and horns.

Water. Quantitatively, water is the most abundant constituent of protoplasm, in which it exists not only in the "free state" but also in combination with many chemical compounds, such as carbohydrates. In the free state, water may be present in protoplasm in proportions ranging from 40 to 96 per cent by weight. For example, water constitutes over 65 per cent of adult man and 96 per cent of some jellyfish. The gray matter of the brain of man is 80 per cent water.

Water plays an essential role in many life activities. It dissolves a greater number of substances than any other liquid and thus in large measure assists chemical reactions among the dissolved substances in the protoplasm.   It makes protoplasmic movement possible.   In general, the more water present, the greater the protoplasmic activity. Tissues of young and more active organisms contain more water than those of older organisms.   Water regulates the temperature of the organism and assists in the digestion (hydrolysis) of many compounds. Moreover, the atoms of hydrogen and oxygen, of which water is composed, play a real part in the synthesis and decomposition of the various chemical compounds found in protoplasm.

Salts.   A salt familiar to all of us is ordinary "table salt" or sodium chloride (NaCl).   Some of the more common salts found in animals

Type of Salt	Example	Formula
Chlorides adding Cl	Sodium chloride	$NaCl$
Sulphates adding SO_4	Sodium sulphate	Na_2SO_4
	Potassium sulphate	K_2SO_4
Nitrates adding NO_3	Sodium nitrate	$NaNO_3$
	Potassium nitrate	KNO_3
Phosphates adding PO_4	Sodium phosphate	Na_2HPO_4
Carbonates adding CO_3	Calcium carbonate	$CaCO_3$

and plants are shown in the table.   Other salts could be added to this list, such as nitrates, nitrites, chlorides, and calcium carbonate.

Salts furnish raw material for food synthesis.   Most salts are readily soluble in water.   They enter into the formation of protoplasm and play important roles in the life processes of cells.   Many supporting structures in organisms are made up chiefly of inorganic salts, for example, the phosphates and calcium carbonate found in bone.

DEFINITE ORGANIZATION

By necessity the very earliest biologists were interested in those structures of animals and plants that they could see with the unaided eye.   About 1600, the use of glass lenses for magnification was discovered.   Many scientists became interested in constructing magnifying instruments, particularly spectacles.   Later, crude microscopes were built, and many observations were made of the more minute details of plant and animal anatomy.   Robert Hooke (1665), using his penknife, made some thin sections of cork which he examined with his microscope; he found the cork to be made up of "little boxes or cells distinguished from one another" (Fig. 11).   Hooke's observations were confirmed by others, and through the years there accumulated a mass of observations made microscopically on different plants and animals. As is the method of science, these observations, or data, were critically studied, and about 1840 led to the formulation of a far-reaching generalization or conclusion known as the **cell theory** or **cell doctrine.** The cell theory holds that **all living animals and plants**

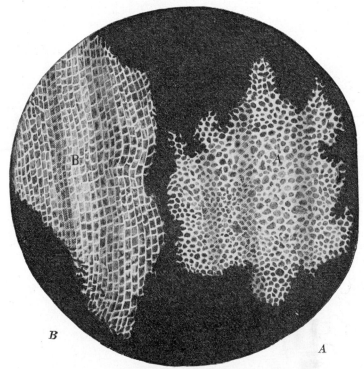

FIG. 11. Cork cells, cross (*A*) and longitudinal section (*B*), as Robert Hooke saw them under his microscope. *Reduced facsimile reproduction from his "Micrographia," published in 1665.*

are either single cells or complexes of cells and cell products, and the life of the organism as a whole is the combined life of its individual cells. Living animals may be composed of both living and non-living material. There is no living matter in a hair except at its root, and very little in bone. Teeth, feathers, finger nails, skin, and the horns of animals contain much lifeless material, all of which is derived from living cells.

The cell. Just as the living animal or plant is an organization of these cellular units, so is the individual cell organized and its protoplasm differentiated. The cell, irrespective of its shape and size, is usually made up of two well-defined parts, a nucleus (*nucleus*—nut or kernel) and the surrounding **cytoplasm** (*cytos*—hollow; *plasma*—something formed) (Fig. 13). Enclosing the cytoplasm is the **cell membrane** which controls to a large extent the movement of ma-

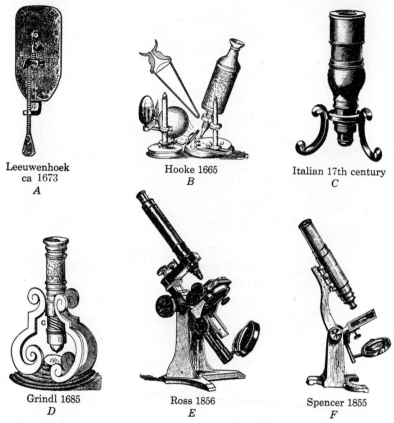

Leeuwenhoek
ca 1673
A

Hooke 1665
B

Italian 17th century
C

Grindl 1685
D

Ross 1856
E

Spencer 1855
F

Fɪɢ. 12.   Early microscopes.   *Photographs furnished by the American Optical Company, Instrument Division, Buffalo, New York.*

terials into and out of the cell.   Cell walls surrounding the cell membrane are very prominent in plants but in animals they may be missing or at best hard to demonstrate.

The great bulk of most cells is made up of the cytoplasm.   Included in the cytoplasm may be stored food in the form of starch, fat droplets, yolk granules, and other material.   Fluid-filled cavities known as **vacuoles** are often present; they play an important part in the metabolic or energy processes of the cells.   Each vacuole is bounded by a protoplasmic membrane which influences the movement of materials into and out of the vacuole.

Near the nucleus, in the cells of most animals there is usually present a somewhat denser area of cytoplasm known as the **centrosome,** which is active in cell division.

Other cytoplasmic bodies that may be present are **chondriosomes** or **mitochondria** in the form of granules, rods, or filaments of various size. Near the nucleus there may be an irregular threadlike network called **Golgi bodies** or **dictyosomes.** The function of these structures is not known.

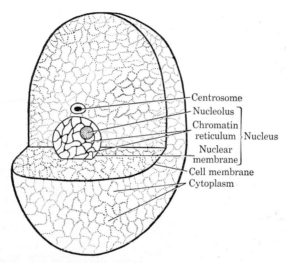

FIG. 13. Schematic drawing of animal cell.

The nucleus is usually a somewhat spherical body having a variable position in the cell (Fig. 13). It is surrounded by a definite **nuclear membrane** of firmer consistency than the surrounding cytoplasm. Enclosed by the nuclear membrane is the **nucleoplasm,** which makes up the ground substance of the nucleus. The most noticeable material in the nucleus is the **chromatin reticulum** (*chromos*—color), which becomes clearly visible when stained with various dyes. Studies seem to indicate that the chromatin reticulum is composed of numerous delicate threads called **chromonemata** (*chromos; nemos*—thread). This chromatin reticulum is vitally concerned in heredity. Often one or more definite bodies of unknown function called **nucleoli** are present.

The nucleus governs and regulates the activities of the cell. The nucleus and the cytoplasm are mutually dependent. Cytoplasm cannot long exist without the nucleus, and the cell dies if the cytoplasm is paralyzed even though the nucleus is unimpaired. Apparently mutual interchange of materials must take place between these two parts of the cell if the cell is to carry on its normal functions.

Size and shape of cells. As shown in Fig. 14 cells vary greatly in shape, depending on their position and function in the organism.

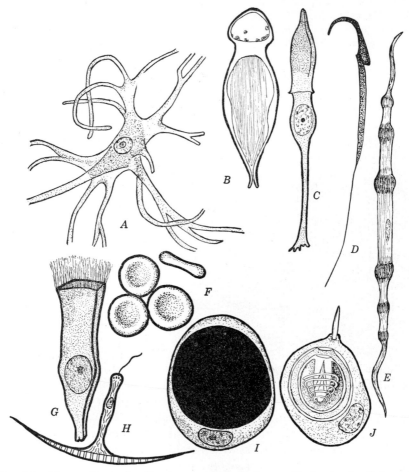

FIG. 14. Types of animal cells: *A*, nerve cell; *B*, flame cell; *C*, visual cell (cone) from human eye; *D*, spermatozoon of a rat; *E*, smooth muscle cell; *F*, red blood cells (corpuscles); *G*, ciliated epithelial cell; *H*, epitheliomuscular cell; *I*, fat cell; *J*, sting cell (nematocyst).

They may be cubelike, columnar, spherical, branched—in fact, the number of shapes is too great to be listed here. Just as the biologist's concept of cell form has changed since the time of Hooke, so has interest shifted from the shape of the container to the substance contained, that is, to the protoplasm itself. The contained protoplasm is now designated the **protoplast** (*protos*—first; *plastos*—something formed), and these protoplasts make up the structural units of the organism. Thus the term "cell" is now used to designate the protoplast with its confining membrane instead of an empty chamber enclosed by the wall.

Cells vary not only in shape but also in size. Some cells are so small as to be almost invisible through the microscope. The largest living cell known at the present time is the ostrich egg, whose yolk is really the cell proper. Nerve cells, such as those in the lumbar region of the spinal cord, which are invisible to the naked eye, may have processes extending from the small of the back to the toes and may thus attain a length of several feet. However, most cells are microscopic.

For a number of years certain experimental evidence indicated that there were living units called viruses and bacteriophages, whose presence was known only by their reactions. Today, by the aid of the electron microscope (Fig. 15), these formerly invisible units have been made visible, furnishing additional evidence in support of the earlier conclusions. There is a difference of opinion among biochemists as to whether the unit particles of viruses and bacteriophages are elementary living units or merely enormous protein molecules with certain properties peculiar to living cells. Some viruses are smaller than protein molecules, and others are larger than certain bacteria.

In animals, viruses cause certain specific diseases, such as measles, common cold, whooping cough, and influenza.

The cell is not only a structural unit comparable to the separate bricks in a brick building, but also a functional or working unit. Thus, what an animal or plant is or does is what "its cells are or do." All life activities are cell activities, and it is only as we gain more knowledge of biology that the full significance of the cell theory is realized.

Just as we have seen that protoplasm is organized into units called cells, so we find that groups of similar cells which perform some particular function are organized into **tissues.** These tissues in turn may be grouped and organized to form an **organ,** such as the heart of an animal or the leaf of a plant. Organs may be grouped and closely interrelated because of some special function to form a **system,** such as the digestive system of man with such organs as the stomach, liver, and pancreas. Finally, in most of the multicellular (many-celled) plants and animals these systems together with certain other tissue combinations may constitute an organism, a living entity such as a plant and an animal. In unicellular (one-celled) plants and animals, we find no tissues or organs such as have just been described. How-

FIG. 15. An electron microscope. *Photograph furnished by the Radio Corporation of America.*

ever, there are differentiations and specializations of the constituent protoplasm by which certain essential life functions are carried out.

Organismal theory. Some biologists have maintained that the cell is not the fundamental unit of structure and function but rather the unit is the organism as a whole. According to this interpretation the organism is more than a mere aggregation of individual cells. Each plant and animal is regarded as a more or less continuous mass of protoplasm within which cells are formed as centers of differentiation. The scientists who advance this view regard it as a more logical basis for the explanation of development, differentiation, and correlation. In all such activities the coordination among the cells and tissues is brought about by the organism functioning as a unit, just as, in the game of football, the team is the unit rather than any one of the individual players. Because of this emphasis on the organism as a whole, the theory has been called the **organismal theory.** When first proposed the idea encountered general skepticism, but it has been more and more favorably received by an increasing number of biologists. Perhaps we may ultimately discover that the cell theory and the organismal theory merely emphasize two different aspects of living organisms. We may think of the cell theory as an interpretation of the plan of structure and the organismal theory as an explanation of the correlation and coordination of the individual cells. The two views incorporated in one biological theory may help us to understand more fully the nature of the organism.

METABOLISM

It is common knowledge that one must eat in order to live and grow. Living, as we think of it, involves a constant outgo of energy in the form of heat and mechanical movement. This flow of energy is maintained by the intake and assimilation of food. If we think but a moment we realize that food is imperative not only for man but for all living animals and plants, since all are composed of that basic substance, protoplasm. Now when we extend this idea of energy release to all animals we find that, in addition to the energy expended as heat and motion, energy may be released in the form of light (fireflies) and electricity (certain fishes, such as the electric ray).

In this release of energy living protoplasm is consuming its own material, particularly the carbohydrates and fats, by burning them or, scientifically speaking, by **oxidation.** The burning of coal and wood is an oxidative process, but oxidation in organisms goes on at much lower temperatures. Oxidation in the living organism is known as **respiration**(*re*—again; *spirare*—to breathe). It usually involves the intake of free oxygen into the cell where cell contents are oxidized to release energy, with the consequent formation of carbon dioxide (CO_2) and water (H_2O) as waste products. Some types of organisms may live in the absence of oxygen; in fact, free oxygen is toxic for certain forms of bacteria. Respiration is constantly taking place in all organisms. Its cessation means death, and thus it is *one constant invariable characteristic of living matter.* Oxidation of carbohydrates and fats may be summarized by the following equations:

Carbohydrate: $C_6H_{12}O_6 + 6O_2 \rightarrow 6CO_2 + 6H_2O + Energy$

Fat: $C_{57}H_{104}O_6 + 80O_2 \rightarrow 57CO_2 + 52H_2O + Energy$

This oxidation of carbohydrates and fats, which we have just called respiration, is not the only decomposition process going on in the cell. Proteins likewise may be broken down to furnish energy. All protoplasm may be broken down into simpler substances much less rich in energy, which are finally given off or eliminated from the organism, as carbon dioxide, water, urea, and various salts.   This complete breaking-down process is called **catabolism;** in it we see the organic material of the cell broken down and changed back to inorganic material.

As pointed out above, the organism is constantly receiving fresh supplies of material, which it distributes to its cells where it is worked over and synthesized into new proteins, fats, and carbohydrates.   In fact, new protoplasm is being built to replace that lost in catabolism. This building-up phase of metabolism is known as **anabolism.**

If the organism is to continue to live, that is, if life is to remain in the protoplasm, both processes must go on, anabolism building protoplasm and furnishing potential energy, and catabolism transforming the potential energy to kinetic.   If anabolism exceeds catabolism, as so often happens in young animals and plants, material accumulates in the cell and growth takes place.   In old age catabolism exceeds anabolism, and eventually and inevitably death ensues.   In this life process (metabolism) we see the inorganic material being synthesized into organic and new material constantly replacing the old, which is thrown back to the inorganic world.   But through all these material and energy changes the organism retains its peculiar individuality, whether it be a camel or a stalk of corn.   This is life. The various aspects of metabolism will be discussed in more detail in subsequent chapters.

GROWTH

Another characteristic of living protoplasm is its ability to grow. As has been pointed out, when anabolism exceeds catabolism, i.e., when synthesis exceeds decomposition, material accumulates within the cell, and additional living protoplasm is built up from inorganic or non-living material.   In marked contrast is the method of growth of such inorganic things as crystals, snowballs, or icicles, where new material is added to the outside.

Now there are limits to the size that an individual cell can attain. If anabolism continues to exceed catabolism, the cell may divide to form two daughter cells, each with the same characteristics as the original cell.   These in turn may grow and divide.   Thus, a many-celled organism grows not only by the increase in size of its individual cells but also by the increase in number of cells by **cell division** or cell multiplication.   Growth of the organism may continue by a combination of these two processes until a certain size limit is reached, when the organism stops growing.

REPRODUCTION

If life is not to perish from the earth, all living things must give rise to others of their kind before they die. Thus all animals have the power to produce new individuals closely resembling the parents. This is called reproduction—a process which takes place sometime in the life cycle of the organism or at some period between its birth or generation and its death. There are two general types of reproduction: **asexual reproduction,** which is a relatively simple process, and **sexual reproduction.**

In asexual reproduction new animals may arise by fragmentation of the parental body. The two following examples will serve to illustrate asexual reproduction. In **fission,** the parent divides into two new individuals and loses its identity. This process is characteristic of the lowest and simplest animals (Figs. 91 and 140). **Budding** is found also in animals. In budding, the parent retains its individuality, and the offspring, taking control of a portion of the parent protoplasm, separates from the parent (Figs. 91 and 148).

In sexual reproduction the organism forms specialized cells called **sex cells** or **gametes** (*gamein*—to marry). These gametes are usually dissimilar in size, the female gamete or **egg** being much larger than the microscopic male gamete or **spermatozoon.** The union of a male and a female gamete forms a new cell, the **zygote** (*zygotes*—yoked), which is the first stage in the life cycle of a new individual.

SENSITIVITY

Another characteristic of living protoplasm is its peculiar inherent capacity to receive and respond to stimuli. A **stimulus** is any change, in the external or internal environment of the organism, which evokes a response. Now it has already been pointed out that the process of metabolism must go on in protoplasm or death will result. This means then that in order to live the organism must have an environment which affords an adequate supply of food and water as well as certain other favorable conditions such as temperature, humidity, light, water currents, chemicals such as gases, and other excitants. Protoplasm, if sensitive or responsive, is evidently so affected by stimuli that temporary adjustments are made from time to time by either the whole or a part of the organism. Such adjustments or **responses** may result in movement from an unsuitable environment to one more favorable. Thus, if there is lack of oxygen in a certain pool, an aquatic animal may move to some other part of the stream. The response just described is movement. Other stimuli, such as the sight or the taste of food, may result in secretion by certain glands.

Thus the property of sensitivity makes possible the adaptation or adjustment of the organism to its environment. Such changes are quite often advantageous and may result in new modifications in structure and behavior. When such adaptive changes can no longer be made because of a decrease in sensitivity or responsiveness, the result is death for the organism.

MOVEMENT OR MOTILITY

We cannot close the general discussion of the characteristics of protoplasm without pointing out that spontaneous movement of the protoplasm is characteristic of plants and animals. Children and primitive men believed that all moving objects were alive. In fact, we adults are somewhat inclined to the same notion. However, we have learned that the flight of a baseball is the result of contact with a baseball bat or of certain movements of the arm. Thus, the movement of the ball is the result of **extrinsic** forces and the movement of the arm is **intrinsic** or spontaneous—inherent within itself.

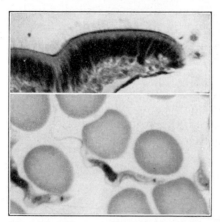

FIG. 16. *Upper,* cilia and, *lower,* flagella. *Photomicrographs furnished by the General Biological Supply House.*

There is protoplasmic movement within the cell which undoubtedly assists in the distribution of food and the elimination of wastes. This intracellular movement of protoplasm is called **cyclosis.** In some of the lower animals we find specialized protoplasmic hairlike structures called **cilia** and **flagella** by which the organism is propelled and drawn through the water (Fig. 16). These structures also occur on the sex cells of certain animals. Rhythmic movements of the cilia on the cells lining the windpipe maintain the flow of mucus over the walls toward the outside. The lowly ameba moves by means of **pseudopodia,** which are outpushings of protoplasm. The white blood corpuscles progress through the body by similar **ameboid motion.**

In the higher animals we find this inherent property of protoplasm (spontaneous movement) more pronounced with consequent greater specialization. Accordingly, here are well-developed structures like legs, wings, and fins with such supporting structures as bones and cartilages moved by the contraction of certain specialized cells known as **muscles.**

This capacity for movement is an essential adaptive mechanism in all animals, and its inception is explained by the characteristic intrinsic motility of all protoplasm.

3

Metabolism
The Animal Digestive Machine

Foods cannot be utilized by living organisms until they are converted from insoluble into soluble substances. Every living animal cell must receive new replacements for materials consumed in the process of metabolism. Food—carbohydrates, fats, and proteins—whether animal or vegetable material, must be broken down, absorbed, and transported to the various parts of the animal where it is resynthesized or assimilated into other compounds making up the animal structure. The transformation of food from an insoluble to a soluble form, and from a non-diffusible to a diffusible condition, is known as **digestion.**

The alimentary tract. In all the higher animals the process of digestion takes place in the **alimentary canal** (*alimentum*—nourishment) which, with its various regions and associated digestive organs, is practically the same in all backboned animals (vertebrates). In some of the higher non-backboned forms (invertebrates), such as the crayfish and earthworm, the alimentary canal has somewhat the same general regions. We shall now study the alimentary canal and associated digestive organs of man, a backboned animal; later we shall compare the structures and functions of the digestive organs of various animals.

In the alimentary canal the food is acted upon by secretions derived not only from the canal itself but also from the associated glands or organs. The process of digestion is also facilitated by mechanical movements of the wall of the canal.

The body of all higher animals is essentially a double-walled tube. The outer tube is the outer body wall with which we are familiar, and running through this is an inner tube, the alimentary canal. Between the alimentary canal and the body wall is a space called the **coelom** or **body cavity,** in which are found most of the digestive organs of the body. These organs and the alimentary canal are anchored to the

36

outer body wall and suspended by sheets of tough tissue called **mesenteries.**

The entrance to the alimentary canal is the **mouth,** which opens into the **buccal cavity** (*bucca*—cheek), bounded by the **upper** and **lower jaws.** Normally in both the upper and lower jaws of man there are **teeth,** differentiated into **incisors, canines, bicuspids,** and **molars** (Fig. 17). In many species of vertebrate animals, all the teeth have the same pattern. A tooth consists of the **crown,** the portion exposed above the gum, and the **root** embedded in the jaw bone (Fig. 18). The crown is covered with resistant **enamel.**

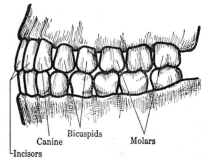

FIG. 17. Human teeth.

Under the enamel is the **dentine,** containing the central **pulp cavity,** in which are blood vessels, nerves, and connective tissue (Fig. 18). Opening by ducts into the buccal cavity are the salivary glands (Fig. 19) whose secretions assist in the digestion of foods.

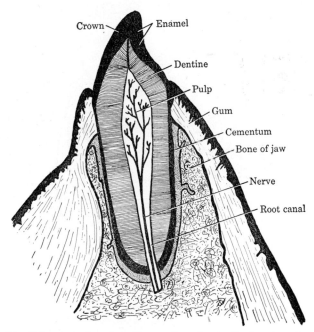

FIG. 18. Schematic drawing of a section of a tooth showing structure.

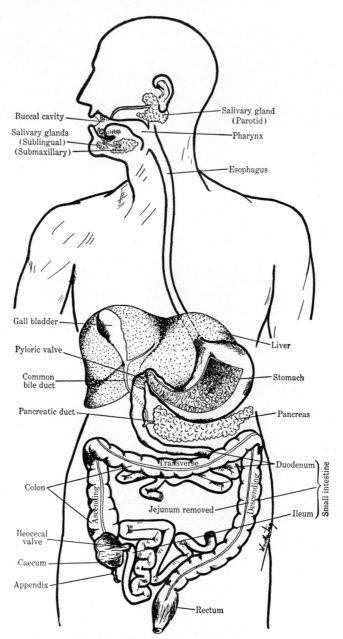

Buccal cavity

Salivary glands
(Sublingual)
(Submaxillary)

Salivary gland
(Parotid)

Pharynx

Esophagus

Gall bladder

Pyloric valve

Common
bile duct

Pancreatic duct

Liver

Stomach

Pancreas

Transverse

Colon

Ascending

Ileocecal
valve

Caecum

Appendix

Duodenum

Jejunum removed

Descending

Small intestine

Ileum

Rectum

FIG. 19. The alimentary tract of man.

The most important paired salivary glands are the **parotids,** located below and in front of the ears. These glands become painfully inflamed in mumps. The

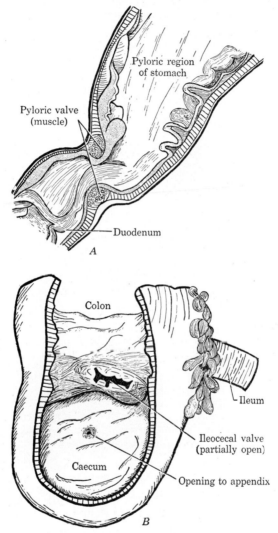

FIG. 20. Pyloric and ileocecal valves.

submaxillary glands lie between the posterior halves of the lower jaw bone; and the **sublingual glands** lie beneath the floor of the mouth between the back of the tongue and the lower jaw.

The buccal cavity merges imperceptibly into the **pharynx** or throat, from which extends a more or less elongated tube, the **esophagus,** leading into an enlarged saclike **stomach.** From the stomach the alimentary canal continues as the much-coiled **small intestine.** Opening into the small intestine by ducts are two large digestive glands, the **pancreas** and the **liver** (Fig. 19). The pancreas is a somewhat elongated, strap-shaped organ lying close to the stomach along the duodenum and secreting the **pancreatic juice,** which is carried to the duodenum by the **pancreatic duct.** The portion of the pancreas secreting the pancreatic juice is a compound alveolar gland. The liver, the largest gland in the body, is a reddish-brown lobed organ located somewhat to the right in the upper part of the abdominal cavity. Bile, the secretion of the liver, is stored in the pear-shaped **gall bladder,** whence it passes through the **common bile duct** to the duodenum at the point where it receives the pancreatic duct. In addition to the secretion of bile, the liver has other functions.

The small intestine leads into the **large intestine** or **colon,** the lowest region of which, the **rectum,** opens to the outside through the **anus.** The opening of the stomach into the small intestine is controlled by the **pyloric valve** (*pyloros*—gatekeeper), which is a ring of specialized muscle (Figs. 19 and 20). The entrance of the small intestine into the colon is regulated by the **ileocecal valve,** similar in structure to the pyloric valve.

At the junction of the small intestine with the large intestine there is a small blind sac called the **caecum** (*caecus*—blind). Extending from the end of the caecum, in man, is a small fingerlike, hollow outgrowth, the **vermiform appendix** (Fig. 20). An infection of this appendage together with the resultant inflammation is **appendicitis.**

Starting anteriorly, the small intestine is divided into three general regions: the **duodenum,** the **jejunum,** and the **ileum.** The colon likewise has three main regions named from their relative positions: the **ascending, transverse,** and **descending colon** (Fig. 19).

Tissues. A group of similar cells coordinated in the performance of some definite function is known as a **tissue.** Tissues are organized into certain structural units which have definite functions to perform. These units are called **organs.** There are four principal groups of animal tissues: **epithelium; connective** or **supporting; contractile** or **muscular;** and **nervous** (Fig. 21).

Epithelium (*epi*—upon; *thele*—nipple). Epithelial tissue covers or lines parts of the body. It may function to protect surfaces, to form the secreting parts of glands, or to aid in absorption. Some epithelial tissues are sensory and others are reproductive in function.

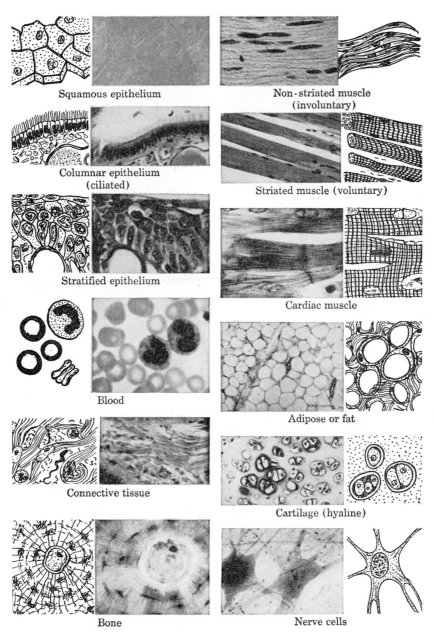

Squamous epithelium

Non-striated muscle
(involuntary)

Columnar epithelium
(ciliated)

Striated muscle (voluntary)

Stratified epithelium

Cardiac muscle

Blood

Adipose or fat

Connective tissue

Cartilage (hyaline)

Bone

Nerve cells

FIG. 21. Types of animal tissues. *Photomicrographs furnished by the General
Biological Supply House.*

Various types of epithelial tissue are recognized and classified according to the structure, shape, and arrangement of the cells (Fig. 21).

Squamous epithelium is made up of flattened, tilelike cells, as may be seen in the covering of the intestine.

Cuboidal epithelium, made up of cells that are of equal dimensions, lines the ducts of glands.

Columnar epithelium is composed of cells whose height exceeds the width. An example is the mucosa or digestive epithelium of the intestine.

Ciliated epithelium is made up of cells which may have fine hairlike structures called **cilia** on the free surface. Columnar cells bearing cilia form **ciliated columnar epithelium,** as the lining of the trachea or windpipe.

Stratified epithelium occurs when a surface is covered with an epithelium several cell layers thick. The outer cells, which are hardened (cornified), are constantly worn away to be replaced by others from a deeper layer. Stratified epithelium is found on surfaces constantly exposed to abrasive action, such as the skin of the body and the inside of the cheek.

Connective or Supporting Tissue. Supporting tissues serve somewhat as a framework to support and bind together various parts of the animal body. Sometimes they are used for food storage (fat cells) and sometimes for transportation (blood and lymph). Sometimes, as in cartilage and bone, the support afforded by these tissues does not depend on the cells proper but on intercellular materials formed on the surfaces of and between the cells. The commoner types (Fig. 21) of supporting tissues are:

Connective tissue proper, of various types, is used to bind other tissues together to form structures and organs. This tissue is pliable and often occurs in sheets called mesenteries, or forms cords or **ligaments.** Toughness of meat is due to an abundance of connective tissue.

Cartilage is somewhat less elastic and of firmer consistency than connective tissue. It is much less rigid but more elastic than bone. The support of the outer ear is cartilage, as is also the voice box or larynx, familiarly known as "Adam's apple."

Bone is the most rigid, non-elastic supporting tissue. The bulk of the bone is made up of the secretion of the bone-forming cells (**osteoblasts).** The solid portion is intercellular and is laid down in sheets called **lamellae** (*lamella*—small plate). The bone is covered with a membrane called the **periosteum** (*peri*— around; *osteum*—bone) which can form new bone after an injury.

Adipose or *fat tissue* is made up of cells which are almost entirely filled with oily fat. The nucleus and cytoplasm are crowded to the side of the cell, which causes it to resemble a signet ring.

Blood and *lymph* are commonly regarded as connective tissue having a liquid intercellular matrix which is not produced by the blood cells found floating in the fluid.

Muscular or Contractile Tissue. Muscle tissue is made up of elongated cells in the form of **fibers** specialized for contractility (Fig. 21).

This power of contraction is due to a special substance organized into **myofibrils** (*mys*—muscle; *fibrilla*—a small fiber) which are found inside the cell and, grouped together, form a muscle fiber surrounded by an elastic membrane, the **sarcolemma** (*sarx*—flesh; *lemma*—skin). These fibers in turn are bound together by connective tissues to form the muscle, which is surrounded by a tough sheath of connective tissue. This tissue may continue as a **tendon** by which the muscle is attached to the bone. There are three types of muscle.

Striated or *voluntary muscle* is distinguished by the presence of alternating light and dark stripes across the fibers. Striated muscle is usually found where rapid motion is required. Most muscles under control of the will are of this type, but there are some exceptions which will be pointed out later. The huge muscles that move the limbs are striated muscles.

Non-striated or *smooth muscle* is a primitive type of muscle in which there are no cross striations. Smooth muscle, often called **involuntary muscle,** is found most often in the internal organs, such as those of the digestive tract, whose movements are automatic and not under control of the will (Fig. 21). Smooth muscle is quite common in the lower animals.

Cardiac muscle is a special kind of muscle found in the heart of backboned animals. Although this muscle is involuntary in function, it has striations characteristic of voluntary muscles. The fibers branch and unite with fibers from adjoining cells. The cells of this tissue, not separated by cross walls, form a mass of protoplasm containing many nuclei. Such a tissue is a **syncytium.**

Nervous Tissue. Nervous tissue is made up of specialized cells called **neurons.** The function of this tissue is to receive and transmit impulses from one part of an animal to another. Neurons may be grouped into masses called **ganglia,** from which may extend **nerve fibers** grouped within a common sheath to form a **nerve** (Fig. 21).

Glands. Single cells or groups of cells which are specialized for the synthesis and secretion of particular substances are known as **glands.** The secreting tissue of a gland is an epithelium. There are various types of glands (Fig. 22).

Unicellular Glands occur as scattered cells concerned in secretion. Such cells or glands are found in the digestive epithelium of the intestine and in the outer epithelium of the earthworm. Sometimes these gland cells may enlarge and push down from the epithelial layer into the underlying connective tissue.

Simple Tubular Glands occur when localized regions of the epithelial layer become infolded or invaginated, forming tubular structures lined with secretory epithelial cells. The cavity of the gland is called the **lumen,** and the tube leading from the gland proper to the place where it empties on the surface is known as the **neck** or **duct.** A good example of a simple tubular gland which is coiled in its deepest portion is the sweat gland of the skin (Fig. 22).

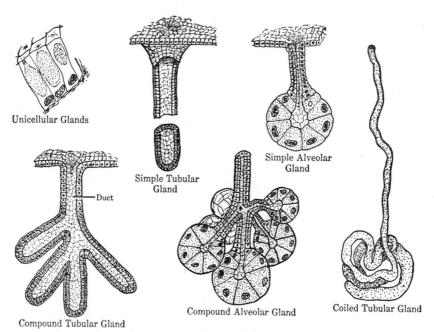

Unicellular Glands

Duct

Simple Tubular Gland

Simple Alveolar Gland

Compound Tubular Gland

Compound Alveolar Gland

Coiled Tubular Gland

FIG. 22. Types of glands.

Simple Alveolar Glands may have the same origin as the simple tubular glands, but they are flask shaped or bulblike. Glands of this type are found in the frog's skin (Fig. 22).

Compound Tubular Glands are branched tubular glands which have a common duct that drains many branched tubes. The liver is a good example of a gland of this type.

Compound Alveolar Glands consist of a number of sacs whose ducts join and empty by a common duct. The structure of a gland of this type has often been compared to that of a bunch of grapes. Each grape represents an alveolus; the stem of the grape is the duct draining the alveolus; and the main stem of the bunch, where it is attached to the vine, corresponds to the duct of the gland. The pancreas and salivary glands are good examples of compound alveolar glands (Fig. 22).

Microscopical anatomy of the intestine. A study of the microscopical structure of the intestine of a vertebrate animal will serve to illustrate how various tissues are combined and correlated to form an organ. We find the intestinal cavity lined with a layer of cells known as the **mucosa** or **digestive epithelium,** under which is the **submucosa** (*sub*—under; *mucosa*) made up of connective tissue (Plate I). In the submucosa are delicate blood vessels. Under the submucosa, that is, toward the outside or periphery of the intestine, is found a layer of **circular muscles** whose fibers encircle the intestine, and outside these is a layer of **longitudinal muscles** whose fibers run lengthwise of the intestine. Covering the outside of the intestine is a layer of flattened cells (squamous epithelium) called **visceral peritoneum.**

It is interesting to note that the muscular arrangement just described is the same as that found in most tubular organs in the animal kingdom—circular muscles which contract to decrease the diameter of the cavity or lumen of the vessel, thereby elongating the vessel, and longitudinal muscles which contract to shorten the vessel and enlarge the diameter of the lumen. In the alimentary canal, the alternating contractions and relaxations of the muscle fibers in these two layers are responsible for the propulsive wave or series of waves known as **peristalsis** (*peri*—around; *stellein*—to place) which traverse the intestine and propel the food through the canal. This longitudinal-circular muscular arrangement is responsible to some extent for locomotion in the common earthworm, for the pumping action of the insect heart, and for the action of other tubular mechanisms found in the higher groups of animals. In general, also, if the organ or structure has a cavity, some type of epithelium will be found lining it.

THE DIGESTIVE SYSTEMS OF SOME OTHER ANIMALS

The digestive systems of other backboned animals are essentially the same as man's, though variations are encountered (Plate II). In fishes there are passages known as **gill slits** leading from the pharynx to the exterior. The esophagus is much shortened, as would be expected in the absence of a neck. Frogs and their relatives have a short esophagus; also, the rectum, instead of opening to the exterior through the anus, discharges into a structure which receives not only the intestinal wastes but also the wastes of the kidneys, and the gametes from the genital organs (ovaries and testes) as well. Such a structure is known as a **cloaca** (*cloaca*—sewer). The cloaca opens to the exterior through the **cloacal aperture.** It is present in certain fishes, reptiles, and birds.

In some birds the esophagus at its lower end is dilated to form a saccular **crop** used for food storage. The stomach is modified into a glandular region and a lower muscular-walled grinding organ, the **gizzard.** Two elongated **caeca** (blind sacs) lead from the intestine (Plate II).

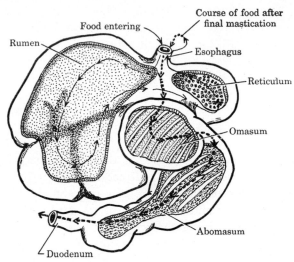

FIG. 23. Stomach of a ruminant or cud-chewing animal (cow). Course of food through the stomach is shown by arrows and dotted line.

Cud-chewing animals, like cows, have what is commonly called a four-chambered stomach (Fig. 23). However, the first three of these are really modifications of the esophagus, and the other is the true stomach. The first chamber of this so-called stomach is the **rumen** or **paunch.** Here the food is stored as it is eaten and then is gradually passed on to the **reticulum,** the second chamber, where it is softened by further mixture with digestive fluids. Later small rounded masses of this food are passed back up to the mouth, where, as the cud, it is thoroughly chewed and mixed with saliva. It is then passed to the third compartment, the **omasum,** and then into the **abomasum,** where characteristic gastric digestion takes place.

The digestive glands of the various vertebrate animals are similar except for the salivary glands, which may vary in number or be missing. The student should study Plate II carefully and compare the digestive tracts of certain backboned animals. In the lower animals there is a wider range in the variations of the machinery of digestion.

4

Metabolism
The Digestion and
Absorption of Foods
Enzymes

It has been pointed out that foods cannot be utilized by living organisms until they are converted into soluble substances. If foods cannot diffuse readily through protoplasmic membranes, their movement from one place to another will be greatly retarded or entirely prohibited. They will be ready for use, if at all, chiefly in the cell where they chance to be. The transformation of food from an insoluble to a soluble form, and from a non-diffusible to a diffusible condition, is known as **digestion.** The chemical changes involved in digestion represent only a few of the many reactions that take place in living cells. These reactions are governed by the same laws that operate in the control of chemical reactions in general. For example, temperature, concentration, and the presence of materials other than the reacting substances all influence the rate and nature of these reactions.

ENZYMES

Catalysis and catalysts. At ordinary temperatures oxygen and hydrogen do not combine to form water. However, if spongy platinum is present the two gases readily combine. The platinum does not enter into the reaction, at least it undergoes no permanent change. Again, if potassium chlorate is heated in a test tube, oxygen is liberated, but the reaction proceeds very slowly. However, if, before heating, a small quantity of manganese dioxide is added to the potassium chlorate, the velocity of the decomposition will be greatly accelerated. But an analysis of the residue in the test tube reveals that the manganese dioxide has not been changed in the reaction. Any such substance that tends to speed up or retard reactions by which compounds are broken down or synthesized, without itself being affected, is known as a **catalyst** (*kata*—down; *lysis*—loosening), and the effect it has on the reaction is called **catalysis.** In the synthesis of water, the spongy platinum acts as a catalyst and in the decomposition of potassium chlorate, manganese dioxide acts as a catalyst. Under the influence of catalysts, reactions which ordinarily take place so slowly that they cannot be detected may be speeded up until they are easily recognized. On the other hand, exceedingly rapid reactions may be retarded until they seem to cease altogether. We do not understand fully how catalysts operate to affect the rate of chemical reactions. Doubtless the activity of these agents is far more common and of much greater significance than has yet been realized. It is generally believed that catalysts are unable to initiate reactions.

How enzymes are named and classified. Included in the list of catalytic agents known to the chemist are certain substances produced in living cells and called **enzymes** (*en*—in; *zyme*—yeast). An enzyme has been defined as an organic catalyst, elaborated by an animal or plant cell, whose activity is entirely independent of any of the life processes of such a cell. Among the processes involving enzyme action, one of the first to be studied was the fermentation of yeast. At that early time, catalyzers, such as the enzyme of yeast, were known to act only in connection with the living cell, and consequently they were called "organized ferments." However, when Büchner in 1897 demonstrated that an active substance was present in the liquid extracted from yeast cells after they were ground up and destroyed, the distinction between organized and unorganized ferments disappeared.

A prominent biochemist lists forty major groups of enzymes. For a full understanding of life, not only is it necessary to know the chemical constituents of protoplasm and their organization, but also we must have complete knowledge of the enzymes and the part they play in chemical reactions. It is now believed that these agents are involved in all chemical reactions that take place in living protoplasm. Here we are interested only in those enzymes that have part in digestion, for they are the active agents in all the chemical processes of this important function. The changes effected by digestion involve the cleavage of compounds into two or more simple substances accompanied by the taking up of water. Such cleavage is called **hydrolysis.** The chemical changes in foods consist of hydrolyses by which the foods are converted into simpler, soluble substances. We have stated that fats are a combination of glycerol and fatty acids. In the digestion of fats this process is reversed, water is taken up (hydrolysis), and the fat is hydrolyzed to glycerol and fatty acids. However, this process cannot proceed without the presence of the specific enzymes. In similar fashion with the assistance of enzymes complex carbohydrates are split into sugars and proteins into amino acids.

Enzymes are named and classified according to the specific reaction with which they are concerned, or the nature of the substance (substrate) acted upon. The four most important general classes of digestive enzymes are:

Lipolytic enzymes, concerned with hydrolysis of fats (lipids).
Proteolytic enzymes, concerned with the hydrolysis of proteins.
Amylolytic enzymes, concerned with the hydrolysis of starch.
Sugar-splitting enzymes, concerned with the hydrolysis of sugars.

In naming the enzyme with reference to the particular substrate on which it acts, the termination *ase* is affixed to some part of the name of the substrate. Thus lipase is the name given to any enzyme involved in the hydrolysis of lipids; amylase (*amylon*—starch) digests starch; and protease digests proteins.

Nature and specificity of enzymes. Although the chemical nature of enzymes has not been determined with any degree of accuracy, it is generally believed that all are colloids resembling proteins in composition. In general, enzymes are most active within a rather narrow range of temperature (30–45°C.), and most of them are entirely destroyed when the temperature rises to 60–75°C. They are inactivated by lower temperatures but again become active when the temperature is increased. A very small amount of an enzyme can effect changes in an almost unlimited quantity of substrate, because the enzyme is not consumed but may be used over and over again like any other catalyst.

Enzymes are specific in their action; that is, some one enzyme is responsible for a particular chemical change in a given substance or group of closely related substances. Thus ptyalin, an animal enzyme, acts only on starch. This evident relation between enzyme and substrate is known as "specificity of enzyme action." At the present time we have no satisfactory explanation of this relationship.

Reversibility of enzyme action. The reaction of some enzymes is known to be reversible; that is, under certain conditions an enzyme will accelerate the breaking up of a given substance into simpler compounds, whereas under another set of conditions the same enzyme may accelerate the combination of simpler substances into a more complex compound. Thus fats that are hydrolyzed by the action of lipase have been synthesized from glycerol and fatty acids by the agency of this same enzyme. Likewise the sugar, maltose, has been synthesized from glucose by the enzyme maltase. Apparently it is the nature of the conditions under which the enzyme is working that determines the direction of the reaction, and therefore the same enzyme may accelerate either the hydrolytic or the synthetic reaction. We know much less about the constructive role of enzymes than about their disintegrating activity, but it seems very probable that we shall ultimately discover that enzymes have a part to play in synthetic processes that is fully as important as their role in digestion.

THE PROCESS OF DIGESTION

Various glands, built on the plans previously described, are associated with the alimentary canal, into which they pour their secretions which are the most important agents in the digestion of food. The food is broken down, usually by hydrolysis, into simpler compounds. Digestion, which takes place in a cavity outside the individual cells, as in the intestine, is known as extracellular digestion.

Digestive glands and enzymes. When food enters the human mouth it is lubricated by **mucus** secreted by unicellular glands in the epithelium lining the buccal cavity. It is thoroughly chewed by the teeth, moved about by the tongue, and thus mixed with **saliva,** which is poured into the buccal cavity from the **salivary glands** (Fig. 24). The salivary glands secrete mucus also.

The alkaline saliva pouring from the ducts of these glands contains, among other substances, an enzyme, **ptyalin,** which changes some of the starch to sugar. Digestion has now begun. The food is moved backward through the pharynx into the esophagus, down which it is propelled by peristalsis.

The esophagus delivers the food to the stomach, where it meets a new digestive fluid, the **gastric juice,** secreted from many compound tubular **gastric glands** in the stomach wall. Although the gastric juice is 99 per cent water, it contains **hydrochloric acid** and the enzymes **pepsin** and **rennin.** Pepsin, when activated by the hydrochloric acid, breaks down proteins into peptones and proteoses. Rennin causes the casein in milk to coagulate. Meantime the food is being thoroughly mixed by the churning action of the stomach muscles and eventually, as a semifluid called **chyme,** passes through the pyloric valve into the upper region of the small intestine known as the **duodenum.**

The food as it passes along through the small intestine is now acted upon by the alkaline pancreatic juice, secreted by the pancreas (Fig.

19), which contains three important enzymes, **amylase, trypsin,** and **lipase.** Amylase continues the work begun by ptyalin in the mouth, changing starches to sugar. Trypsin acts on proteins, breaking them down into peptones and proteoses. Lipase changes the fats to fatty acids and glycerol. The bile secreted by the liver (Fig. 19) accelerates the action of the pancreatic lipase in splitting fats. It also assists ma-

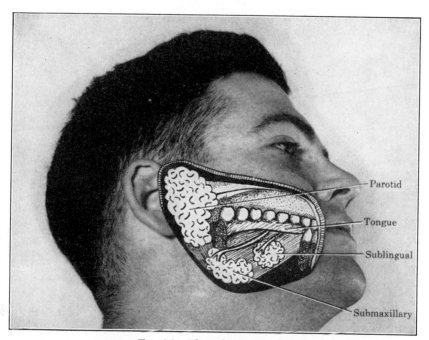

Fig. 24. The salivary glands.

terially in the absorption of fats and neutralizes hydrochloric acid. Additional enzymes are contained in the intestinal juice secreted by hundreds of small glands in the intestinal wall. These enzymes are the sugar-splitting enzymes **maltase, invertase,** and **lactase,** and the proteolytic enzyme **erepsin,** which continues the protein digestion begun by pepsin and trypsin, forming amino acids.

The food is propelled along through the small intestine by peristaltic action. Digestion continues. Eventually the food passes through the ileocaecal valve into the large intestine. It is probable that no new enzymes are added here, but some of the digestive processes going on in the small intestine may be continued for a time. Further decomposition is effected by the action of bacteria. The real function of the large intestine is absorption, particularly of water; the large intestine also serves as a reservoir for the accumulation of unusable residues of foods. These final remains consist of undigested material, bile salts and pigments, and various secretions which eventually are evacuated through the anus.

Constipation. Haggard says, "If we may judge from the money expended in advertising laxatives, America is indeed a constipated nation." In view of the above statement, the following scientific findings should be kept in mind.

(a) There is considerable variation in frequency of bowel evacuation among different persons.

(b) The discomfort such as headache and dullness due to constipation are not the result of harmful bacterial toxins entering the blood from the colon, as many advertisements have it, but are due to the resultant nervous disturbances of reflex origin.

(c) Most cathartics advertised are habit-forming drugs which lead to chronic constipation.

(d) Constipation is caused mostly by bad habits such as functional irregularity, poor posture, and diet deficient in roughage.

The table below serves to summarize the essential facts of digestion and digestive enzyme action.

REGION OF THE ALIMENTARY CANAL	DIGESTIVE JUICE	SOURCES OF DIGESTIVE JUICE	ENZYMES CONTAINED	KINDS OF FOODS ACTED UPON	END PRODUCTS OF DIGESTION, THE TRAVELING FORMS
Mouth	Saliva	Salivary glands	Ptyalin	Starch	Malt sugar
Stomach *	Gastric	Gastric glands	Pepsin	Protein	Peptone, proteoses
		Walls of stomach	Rennin	Milk	
	Pancreatic	Pancreas	Amylase	Starches	Malt sugar
			Lipase	Fats	Glycerol and fatty acids
			Trypsin	Proteins Peptones Proteoses	Some amino acids
Small intestine	Intestinal juice	Intestinal wall Intestinal glands	Erepsin	Peptides	Amino acids
			Invertase	Cane sugar	Simple sugars such as glucose
			Lactase	Milk sugar	
			Maltase	Malt sugar	
	Bile	Liver	None	Fats	Assists in digesting fats

* The stomach also secretes hydrochloric acid, which is not an enzyme but stimulates action of gastric enzymes and partly sterilizes the food.

ABSORPTION

We have already pointed out that the purpose of digestion is not only to break food down into simpler compounds but primarily to render it soluble and diffusible so that it can be transferred to the various parts of the animal. Again we emphasize that each one of the millions of cells making up the organism must have its supply of food for growth or for replacement of material consumed in living. As a result of digestion there are now in the intestinal cavity molecules of glucose, amino acids, and fatty acids and glycerin. These food molecules are in a soluble state but must traverse the cells of the intestinal lining and the walls of tiny blood vessels to get into the blood stream for distribution to the millions of needy cells making up the organism. This transfer of food molecules is, for the most part, purely physical in nature and takes place largely by what is known as diffusion and osmosis.

Solution. It is highly significant that most substances—solids, liquids, and gases—can pass into or out of the cell only when dissolved in water. Whatever the state of matter may be, there is an inherent tendency of the molecules to separate, and this tendency is opposed by their cohesion or mutual attraction. Therefore, when two or more substances are brought together they become intermingled. This intermingling of molecules or particles of different substances is called **solution.** A solution may be defined as a mixture of substances so intimate that they cannot be mechanically separated, as, for example, by filtration.

Diffusion. It has been stated that the molecules of a substance are in constant motion. The distance between molecules is greatest in the gaseous state, less in liquids, and least in solids. Therefore, in gases the cohesive force holding the molecules together is much less than in either liquids or solids, and consequently the molecules of gases have the greatest freedom of movement. If a gas escapes in a room from a leak in the pipe, the gas molecules will pass rapidly through the atmosphere until they are uniformly distributed. In other words, a gas tends to fill all available space. If a cube of sugar is placed in a cup of coffee and the cup is left undisturbed, in time the coffee will be uniformly sweetened. If, after a time, we could taste the liquid most adjacent to the lump of sugar we would find it has a sweeter taste than liquid from near the walls of the cup. Liquid from intermediate regions would be neither as sweet nor as dilute as that from the localities just mentioned. After a time all regions of the coffee would have the same degree of sweetness as a result of the distribution of the moving colliding molecules of sugar and water (Fig. 25). We usually assist the physical process of diffusion by stirring the liquid. If a crystal of potassium permanganate is placed in a glass of water, the coloring of the water adjacent to the crystal indicates that molecules of the substance are passing out into the water, i.e., among the molecules of the water. This movement will continue until all the water in the glass is uniformly colored, or in other words until the molecules of the solute (potassium permanganate) and those of the solvent (water) are equally distributed. This movement of molecules through a medium is called **diffusion,** and the direction of the movement is always away from the place where they are most abundant. Gases and solids dissolved in water may move by diffusion into the cell, through the cell, and out of the cell, the direction being determined by their relative concentration which sets up what is known as a diffusion gradient.

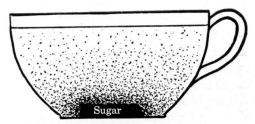

Fig. 25. Diagram illustrating the diffusion of dissolved particles of sugar in a cup of tea.

Osmosis and osmotic pressure. It has just been pointed out that the digested foods must traverse the cellular lining of the intestine and the tiny blood vessels (capillaries). Passage through the plasma membrane of the respective cells is involved. If a sac of animal membrane, such as a piece of bladder, is tied over the mouth of a tube, which is then immersed in water, the water will diffuse through the membrane into the sac, thence up into the tube, and will continue to rise until it has reached the level of the water outside the tube (Fig. 26). When this point is reached diffusion continues, but the amount of water now diffusing out of the tube is the same as that entering the tube; consequently the level inside remains even with the level of the water outside.

If a little sugar is dissolved in the water in the sac, the level of the liquid in the tube will begin to rise above the level of the liquid outside. It is obvious that more water is now passing through the membrane into the tube than is moving out of the tube and membranous sac into the vessel. This may be partly explained by the fact that the invisible pores of the membrane which readily allow water molecules to enter are, for the most part, too small to permit the passage of the larger sugar molecules from the sac. Consequently the outer surface of the membrane is in contact with more molecules of water

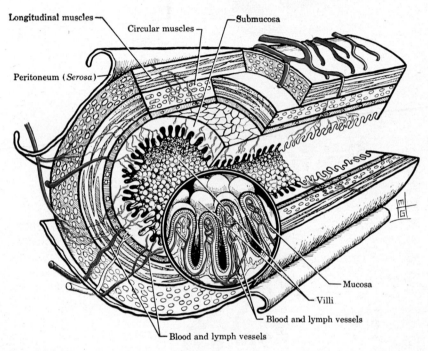

Longitudinal muscles

Circular muscles

Submucosa

Peritoneum (*Serosa*)

Mucosa

Villi

Blood and lymph vessels

Blood and lymph vessels

PLATE I.   Stereogram showing microscopic structure of small intestine.   Arteries, red; veins, blue; lymphatics, not colored.

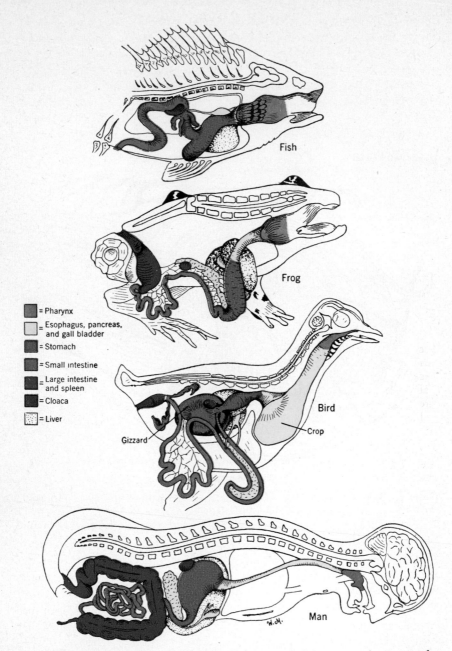

= Pharynx

= Esophagus, pancreas, and gall bladder

= Stomach

= Small intestine

= Large intestine and spleen

= Cloaca

= Liver

Fish

Frog

Bird

Gizzard

Crop

Man

PLATE II. Comparative study of the digestive tracts of different vertebrate animals.

tending to pass through it into the tube, whereas the inner surface of the membrane is partially covered by sugar molecules which block the passage so that fewer water molecules can diffuse outward. The presence of sugar dilutes the water in the tube, and consequently the water on the outside of the membrane is more concentrated. Therefore, in compliance with the general law of diffusion, the water moves from the place of its greater concentration to the region of its lower concentration. The sugar molecules also tend to obey this law but

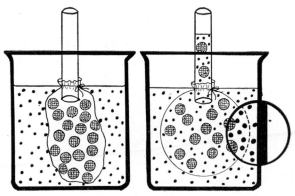

FIG. 26. Diagram representing the passage of water through a differentially permeable membrane. *Left*, the movement of water molecules through the membrane into the more dense solution within the sac is beginning to exceed the outward movement of water molecules. *Right*, after some time has elapsed, this greater inward movement of water molecules has diluted the solution as shown by the distended walls of the sac and the rise of the water in the glass tube.

are prevented from doing so by the membrane, most of the pores of which are too small to transmit the sugar molecules. Moreover, according to one hypothesis, the sugar molecules may have a great affinity for the water molecules and therefore tend to hold them inside the tube (Fig. 26).

If, in the above experiment, we close the upper end of the tube, the rising column of water will compress the air in the enclosed tube. The greater the concentration or the amount of the sugar in solution, the more rapid will be the rise of the water column and the greater the pressure exerted by it. Pressure developed by diffusion under these conditions is called **osmotic pressure**. We can also think of osmotic pressure as that pressure which would be just sufficient to prevent the diffusion of the molecules into the cell.

Differentially permeable membranes. Any membrane that permits the passage of a given substance is said to be permeable to that substance. A membrane that permits the passage of one substance but retards or prohibits the passage of another substance is called a **differentially permeable membrane.** The membranous sac is a differentially permeable membrane because it permits the free passage of water molecules but transmits very few of the sugar molecules dissolved in water. All living cell membranes are differentially permeable. The diffusion of substances through differentially permeable

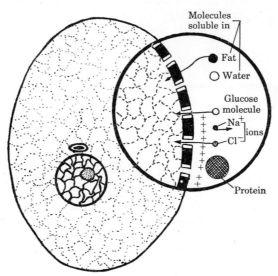

Fig. 27. Passage of substances through the cell membranes. Glucose molecules are thought to penetrate cell membranes through openings too small to permit the passage of protein molecules and fat-soluble molecules. Fat-soluble molecules may pass through the fatty portion of the cell membranes. Plus-charged ions are repelled from the plus-charged cell surface. Minus-charged ions may enter or leave the cell under special conditions. *Adapted from Carlson and Johnson, "The Machinery of the Body," University of Chicago Press.*

membranes is called osmosis. Not all particles can traverse readily all cell membranes. Sometimes the way is barred in some cells and open in others.

Various explanations have been offered to explain the phenomenon of semipermeability. There may be minute pores in the membrane which are too small to admit large molecules (Fig. 27). Again, there may be fatty portions of the cell membrane through which those particles which are fat soluble may penetrate the cell more readily. Further, it appears that there are present on almost all surfaces, electrical charges. Since similar electrical charges repel and unlike attract, a positively charged surface membrane would repel particles that are positively charged and in this way prevent their entrance into the cell.

On the other hand, negatively charged particles may enter. Finally, as so often happens in science, many phenomena of cell membrane permeability cannot be accounted for by the explanations just offered. Here, then, is a field for experimentation and research.

Absorption of food. Although water is absorbed in the large intestine, most of the food absorption in man and the higher animals

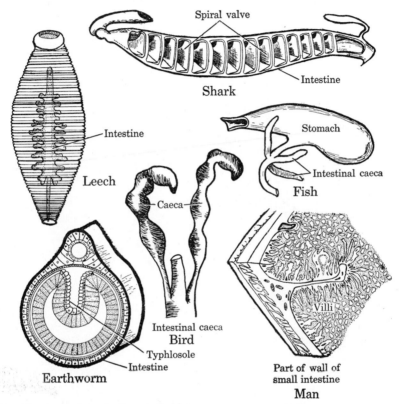

FIG. 28. Some devices that increase the absorptive surfaces of the digestive tracts of various animals.

takes place in the small intestine. Since the space within the body cavity is so limited, the intestines are much coiled, and this, together with certain modifications in the stomach and intestines, greatly increases the amount of absorptive surface (Fig. 28). It is a self-evident fact that a square yard of cloth will absorb more moisture than a square inch. The modifications that increase the surface area of the intestines increase both the amount of absorption and the speed with which absorption takes place. In the walls of the stomach there are many folds.   In the human intestines there are, in addition to folds, millions of minute projections called **villi** (*villus*–hair) (Figs. 28 and 29).   In the intestine of certain sharks the food travels down a sort of spiral staircase, an arrangement called a **spiral valve** (Fig. 28).   In the earthworm the dorsal wall of the intestine is infolded along its length; this internal fold is called the **typhlosole.**   In the large intestine of man the wall is constricted at intervals, forming saclike pockets. All these modifications greatly increase the surface.

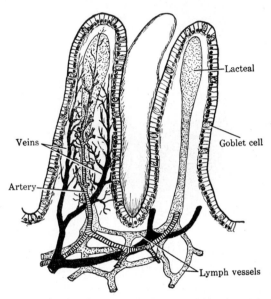

Fig. 29.   Diagram of villi, showing distribution of blood and lymph vessels.

The villi not only greatly increase the digestive surface but at the same time bring countless tiny blood and lymph vessels into close contact with the inner absorbing epithelium of the intestine (Fig. 29).   The lymph vessels of the villi, or the **lacteals** (*lac*–milk), absorb the products of the digested fats.   The lacteals converge into increasingly larger **lymph vessels,** which eventually unite to form a main vessel, the **thoracic duct,** that empties directly into the blood stream anterior to the heart.   The venous capillaries absorb the digested proteins and carbohydrates.   The veins course through the mesentery of the intestine and eventually lead into one main vessel, the **portal vein** (Plate III), which branches through the liver.   Here some of the carbohydrates are stored in the form of **glycogen,** or animal starch.

Glycogen is stored in the liver and also in other parts of the body. The liver acts on the amino acids which come from the intestine, breaking them down still further and removing the nitrogen in the from of **urea.** This process is called **deamination.** From the blood the liver absorbs many toxic substances and converts them into non-toxic ones.

The absorption of foods from the intestines apparently involves more than the simple processes of diffusion and osmosis; it "depends largely upon the properties of the separating wall of epithelial cells." In other words, the living membrane furnishes energy that aids in absorption.

SOLVING THE RIDDLE OF DIGESTION

From what has just been said of digestion, one may get the impression that all is known about this process and that this knowledge was easily acquired. This impression would be far from the truth. The partial solving of this riddle has taken the tireless efforts and life-time studies of intelligent, earnest men.

About the middle of the eighteenth century a Frenchman, Réaumur, fed his pet kite (a species of hawk) some meat inclosed in metal tubes, the ends of which were closed with fine gratings. Later these indigestible pellets were ejected through the mouth and the inclosed meat was found to be partially dissolved. Vegetable matter thus fed was found to undergo no change. Réaumur later sent these tubes on another errand, but this time they were filled with pieces of sponge which brought up a yellowish fluid that had a bitter taste. This fluid was found to act on food placed in glass vessels. Thus began the scientific study of digestion. Later, an Italian, Spallanzani, said that human digestive juice would melt food even though it was outside of the body. In those days this seemed remarkable because digestion was taking place without the "vital influence" of the stomach. Spallanzani, continuing his studies, found that saliva would act on starchy foods even outside the body. However, there were many who refused to believe. Typical of the arguments of these diehards was Hunter's declaration that "some physiologists will have it that the stomach is a Mill; others that it is a fermenting Vat; others that it is a Stew Pan; but in my view of the matter it is neither a Mill, a fermenting Vat, nor a Stew Pan—but a Stomach, gentlemen, a Stomach."

About 1825, our understanding of digestion really began to advance with Dr. Beaumont's experiments on a man named St. Martin. St. Martin accidentally shot himself in the stomach. Beaumont sewed the edges of the stomach to the skin. St. Martin got well, although he now had a hole in his stomach and abdomen. Through this hole Beaumont could see the stomach move and digestive juice pour out. He thought he would see how this gastric juice worked. Through

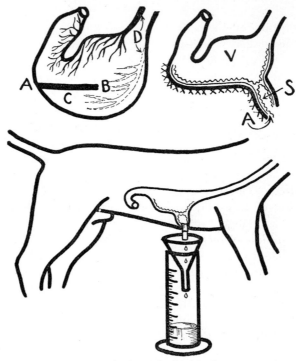

Fig. 30. Drawings showing Pavlov's method of making a gastric pouch. A, incision A–B is made in the stomach wall, leaving a flap, C, which is turned down so that pouch S forms an isolated miniature stomach in the side of main stomach V. Lower drawing shows the method by which gastric juice is drained from the miniature stomach S while digestion is going on in the main stomach. *Redrawn from Best and Taylor, "The Living Body," by permission of the authors and publisher, Henry Holt and Co.*

the opening he stuck some meat tied to a string, and two hours later pulled out the string. The meat had entirely dissolved! Later, by means of a rubber tube, he extracted from the stomach some gastric juice which on analysis was found to contain hydrochloric acid. These and other studies of Beaumont are classics in the early history of the study of digestion.

Other interesting experiments on digestion are those of Pavlov, a Russian, and those of Carlson, an American. Carlson's "experimental animal" was a man whose esophagus was so badly burned with lye that he had to be fed by a tube leading directly through the abdomen to the stomach. In this way Carlson was able to study the amount of flow of the gastric juice when the man smelled appetizing and non-appetizing food. The reactions in the stomach caused by the sight of foods and the chewing of food were observed and measured. These observations showed that the flow of digestive fluids is influenced by nervous reaction and that the digestive machinery begins to operate before the food ever enters the mouth. By cutting out of the duodenum of a dog a section containing the opening of the pancreatic duct, and sewing the piece to the body wall in such a way that the duct opened to the outside, Pavlov was able to study the amount of flow and the nature of the dog's pancreatic juice. The dog under careful dieting continued to live. The pancreatic juice could thus be collected and analyzed, and its digestive action could be studied. Dogs have been found to secrete 200–750 cc. of pancreatic juice per day. Many of the important facts of digestion have been uncovered by other ingenious experiments on the lower animals, particularly dogs, cats, and guinea pigs (Fig. 30).

The role of the various intestinal regions in absorption has been determined by removing the small intestine and attaching the stomach directly to the large intestine. The importance of the large intestine has been learned by its removal, or by making an outlet for the small intestine so that the food was unable to reach the large intestine. It would be possible to describe many other interesting and ingenious experiments which man has made in his efforts to solve the riddle of digestion.

5

Foods and Their Uses
Nutrition

As we have previously pointed out, all organisms in order to live must have an adequate food supply. Man is no exception. Naturally the choice of food varies with the animal. **Herbivorous** animals (*herba*—herb; *vorare*—to devour) feed entirely on vegetation; **carnivorous** animals (*caro*—flesh; *vorare*) devour the flesh of other animals, and **omnivorous** (*omnis*—all; *vorare*) eat both fleshy and herbaceous food. The choice of food is determined by several factors, among which may be listed climatic conditions and availability. Animals in northern latitudes require more heat to withstand the cold than those in the tropics. This heat is furnished by the supplies of energy stored in the fats of other animals. For example, the Eskimo eats blubber because he needs it and because it is readily available. Environment also plays its part in determining food habits. The food of aquatic animals differs from that of land forms. The animal pattern or form influences food choice; for example, the food of an oyster is very different from that of a tiger. So far as we know man is the only animal which should be able to select food intelligently to satisfy energy and structural needs. In the centuries past, man was guided by his "stomach" rather than his brain in the selection of his menu. This is still true for many people of today, but in the light of modern knowledge of nutrition it is time to change guides.

Food synthesis. The building stones for the formation of other kinds of food substances are the carbohydrates. At the present time the source of our carbohydrates is the green plant which manufactures them by a process of photosynthesis from the elements of water (hydrogen and oxygen) and carbon dioxide (CO_2) in the air. Water is taken into the roots of the plant from the soil and passes up the stem to the green leaf. Carbon dioxide enters the leaf through small openings and moves into certain cells of the leaf which contain green bodies known as **chloroplasts**. The green chloroplasts of the leaf—in fact in whatever green plant they may be found—through the energy of sunlight converts the inorganic materials, carbon dioxide and water, into the organic carbohydrates, that is, sugars and starches. In this process energy from the sun is stored in the molecules of the sugars and starches manufactured by the green plant.

The synthesis of fats and proteins in animals starts with carbohydrate materials. Like starch, fats and oils are inactive storage substances—reservoirs of energy—and before they can be used or transported they must be converted by digestion into water-soluble substances. In the synthesis of fats, fatty acids and glycerol formed from carbohydrates are combined to form fats and oils (lipids) (Fig. 31). In the liquid state fats are usually called oils.

CARBOHYDRATES

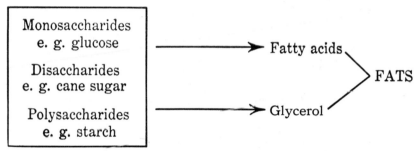

| Monosaccharides e. g. glucose |
| Disaccharides e. g. cane sugar |
| Polysaccharides e. g. starch |

→ Fatty acids

→ Glycerol

FATS

FIG. 31. Diagram of the synthesis of fats.

The synthesis of proteins also begins with the carbohydrate molecule. However, proteins are far more complex compounds than either carbohydrates or fats. To get some appreciation of the size and complexity of the protein molecule we need only to glance at the empirical formulas of two common proteins:

Zein (a protein found in corn) $C_{736}H_{1161}O_{208}N_{184}S_3$

Egg albumin $C_{696}H_{1125}O_{220}N_{175}S_8$

In addition to carbon, hydrogen, and oxygen, all proteins contain the elements nitrogen and sulphur, and some of them also contain phosphorus, iron, and other elements. The fundamental components of proteins are the **amino acids**. In the synthesis of proteins in the plant, nitrogen, phosphorus, and sulphur are incorporated with various carbohydrates to produce the protein molecule.

The living protoplasm alone is responsible for the synthesis of proteins and fats. Because of their complex chemical composition and their peculiar physical properties, proteins are especially useful in the building of protoplasm.

There are several theories that attempt to explain how proteins are synthesized. Although the process is not yet fully understood, it is quite generally believed that the nitrates obtained from the soil are

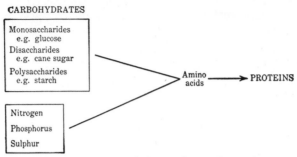

CARBOHYDRATES

FIG. 32. Diagram of the synthesis of proteins.

changed into ammonia (NH_3) within the plant. This ammonia combines with certain acids derived from the carbohydrates to form **amino acids**—so called because each molecule contains the **amino group** (NH_2) and the **carboxyl group** ($COOH$). The simplest amino acid is glycine, and its molecular composition may be indicated thus:

$$\begin{array}{c} H \\ | \\ H-C-NH_2 \\ | \\ O=C-O-H \end{array}$$

See Fig. 10. Just as many glucose molecules may be joined to form a starch molecule, so numbers of amino acid molecules may join to form a molecule of protein. It is believed that some protein molecules are formed by the union of a hundred or more amino acid molecules.

Energy value of food. One of the earliest studies of nutrition was made by Sanctorius in 1614 (Fig. 33). He weighed himself before and after meals to find how much of the food eaten vanished in the form of "insensible perspiration" and "heat." Other investigators discovered that the food was oxidized in the body, releasing energy, and that the energy content of foods could be measured. The unit of measurement adopted was the **Calorie** (*calor*—heat). A food Calorie is approximately the amount of heat required to raise one kilogram of water one degree centigrade.

After the establishment of this unit of energy the next step was to measure the energy values of known weights of various foods, particularly the carbohydrates and fats. Protein has been found to be expensive as an energy food, but it is needed for the replacement of certain components of the organism which are continually being torn down and lost.

A certain amount of energy is necessary to keep an animal living, even during complete relaxation and repose. This amount of basal energy or minimal heat produced is the measure of the **basal metab-**

FIG. 33. How Sanctorius tried to count calories in 1614. *After Jean, Harrah, Herman, and Powers, "Introductory Course in Science for Colleges, II."* By *permission of the publisher, Ginn and Co.*

olism of an organism (Fig. 34). It varies with the weight of an animal, but for each square meter of body surface exposed, it is practically the same in all mammals. It can be readily seen that, in addition to the basal metabolic requirements, man needs fuel to provide energy for his occupational and recreational activities (Fig. 34).

For an individual of given weight the number of Calories required varies with age, occupation, and recreational habits. For those engaged in sedentary occupations the daily requirement varies from 2,200 to 2,800 Calories; an individual who does manual labor with pick and shovel will require daily from 4,000 to 6,000 Calories. If man is to balance his food according to his needs, it will be necessary for

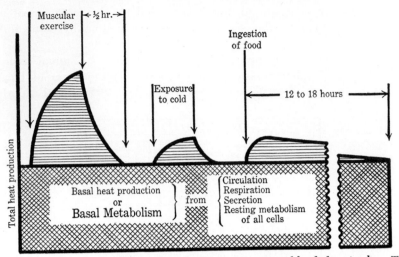

Fig. 34.   Factors modifying heat production in warm-blooded animals.   The basal heat production necessary to sustain life is represented by the cross-hatched region.   Additional heat may be derived from muscular exercise (part of which heat is liberated after exercise is stopped), from exposure to cold, and from ingestion of food.   *Redrawn from Carlson and Johnson, "The Machinery of the Body."   By permission of the publisher, University of Chicago Press.*

him to have some accurate measurement of food values in Calories to satisfy his daily requirements.

Water and minerals.   The importance of water to the organism has already been pointed out.   In addition to water, proteins, carbohydrates, and fats, the organism must have certain minerals.   In the higher animals calcium and phosphorus are especially necessary for bone and teeth formation.   Calcium is necessary for the clotting of blood, and it aids in muscular regulation.   In such lower animals as oysters and clams, calcium is necessary for shell formation.   Iron is a necessary constituent of the hemoglobin or red part of the blood. Copper in minute amounts serves as an aid to iron utilization, although it is not a constituent of hemoglobin itself.   As will be seen later, iron is very necessary to insure normal growth and development.   Phosphorus, calcium, magnesium, sodium, and potassium, in the form of various salts, perform an important function in regulating the acidity and alkalinity of the blood.

VITAMINS

Modern science has demonstrated that man does not live by bread alone nor by any fixed quota of carbohydrates, proteins, fats, and minerals. Substances called **vitamins** (*vita*–life; amine) play an important part in man's nutritional program and undoubtedly do the same for all other animals, though our knowledge of their role for other groups is slight compared to what we know of it in man, rats, mice, guinea pigs, and various domesticated animals.

Long ago it was recognized that certain foods were beneficial for various diseases. In 1720 Kramer was of the opinion that scurvy could not be cured by medicine or an operation. He wrote: "But if you can get green vegetables; if you can prepare a sufficient quantity of fresh, antiscorbutic juices, if you have oranges, lemons, citrons, or their pulp and juice preserved with whey in cask, so that you can make a lemonade or rather give to the quantity of 3 or 4 ounces of their juice in whey, you will, without other assistance, cure this dreadful evil."

In 1912, Funk found that he could cure polyneuritic pigeons by a substance which he extracted from bran. Funk finally gave the name **vitamin** to these new principles. In the early days of vitamin research, the chemical structures of these substances were unknown, and so they were labeled vitamin A, vitamin B, and so on. Today the chemical formulas of most of them have been determined and the majority of them have been synthesized in the chemist's laboratory. Water-soluble vitamin B is now known to consist of at least twelve or more food factors! So in the light of modern research it has been suggested that it might be better to list these essential food factors by using their chemical names rather than the old terms.

The basic source of vitamins is the plants, which supply not only the vitamin itself but often the precursor from which the vitamin is built. Vitamins and their precursors are found in various parts of the plant, such as the leaves, roots, and fruits. Lack of vitamins in the diet of man and other animals often causes non-infectious diseases called **deficiency diseases.**

Vitamin A ($C_{20}H_{29}OH$). The precursor of this vitamin occurs in plants in the form of a yellow pigment called **carotene.** The animal may obtain carotene from fresh vegetable food and convert it into vitamin A. This vitamin has been extracted in the pure form from the oil of fish liver and has been synthesized in the chemical laboratory. Both vitamin B and carotene occur in butter and eggs.

Lack of vitamin A, or the precursor carotene, in the diet may result in disturbances in the epithelial tissues. Often the skin may become dry or horny, a condition which also affects the alimentary canal, respiratory tissues, and the genito-urinary tract. Frequently the front of the eye becomes rough and dry, a condition called "dry eye" (xerophthalmia), and as a result the eye may become a ready prey for infection (Fig. 35). After a famine this condition has been very prevalent among children in various parts of the world, particularly in India and Japan. The first indication of vitamin A deficiency is a type of **night blindness,** that is, a partial loss of sight in dim light. During the earlier stages in the life of the individual, the absence of this vitamin may indirectly affect growth. Vitamin A is essential for normal cell metabolism. There is no conclusive evidence, however, that vitamin A may assist in building up resistance to common colds although it may shorten the duration of the attack. In four-footed

Fig. 35. Xerophthalmia in white rat caused by a diet deficient in vitamin A, and recovery when given vitamin A. *By permission of Mead Johnson & Co.*

animals and poultry there is evidence that vitamin A is essential for normal reproduction.

Some of the principal sources of the precursor carotene are: raw carrots, lettuce, tomatoes, cantaloupes, sweet potatoes, and most yellow fruits and vegetables. The vitamin itself is found in oysters, egg yolk, liver, butter, and fish-liver oils such as cod-liver oil and halibut-liver oil.

Vitamin B complex. Once it was thought that certain nutritional defects observed in experimental animals resulted from the lack of a single dietary essential designated as vitamin B. As a result of further investigation, it has been discovered that vitamin B is really a complex of a number of distinct chemical compounds or fractions. Sometimes these are designated as B_1, B_2, but today they are usually designated by their chemical names.

Thiamine ($C_{12}H_{17}CIN_4OSHCl$), sometimes called vitamin B_1, was one of the first vitamins to be discovered. Eijkman, a Dutch physician who lived in Java, observed many cases of an Oriental paralytic disease known as **beriberi,** which translated means "extreme weakness." People afflicted with beriberi find their muscles becoming stiff and painful. Neuritic pains caused by inflammation of the nerves occur, and eventually the patient may become completely paralyzed as a result of degeneration of the nervous tissue. Under experimental conditions, lack of thiamine in man's diet results in loss of appetite, irritability, inertia, and such early onset of fatigue that individuals cannot carry on their daily work.

For a time the remedies applied consisted mostly of exercise and improved sanitation. In 1897, Eijkman noticed that fowls fed on polished rice—rice with the hull removed—were afflicted with the disease called **polyneuritis,** a disease very similar to beriberi, but that those fed on the whole grain remained normal (Fig. 36). This

FIG. 36. Pigeon afflicted with polyneuritis. *A,* afflicted bird; *B,* same bird after recovery following feeding with food containing thiamine. *By permission of Merck and Co.*

discovery opened the way for the study of human beriberi, and, to make a long but interesting story short, it was discovered that the hull of the grain contained something which prevented this disease—another case where coarse food is better than refined. Thus whole-wheat bread is more healthful than white.

Thiamine is found in a number of foods—whole-grain cereals, raw cabbage, raw carrots, lettuce, other vegetables, meats, and eggs. Since it is soluble in water and is also destroyed by heat, food cooked in water tends to lose thiamine.

Riboflavin ($C_{17}H_{20}N_4O_6$) is one of a group of yellow substances found in many plant and animal tissues. If riboflavin is lacking in man's diet there result a reddening of the eyes owing to the development of visible, fine blood vessels in the cornea, and an intolerance to bright light. In cattle, swine, dogs, rats, and chicks riboflavin promotes growth and prevents certain abnormalities of the nervous system and skin.

Niacin or **nicotinic acid** ($C_6H_5O_2N$) is a vitamin found most often in yeast, fresh vegetables, and meat. In those areas of the country

where corn meal forms a large part of the diet, there often occurs
the deficiency disease, **pellagra.** Corn meal has very low niacin content. Some of the symptoms of pellagra are soreness of the mouth,

digestive disturbances, and red and
inflamed patches of the skin, particularly where the sun strikes it. In
the later stages of the disease there
are nervous twitches and disorders.
For sometime it was thought that
this disease was the result of a
lack of niacin in the diet, but now
studies apparently indicate that there
is also a relationship between pellagra
and the amino acid tryptophane.
Irrespective of the specific factors involved it is known that a diversified
diet of meat and plenty of leafy
vegetables will prevent and cure the
disease. Thiamine, niacin, and riboflavin assist in transport of energy in
carbohydrate metabolism.

A

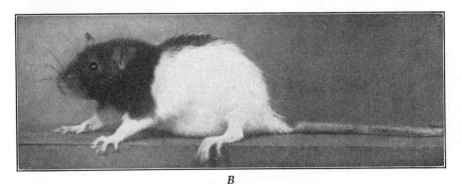

B

FIG. 37. *A,* rat fed for seven weeks on a diet deficient in riboflavin gained only
15 grams, whereas a normal rat (*B*) given a balanced diet gained 90 grams in the
same period. *By permission of Mead Johnson & Co.*

The lack of another vitamin, **pyridoxine** ($C_8H_{11}NO_2HCl$), in experimental animals such as rats, chicks, dogs, and pigs produces painful
swelling and ulceration of the feet, nose, and regions around the mouth.
The growth of the animals may be retarded. Pyridoxine is apparently
essential in the conversion of proteins to carbohydrates.

Biotin (formerly known as vitamin H) is apparently a growth-promoting vitamin. Although its role is not well understood there is evidence that it is involved in fat metabolism. It is found abundantly in growing tissue and in tumorous growths.

Folic acid ($C_{19}H_{19}O_6N_7$) or vitamin B_{12} is effective in the treatment of pernicious macrocytic anemia and other anemias following pellagra, sprue, and certain diseases of the liver. It plays a part in bone metabolism. The liver and kidneys are important sources of this vitamin, and small amounts may be present in green vegetables and cereals.

Some other factors of the vitamin B complex whose exact functions are not clear are **choline** concerned with fat metabolism and **pantothenic acid** which may play a part in carbohydrate metabolism.

Vitamin C. The disease **scurvy** has been known for a long time. The patient afflicted with scurvy has bleeding gums, loosened teeth, swollen joints, and brittle bones; the blood vessels rupture easily, those in the skin leaving red blotches. The individual becomes "lazy." Plagues of this non-infectious disease were frequent among people in the more northern countries and among sailors who made long voyages on the slow-going sailing ships. It was the bane of Arctic explorers.

About 1757, Lind, a British surgeon, discovered that citrus fruits contained something that prevented this plague, and so the British navy included lime juice in its rations. Today we know this anti-scorbutic substance as vitamin C, or as **ascorbic** or **cevitamic acid** ($C_6H_8O_6$). It is essential in the metabolism of amino acids. It can be extracted in pure form and can be synthesized in the chemist's laboratory. Apparently the only species of animals that need vitamin C are man, monkeys, and guinea pigs. Other animals seem to be able to synthesize the substance from certain dietary components.

Vitamin C is abundant in lemons, limes, oranges, and such raw vegetables as cabbage, lettuce, spinach, tomatoes, and peppers. It is practically lacking in foods of animal origin. Cooking and canning, except of acid foods, usually result in loss of vitamin C.

Vitamin D. Through the centuries a condition known as rickets ("twists") has been present in the human population. The condition was, and is, particularly prevalent among the poor children in large and crowded cities. Rickets usually appears in children under two years of age and has a marked effect on the bones, especially those of the arms and legs, which become abnormally soft because of a lack of calcium. In this weakened, non-rigid condition, they tend to twist and bow (Fig. 38). In rickets, the head of the individual becomes abnormally large and the forehead bulges. Because of the malformation of the ribs, the chest narrows to form a so-called "pigeon chest." The teeth are also affected.

Rickets is found not only in man but also in dogs, chickens, and other domestic animals. Mellanby, an Englishman, discovered that rickets in dogs was due to a diet deficiency. Later McCollum, an American, demonstrated that rickets in man was caused by lack of some vitamin factor.

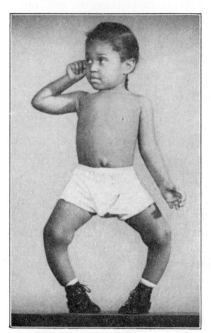

Rickets is a disturbance of the calcium and phosphorus metabolism of the body, and the structures richest in these substances are most affected. We now know that vitamin D assists in the absorption of the calcium from the gastrointestinal tract and is the regulator of the calcium level in the blood. Thus vitamin D holds calcium and phosphorus in the body and so regulates both the necessary calcification of the bones and teeth and the normal functioning of the muscles and the nervous system. Incidentally, this vitamin is necessary for numerous functions in other animals. In poultry a lack of it causes a decrease in egg production, and in cows, lactation is affected.

FIG. 38. A case of rickets caused by a diet deficient in vitamin D. *From film, "Foods and Nutrition," Encyclopædia Britannica Films, Inc.*

Vitamin D is not so widely distributed in nature as the other known vitamins. Food substances most rich in vitamin D are egg yolk, cod-liver oil, and other fish oils. There is a variable amount in butter. It had been observed that rachitic children, when exposed to sunlight, were definitely benefited, and, in some of them, the defect was prevented if the sunlight treatment was begun in time. In 1919 it was demonstrated that exposure to ultraviolet light would cause a deposition of calcium in the bones of rachitic animals and cure the disease. Later it was demonstrated that food materials could be made antirachitic by exposing them to ultraviolet light. Further experimentation revealed that the sterols, a type of fat found in certain fish-liver oils, contain some precursor which, when irradiated, became the effective agent of vitamin D. The activated sterol, **ergosterol,** is the most important commercial source of vitamin D. There occur several forms of vitamin D in nature, all of them closely related chemically, however, **calciferol** seems to be the pure vitamin.

It now appears that in most animal bodies there is present a precursor of vitamin D which becomes active under the influence of the ultraviolet rays of the sun. Cattle kept in the pasture fields during the summer never need to have their diet enriched by vitamin D. The body need not be in direct sunlight to be benefited, for light from a northern sky and reflected rays from snow and water are also effective. However, certain types of window glass, clouds, smoke, and dust effectively cut off these activating rays of the sun.

From what has been said, we see that control of rickets is a problem which involves not only biology as it concerns food but also sociology and economics, including such factors as crowding of population, housing, and community planning. There must be proper spacing of houses and control of excess smoke which filters out the necessary rays of the sun.

Vitamin E. It has been observed that when rats are fed on a diet lacking vitamin E, the reproductive tissues are found to be degenerated in males, and in pregnant females the young fetuses die and are resorbed. Although the females can be cured by the addition of vitamin E to their diet, the males never regain their reproductive capacity. It has been definitely proved that vitamin E is essential for normal reproduction in rats, mice, and poultry. There is no definite evidence of its effect upon humans.

Vitamin E is found in the green forage of domestic animals and is abundant in the germ of cereal grains as well as in cottonseed oil and corn oil.

Vitamin E has been isolated as **alpha tocopherol** ($C_{29}H_{50}O_2$). It is not readily destroyed by heating or cooking, but it is destroyed if the oil containing it becomes rancid.

Vitamin K ($C_{31}H_{46}O_2$). This anti-hemorrhagic vitamin is found in such vegetables as spinach, cabbage, and other green foods. Its presence prevents bleeding diseases caused by a lack of prothrombin, a substance found in the blood and necessary to bring about clotting. It is needed especially by farm animals but is not so important in man unless the bile does not enter the intestine, under which circumstances there is a tendency to bleed if an operation is performed. Vitamin K is used to correct the hemorrhagic diseases of the newborn.

Menadione ($C_{11}H_8O_2$) resembles vitamin K in its activity in connection with blood clotting. It is a pure chemical compound.

The investigations in the vitamin field are exceedingly numerous, and new discoveries are being announced frequently. So rapid is the development in this field that, even by the time these words are being read, new discoveries may demand a revision of the statements.

Vitamin propaganda. Since their discovery, much has been said, written, and taught about vitamins, some of which has been true, some unintentionally misleading, and some misinformation broadcast deliberately for commercial gain. Vitamins share with hormones the spotlight in patent-medicine advertising. True, vitamins A, the B complex, C, D, K, and perhaps E are necessary to maintain normal health and prevent certain diseases. Adequate amounts of these vitamins can be obtained in the ordinary average diet, and only under exceptional conditions is it necessary to secure a more than usual supply by the use of commercial preparations. Under these circumstances, it is best to get the advice of a physician.

A chart summarizing information about certain vitamins follows.

VITAMINS—CHEMISTRY, SOURCES, EFFECT OF DEFICIENCY

VITAMIN	SOURCE xxx—abundant xx—good	CHIEF RESULTS OF DEFICIENCY IN DIET
A $C_{20}H_{30}O$ Precursor—carotene (p. 67)	Cod-liver oil xxx Halibut-liver oil xxx Carrots, raw xx Lettuce xx Tomatoes xx Cantaloupe xx Pineapple xx Egg yolk xx Butter xx	Keratinization of epithelial tissues. Liability to infection of the skin. Night blindness. Failure of growth.
B complex $C_{12}H_{17}N_4OSCl$ Thiamine (p. 68)	Cabbage, raw xx Carrots, raw xx Lettuce, raw xx Potatoes, raw xx Tomatoes, raw xx Rice, unpolished xx Wheat, whole xx Meat xx Egg yolk xx Cornmeal xx	Beriberi in man. Polyneuritis in birds. Growth affected. Essential to utilization of carbohydrates. Aids appetite and digestion.
$C_{17}H_{20}N_4O_6$ Riboflavin (p. 69)	Green, leafy vegetables xxx Liver xxx Kidney xxx Other meats xxx Egg yolk xxx Milk, whole xxx Cornmeal xxx	Not found in man under natural conditions. Lack in man causes fissures and cracks at angles of mouth, and itching, burning of eyes, and poor vision. Dogs and chicks lose weight. Cataract in cats. Pellagra (?).

VITAMINS—CHEMISTRY, SOURCES, EFFECT OF DEFICIENCY (*Continued*)

VITAMIN	SOURCE xxx—abundant xx—good	CHIEF RESULTS OF DEFICIENCY IN DIET
Nicotinic acid or niacin $C_6H_5O_2N$	Yeast xx Fresh vegetables xx Meat xx	Pellagra (?). Soreness of mouth and tongue. Red and inflamed patches of the skin.
Folic acid $C_{19}H_{19}O_6N_7$	Liver xx Kidney xx	Pernicious macrocytic anemia.
C $C_6H_{10}O_6$ Ascorbic or cevitamic acid (synthesized) (p. 71)	Cabbage, raw xxx Lettuce xxx Potatoes, raw xxx cooked xx Citrus fruits xxx Carrots, raw xx Celery, raw xx Cucumbers, raw xx Peas and beans xx Other fruits xx	Scurvy.
D Precursors Sterols, particularly ergosterol Sunlight (p. 71)	Egg yolk xxx Cod-liver oil xxx Halibut-liver oil xxx Butter xx Oysters xx	Rickets in both man and domestic animals. Diminishes egg production in poultry. Necessary for normal function of muscles and nerves.
E $C_{29}H_{50}O_2$ Tocopherol (p. 73)	Lettuce xxx Tomatoes xx Beef xx Egg yolk xx Butter xx	No definite evidence of effect on man. Necessary for reproductive capacity of rats, mice, and poultry.
K $C_{31}H_{46}O_2$ (p. 73)	Spinach xxx Cabbage xxx Other green fruits and vegetables xx	Blood does not clot owing to lack of prothrombin in certain liver diseases in man. Hemorrhagic diseases in the newborn.

6

The Blood and
Circulatory System

We have previously stated that the cell is not only the structural unit of the organism but also the functional or physiological unit, and that the life and behavior of the organism are in a measure the result of the actions and reactions of its living component cells. Every living cell then must carry on metabolism, which means that the countless millions of cells must be supplied with new materials to replace those used up, and waste must be removed. To meet these requirements efficiently a transportation system through the organism is needed which will serve every cell either directly or indirectly. In animals these transportation systems are the blood and lymph circulations together with their systems of vessels and spaces (sinuses or hemocoeles).

THE CIRCULATORY SYSTEM

Vessels. The circulatory system is made up of the **heart** and a system of vessels. The rhythmic contractions of the heart maintain a flow of blood *out through the* **arteries,** which are vessels with fairly thick walls (Plate III and Fig. 39). The arteries branch and subdivide, gradually decreasing in diameter until they empty into minute vessels called **capillaries** (*capillaris*—hair). The capillaries branch, extending into intercellular spaces of all the organs and tissues and forming a continuous network through the organism. Their thin walls—they are composed of but a single layer of flat epithelial cells—allow ready exchange of materials between the blood and the various cells of the body by diffusion and osmosis. These capillaries unite to form small vessels called **veins,** which have thinner walls than the arteries (Plate III and Fig. 39). These veins in turn join to form larger veins, which carry the blood back to the heart, thus completing the circulation.

It is estimated by Dr. Krogh, who was awarded the Nobel prize for his studies of the human circulation, that, if all the capillaries in the body of an average man were cut and spread open, the total surface exposed would cover a city block. If the capillaries were placed end to end with the other blood vessels, we would have a string of blood vessels which would encircle the earth two and one-half times.

The heart. The human heart is a thick-walled muscular organ lying inside the **pericardial cavity,** which is enclosed by a tough sac of connective tissue, the **pericardium** (*peri*—around; *cardia*—heart)

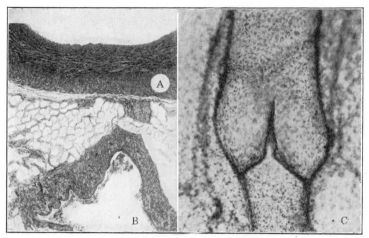

FIG. 39. *A,* portion of the wall of an artery. *B,* portion of the wall of a vein. Notice the difference in thickness of the walls. *C,* longitudinal section of lymph vessel. Note the thin walls of the lymph vessel. *Photomicrographs by permission of the General Biological Supply House.*

(Fig. 40). The heart is divided into four compartments; the **right auricle** (*auricula*—little ear), **left auricle, right ventricle,** and **left ventricle.** The walls of the ventricles are much more muscular and thicker than those of the auricles. The right auricle and the right ventricle are completely separated from the left auricle and the left ventricle. The **venous blood,** often but incorrectly spoken of as the "impure" blood because of its low oxygen content, is collected from the body and poured into the right auricle. A wave of muscular contraction originating in the wall of the right auricle sweeps down across the two auricles and thence over the ventricles, causing a muscular contraction of the heart which seems to twist and wring the blood from it. This is the heart beat. The right and left sides of the heart are contracting simultaneously. However, in order to present a clearer understanding of its mechanism, each side of the heart will be discussed separately.

The blood, acted upon by gravity and the muscular contraction of the walls of the right auricle, flows through an opening over flaps of tough connective tissue, the **tricuspid valve** (*tri*–three; *cusp*–tooth) (Fig. 40). The increased pressure on the blood as the ventricle con-

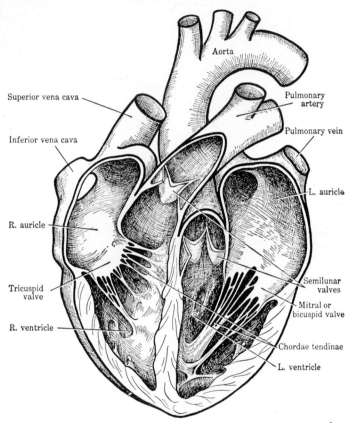

Aorta

Superior vena cava

Pulmonary artery

Pulmonary vein

Inferior vena cava

L. auricle

R. auricle

Tricuspid valve

Semilunar valves

Mitral or bicuspid valve

R. ventricle

Chordae tendinae

L. ventricle

Fig. 40.   Diagram showing the internal anatomy of the heart.   *Redrawn from Haggard, "The Science of Health and Disease." By permission of the publishers, Harper and Brothers.*

tracts pushes the three flaps composing the tricuspid valve away from the heart wall and against each other, thus closing the opening between the auricle and the ventricle (Fig. 41).   All the valves of the heart operate on this same general principle.   When the right ventricle contracts, the tricuspid valve closes and the blood is forced out through another opening into the **pulmonary artery** (*pulmo*–lung), which leads to the lungs.   At the opening of the pulmonary artery into the right ventricle there are three small, half-moon-shaped pocketlike flaps, **semilunar valves** (*semi*—half; *luna*—moon) which prevent the backward flow of blood into the heart.

The blood has now reached the lungs, where it loses carbon dioxide and receives oxygen. The **oxygenated blood** returns from the lungs to the left auricle through the **pulmonary veins.** When the left auricle contracts, the blood flows into the left ventricle through the opening between the left auricle and left ventricle over the **bicuspid** or **mitral valve.** When the left ventricle contracts, the mitral valve prevents the flow back into the auricle and the blood is forced into a

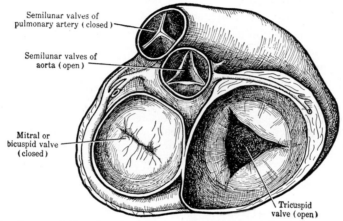

Semilunar valves of
pulmonary artery (closed)

Semilunar valves of
aorta (open)

Mitral or
bicuspid valve
(closed)

Tricuspid
valve (open)

FIG. 41. Action of the valves of the heart. *Redrawn from Haggard, "The Science of Health and Disease." By permission of the publishers, Harper and Brothers.*

large vessel, the **aorta** (Fig. 41). In the opening between the aorta and the left ventricle are three **semilunar valves** similar to those at the base of the pulmonary artery and functioning in the same manner.

Sometimes as a result of disease or other causes the valves fail to close properly and some of the blood pushes back into the chamber which it has just left. This is known as **leakage of the heart.** Thus when the left ventricle contracts leakage of the bicuspid valve allows blood to escape into the left auricle. Such leakage may be caused by weakness in the valves or by growths on them which prevent proper closure.

From the aorta, arteries lead off to the neck and head, the arms, the alimentary tract—in fact to all the organs and structures of the body except the lungs. It has been estimated that, in pumping this blood through the body, the work done by the heart every 24 hours would be sufficient to raise a man weighing 150 pounds to a height 200 feet above the top of the Empire State Building in New York City.

If the heart exerts so great a pressure, then the walls of the vessels through which the blood flows must also be under constant pressure, those of the arteries nearest the heart being under the greatest pressure. Consequently the walls of the arteries are much thicker than those of the veins (Fig. 39). The walls of both the arteries and veins have the same structural plan, but the arteries have more muscle and elastic tissue. This is particularly true of the aorta. After the blood passes through the capillaries and gets into the veins, there is a steady flow toward the heart but not nearly so strong as the flow in the arteries. The veins contain small valves that prevent any backward flow of the blood (Fig. 39).

The first rush of blood from the heart distends the walls of the aorta and larger arteries, which maintain this pressure through the contracting muscles and the elastic tissue. This mechanism makes possible a constant pressure which forces the blood to all parts of the body and through the small vessels where the resistance becomes increasingly greater.

Blood pressure is measured by placing around the arm an air-tight rubber cuff into which air is pumped until the pressure causes the collapse of the main artery of the arm. This obliterates the pulse at the wrist. The pressure, measured in milligrams of mercury, is recorded by a gauge. It is the **systolic pressure** or the pressure at the time of the contraction of the heart. Usually "no definite cause can be found for low blood pressure" though it is present in certain chronic diseases. High blood pressure may be the result of overweight, improper diet, infections, age, or the rush and worry of modern life. It may be caused by hardening of the arteries (**arteriosclerosis**).

There are in reality four transportation systems in the human body and in the body of most of the higher animals: the **systemic system,** which carries the blood to the limbs, brain, the organs of digestion, and other parts of the body; a **pulmonary system,** which carries the blood from the right side of the heart to the lungs and returns it to the left side of the heart; and a system called the **hepatic portal system,** which drains the blood from the intestines and carries the digested proteins and carbohydrates through the portal vein to the liver, where, as we have seen, carbohydrates are stored (Plate III). The **lymphatic system** will be discussed later. In some of the backboned animals like fishes and frogs the **renal portal system** (*renes*— kidney; *portare*—to carry) carries the venous blood from the tail regions to the kidneys.

THE BLOOD

The circulating medium or blood is a very complex liquid tissue, much more complex than the average person realizes. In some of the lower animals the blood is almost transparent and much simpler in composition than the blood of the higher forms. In man and the higher vertebrates about 50–60 per cent of the blood is made up of a liquid called the **plasma**. The remaining 50–40 per cent of the blood volume consists of millions of **red** and **white corpuscles** and floating **blood platelets**.

Plasma. The plasma, the liquid part of the blood, is approximately 90 per cent water. Dissolved in the plasma and distributed by it is a great variety of substances. Practically every soluble substance found in any part of the body is also found in the blood in variable amounts on its way to or from the various organs and tissues. The plasma is the medium for the distribution of food, hormones, enzymes, antibodies, and metabolic wastes like carbon dioxide and urea. Glucose is always found in the plasma and is maintained at a concentration of about 0.1 per cent. A reduction in glucose to a concentration of 0.04 per cent or less may result in convulsions, unconsciousness, and death. Seven to nine per cent by weight of the plasma is made up of the plasma proteins. They play an important role in maintaining blood pressure and water balance between the blood and the tissue fluid. One of the proteins, fibrinogen, is necessary in the clotting of the blood. In recent years the physical chemists have developed methods for separating the various proteins of the plasma.

The most useful of the plasma proteins from a therapeutic viewpoint are albumin, gamma globulin, and fibrinogen. The albumin molecules appear to be well suited for the maintenance of blood volume in a person suffering from hemorrhage and shock since they readily bring the water by osmosis from the surrounding tissues to the blood stream and thus raise the blood pressure. Certain of the gamma globulins contain antibodies, a fact shown to be especially true in measles. Fibrinogen has been processed into fibrin foam and fibrin film (Fig. 42). The spongelike fibrin foam is used to control excess bleeding in operations, especially those on the brain. Fibrin film has been cut and fitted into place to repair injuries to the covering of the brain. Fibrinogen with thrombin has been found useful for cementing skin grafts in place.

Blood banks. Almost everyone has heard of blood banks, where "dried" blood is stored which can be given later by transfusions to those in need of it. Such "dried" blood is really only the dried blood serum. Blood is drawn from an individual, and the red and white corpuscles are separated from the serum by centrifuging. The serum is frozen, and the frozen chunks are evaporated, leaving the dried, flaky, yellow-brown plasma, which contains glucose, proteins, and certain other substances of the plasma. For emergency transfusions this dried material is mixed with triple-distilled sterilized water. The Red Cross worker, the surgeon, and the nurse on the battlefield of World War II were equipped with kits containing the materials necessary for making transfusions, and thousands of lives were saved by this means. On the first day after Pearl Harbor,

FIG. 42.   Plasma proteins: A, plasma foam; B, plasma sheet. *Photographs by Fritz Goro; by permission of Life Publishing Co.*

750 pints of plasma were used. Usually, the transfusion of dried blood is followed by a regular transfusion as soon as possible. Serum transfusions have been found to be especially effective in victims of severe burns and after poison-gas attacks.

Red corpuscles. The red color of the blood is caused by the presence of countless, flattened, biconcave, disklike cells called **red corpuscles (erythrocytes)** (*erythros*—red; *cytos*), which contain a red pigment called **hemoglobin.** In man there are about 5,000,000 in a cubic millimeter of blood (Fig. 43). They are formed in the **red**

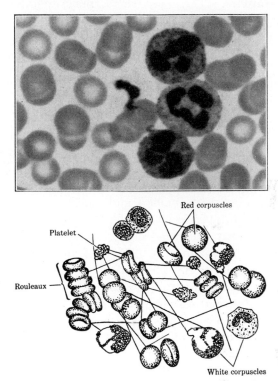

Fig. 43. Blood cells. *Above,* photomicrograph of red corpuscles and three large white corpuscles. *By permission of the General Biological Supply House.*

marrow of the long bones of the body, in some of the flat bones like the ribs, and in some of the bones of the skull. In man these red corpuscles in their later stages have no nuclei. Red blood corpuscles differ in various animals. For instance, those of the frog are oval, nucleated, and biconvex.

Hemoglobin, an iron-containing pigment combined with a protein, enters into a loose combination with oxygen and in this way carries oxygen to the various cells of the body. When the red corpuscles reach places in the organism where the oxygen content is low, the oxygen diffuses from the hemoglobin and passes to these regions of low oxygen concentration. Arterial blood, owing to the large amount of oxygen carried, has a bright red color; venous blood, because of reduced oxygen content, is dark red. The life of a red corpuscle is about 120 days. The worn-out or injured cells are destroyed in the liver and spleen. The iron is returned to the bone marrow, and the hematin fragment of the hemoglobin changes into bile pigment.

White corpuscles. These are small, nucleated, semitranslucent cells, numbering about 8,000 per cubic millimeter. There are a number of different types of white corpuscles, but we shall discuss only the two most numerous, the **leucocytes** and the **lymphocytes** (Fig. 43 and Plate IV). The leucocytes are capable of changing their shape and moving or migrating independently through the intercellular spaces among the tissues by ameboid movement, so called because it resembles the movement of the ameba. The number of these cells depends on the condition of the body. In infection they generally increase rapidly in number, but in typhoid and malaria their number is reduced. Leucocytes are scavengers, or perhaps we might say "soldiers." When bacteria invade any part of the body, the leucocytes gather there in great numbers and attack and feed on the bacteria and broken-down tissues by engulfing the particles. This process is called **phagocytosis** (*phagein*—to eat; *cytos*), hence the leucocytes are often known as **phagocytes.** Some of the leucocytes may be destroyed by bacterial acid. Thus there may result at the focus of the infection an accumulation of blood, tissue fluid, dead and living bacteria, leucocytes, and disintegrating cells. This entire yellowish or whitish mass is known as **pus.** The lymphocytes are smaller than the leucocytes and contain relatively little cytoplasm. They are useful in healing wounds and in replacing broken and torn tissues by transformation into connective-tissue cells.

Blood counts. We have already pointed out that the number of red corpuscles, leucocytes, and lymphocytes is fairly constant under normal conditions for certain specified comparable amounts of blood. In making a blood count a measured amount of blood is drawn and accurately diluted 200 times. A measured amount is spread upon a counting chamber, and the cells are counted under the microscope. The amount per cubic millimeter is then determined. Sometimes the amount of hemoglobin present is estimated by comparing the color of a sample with color charts. By either one or both of these methods the physician diagnoses a case of **anemia** if the red count is low or if the amount of hemoglobin is low. Anemia results in deficient oxygen supply, loss of energy, and general bodily impairment.

Blood platelets. These are small, roughly disk-shaped, granular bodies which aid in the clotting of blood. They probably have the same origin as the red blood corpuscles.

Clotting or coagulation. If blood is allowed to stand in a test tube or remain on the surface of a wound, it soon forms a jellylike mass or clot which gradually contracts, squeezing out a yellowish liquid, the **blood serum.** This very commonplace biological process, which is so frequently seen, in reality is very complex and involves a chain of events. It serves to illustrate how complicated many of the life processes are. Although certain details of blood clotting are not yet definitely understood, the main steps may be described as follows: as a result of a wound the injured tissue cells and the disintegrating blood platelets may release a substance called **thrombokinase.** This in turn acts with the calcium in the blood and another substance, **prothrombin,** to form **thrombin.** Thrombin in its turn acts on another substance, **fibrinogen** (fibrin; *genes*—born of), to change it into the **fibrin** which forms an interlacing network of strands, enmeshed in which are numerous red corpuscles. Fibrin is absolutely necessary for the clotting but does not occur as such in the blood stream. Summarized, this process probably is as follows:

Disintegrating platelets and injured tissue cells → Thrombokinase
Thrombokinase + Prothrombin + Calcium → Thrombin
Thrombin + Fibrinogen → Fibrin
Fibrin and red corpuscles → Clot

In certain diseases the blood loses its clotting power. Also, some unfortunate individuals, called "bleeders," have blood which clots slowly, and often an ordinary wound results in a severe hemorrhage. This condition is hereditary. Clendening reported the case of a butcher's delivery boy who, because of the jars received in jumping down from the wagon, started so many hemorrhages in his joints that he was crippled for life.

Sometimes as a result of injury or disease a clot, known as a **thrombus,** may form in a blood vessel. This clot may shut off the normal supply of blood to an organ or tissue. If it occurs in the heart it may result in death. A thrombus in the legs may cause varicose veins, and in the rectum, it may cause hemorrhoids. Occasionally, part of the thrombus breaks off and is carried free in the circulation; it is known as an **embolus** and, if it lodges in the blood vessels of the brain or the heart, may cause death.

Tissue fluid. The blood pressure in the capillaries causes some of the liquid plasma, minus plasma proteins, to be forced out into the intercellular spaces. This watery liquid fills the intercellular spaces and bathes some part of practically every individual cell of the organism. Someone has aptly said that almost every cell has its own "water front." The intercellular liquid, called **tissue fluid,** and the plasma within the capillaries, form an almost continuous liquid system (Plate IV). Dissolved materials diffuse from the plasma of the blood into the tissue fluid and thus are available to the individual cells. Waste materials are given off by the cells into the tissue fluid, which may diffuse back into the blood stream by way of the venous capillaries or the lymph vessels.

Lymph and the lymphatic system. The lymphatic system extends throughout the entire body. The main lymph vessels resemble the

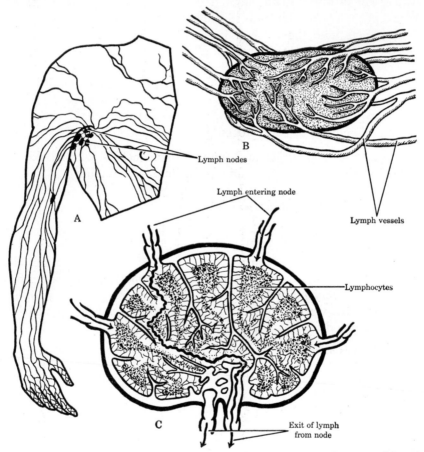

FIG. 44. *A,* lymph vessels and lymph nodes of the arm. *B,* diagram of lymph vessels entering and leaving lymph gland. *C,* diagram of lymph node. The lymph flows slowly through the node (note arrows) by labyrinthine blood passages, and solid particles are filtered from the lymph and engulfed by white corpuscles (not shown). *A and C redrawn from Carlson and Johnson, "The Machinery of the Body." By permission of the authors and the University of Chicago Press.*

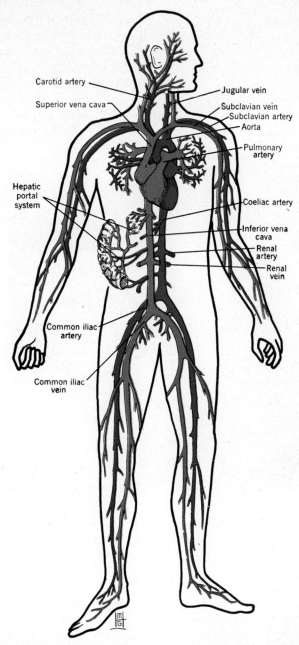

Carotid artery

Superior vena cava

Hepatic
portal
system

Common iliac
artery

Common iliac
vein

Jugular vein

Subclavian vein
Subclavian artery
Aorta
Pulmonary
artery

Coeliac artery

Inferior vena
cava
Renal
artery
Renal
vein

PLATE III. Diagram illustrating the circulation paths of man. Arterial system in
red; venous system in blue; hepatic portal system in purple.

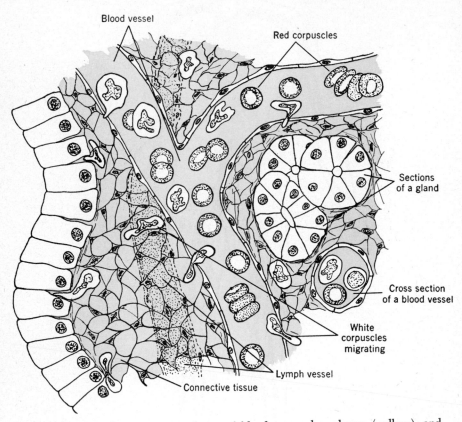

Blood vessel

Red corpuscles

Sections
of a gland

Cross section
of a blood vessel

White
corpuscles
migrating

Lymph vessel

Connective tissue

PLATE IV.   Diagram showing relation of blood corpuscles, plasma (yellow), and
tissue fluid (yellow) to the cells of other tissues.

veins in structure. They have valves but are thinner walled (Fig. 39). The composition of lymph is very much like that of the blood plasma minus the red corpuscles and certain proteins. The movement of the lymph toward the heart is caused by muscular contraction, particularly in the arms and legs, as well as by breathing movements. In some lower animals there may be pulsating "lymph hearts" which assist in keeping the lymph in circulation. The valves of the lymph vessels aid in keeping the lymph flowing toward the heart. At various places along the lymph tubes are rounded swellings called **lymph nodes** (Fig. 44), which aid not only in straining out bacteria and certain foreign particles but also in producing new lymphocytes. The lymph nodes of the lungs of city dwellers often become very dark from the accumulation of soot and dust particles. The "strained-out" bacteria are phagocytized by the leucocytes present in the lymph nodes. Often there is such an accumulation of bacteria and leucocytes in the lymph nodes near the site of an infection that they become swollen ("swollen glands") and sore to the touch.

The spleen. This organ of the vascular system seems to have at least three important functions. It acts as a reservoir for blood in which there is a higher concentration of red corpuscles. In an emergency, such as a rise in environmental temperature, hemorrhage, or emotional excitement, the spleen contracts, throwing reserve blood and corpuscles into the circulation. In the spleen, old and unhealthy red corpuscles are probably eliminated by the action of leucocytes. Finally, the spleen may manufacture lymphocytes.

THE CIRCULATORY SYSTEMS OF OTHER ANIMALS

When the walls of blood vessels in certain regions develop additional muscle fibers and have the power of rhythmic pulsation, they are known as **hearts.** Thus in the earthworm there are five pairs of specialized arches around the esophagus which aid, to some extent, the dorsal blood vessel in pumping the blood through the animal. The heart of an insect is a single muscular tube extending along the back, but it is actually only a specialized blood vessel which may be said to correspond to a ventricle (Fig. 45). The blood collects in a space or sinus around this tube or heart and enters through little openings, called **ostia** (*ostium*—entrance), which are provided with valves that close when the heart contracts. The clam has a heart made up of one ventricle and two auricles (Fig. 45 and Plate V). It pumps only oxygenated blood, since the blood comes to the auricles from the gills and mantle where it has lost carbon dioxide and gained oxygen.

The animals just mentioned, like almost all the non-backboned, multicellular animals, have a more or less well-developed system of

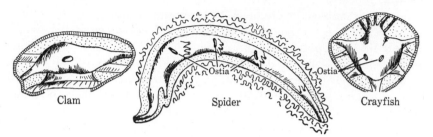

FIG. 45.   Hearts of some invertebrate animals.

arteries and veins.   In addition there are numerous spaces among the tissues and organs through which the blood flows.   This type of circulation in which the blood is not confined entirely to vessels is known as an **open circulation** (Plate V).

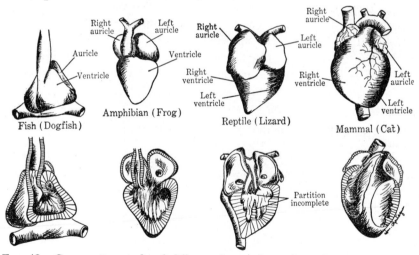

FIG. 46.   Comparative study of different forms of vertebrate hearts.   Note progressive development in the number of auricles and ventricles and the complete separation of the chambers on the right side of the heart from those on the left, thus preventing a mixture of the venous blood and the arterial blood.

There are a number of variations in the heart and blood vessels of the backboned animals, almost all of which have a **closed circulation,** although the lymphatic system might be considered comparable to the open circulation of lower forms. The heart of fishes has one auricle and one ventricle. It contains only venous blood, which is pumped to the gills through **afferent branchial arteries** (*adfero*— I carry toward; *branchus*—gill) where it is oxygenated and then transported to the aorta by the **efferent branchial arteries** (*effero*—I carry away from). This is a **branchial** or **gill circulation** instead of a pulmonary or lung circulation (Plate V).

With the development of lungs as a breathing device, new structural modifications and shifts appear in the heart and blood vessels to prevent the mixing of the arterial with the venous blood. In the amphibians (frogs, toads, water dogs, newts, and others) the heart is made up of a single ventricle and a right and a left auricle separated by a wall, or **septum** (Fig. 46). However, a special valvular mechanism is present which assists in preventing any great mixture of the arterial and venous blood. In reptiles, birds, and mammals a wall or septum is present which divides the ventricle into right and left ventricles. This ventricular septum is complete in birds and mammals but is incomplete in most of the reptiles. With complete septa in both auricles and ventricles there is no mixing of arterial and venous blood. Study carefully the semidiagrammatic sketches in Fig. 46.

THE BLOOD AND BODY DEFENSE—IMMUNITY

Organisms may suffer from two types of disease, **non-infectious** and **infectious**. We have already discussed the cause and cure for certain non-infectious diseases of man, such as pellagra, beriberi, and xerophthalmia. These diseases are not communicable. Mumps, scarlet fever, measles, typhoid fever, tuberculosis, and diphtheria are diseases which practically everyone knows are communicable from one individual to another, or infectious.

The organism has certain natural defenses against the invasion of bacteria and other parasitic organisms, all of which are protein in nature since they are made of protoplasm. Organisms likewise are able to combat bacterial products (**toxins**) and proteins foreign to the organism. The three groups of substances—bacteria, bacterial products, and foreign proteins—are known as **antigens** (*anti*—against; *genes*—born of). When an antigen enters the tissue of an organism, the tissues of the organism secrete a specific substance, known as an **antibody,** which in some way combines with the antigen and nullifies its harmful effects. We know how antibodies act, and, although we do not know in what tissues they are synthesized or their chemical formulas, it is certain that the blood serum contains these antibodies.

There are five general types of antibodies: **lysins** (*lysis*—loosening), which destroy the cell walls of foreign cells and cause dispersion of their protoplasms; **opsonins** (*opsonion*—sauce), which cause the leucocytes to engulf more bacteria; **agglutinins** (*agglutinans*—gluing), which cause bacterial cells and blood corpuscles to clump together; **precipitins,** which aggregate the molecules of a protein with formation of a precipitate; and **antitoxins** (*anti*-against; *toxin*—poison), which neutralize the poisons given off by some organisms, such as bacteria. The first three groups of antibodies attack bacteria or entire cells, whereas the last group mentioned neutralizes bacterial products or toxic substances. Since these reactions increase specific resistance to disease-producing agents, or produce **immunity,** they are called immunological reactions, and all such reactions are highly specific. A typhoid bacterium, an antigen, can be detected by an antigen-antibody reaction; for example, an immune animal's serum may be diluted many thousandfold and yet cause agglutination of typhoid cells, whereas a non-immune animal might not show this reaction after a hundredfold dilution of its serum.

Cytolysins (*cytos*—cell; *lysis*—loosening). When foreign tissues, such as red corpuscles or living or dead bacteria, are injected into the blood stream, protective substances called lysins are formed which will dissolve (lytic action) the walls of the foreign cells and break up the cells. For example, if the serum of a rabbit which has had human red corpuscles previously injected into its blood is added to a mixture of human and rabbit blood in a test tube, the human corpuscles will be dissolved but no others will be affected. Thus we see that cytolysins are specific in their reactions.

This knowledge concerning lytic action is utilized in inoculations against typhoid fever, smallpox, and other diseases. Dead typhoid germs are injected into the animal intramuscularly, causing the formation of a specific cytolysin. Later, if live typhoid germs invade the body, they will be destroyed by the cytolysin present. The lytic reaction is also the basis of the Wassermann blood test for syphilis as well as for other diagnostic tests.

Opsonins. Wright discovered that the leucocytes could not take up the bacteria unless they had first been acted upon by serum. The blood serum from immune animals "prepared" bacteria or "made them more appetizing" than did the serum of normal blood. This seemed to indicate the presence of something in the blood serum which caused the white corpuscles to engulf more bacteria, hence the name opsonin. Increased production of these opsonins can be stimulated by injections of various kinds of dead or living bacteria into the blood stream.

Agglutinins and precipitins. These two kinds of substances are so similar in their action that they may properly be grouped as the same type of antibody. Agglutinins cause bacteria or foreign cells

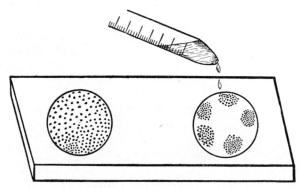

Fig. 47. Diagram showing agglutination of bacteria. *A*, uniform distribution of bacteria within a droplet of culture. *B*, clumping of bacteria after the addition of blood serum containing agglutinin.

and blood corpuscles to clump together; precipitins act on smaller units, such as molecules. Both reactions tend to localize the foreign protein and render it more available to the phagocytes.

Agglutinins are specific in their reactions and are used for laboratory diagnosis of disease. Thus, in the Widal test for typhoid fever, blood serum from the suspected patient, if added to a culture of known typhoid bacteria, will cause the bacteria to clump or agglutinate (Fig. 47). Clearly, this would not happen if the patient had some other disease. Types I, II, and III of pneumonia may be diagnosed by the same general method.

Precipitins can be readily built up in the blood by repeated injections of some specific foreign protein. To illustrate, if chicken serum is repeatedly injected into the circulation of a rabbit, a precipitin is formed. Now if some blood serum from the injected rabbit is added to some chicken serum, a visible precipitate is formed. Not only chicken serum but also serum of animals closely related to the chicken will be precipitated in this way. The closer the relationship, the more marked is this precipitating reaction (Fig. 48). Therefore this method can be used to detect animal relationships. Precipitins are fairly specific in their reactions. For example, if cow's milk is injected

into the rabbit's blood stream there will be produced a precipitin
which will precipitate the casein of the milk. The precipitin reaction
has been made use of in medicolegal cases to determine whether or
not a stain was made by human blood.

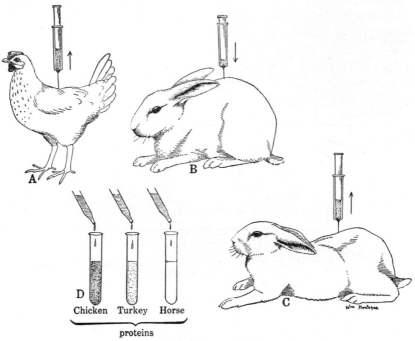

D
Chicken Turkey Horse
proteins

FIG. 48. Diagram showing preparation and reaction of precipitins. A, withdrawing serum (protein) from a chicken. B, injecting chicken protein into a
rabbit. C, withdrawing serum from the rabbit after an interval of several days.
D, result of adding this serum to different proteins. Note the dense precipitate
when mixed with chicken protein, a slighter reaction with turkey protein (an
animal closely related to the chicken), and no reaction with horse protein.

Antitoxins. Some disease germs or bacteria, such as those causing
diphtheria, owe their deadliness to the toxins or poisons which they
throw off into the blood stream as a result of their metabolism.
Diphtheria toxin produces characteristic effects upon heart muscle;
tetanus toxin causes marked changes in the central nervous system.
To counteract or neutralize the effects of these toxins, the living
cells of the infected animal form chemical substances called **antitoxins.** Antitoxins unite with the toxins in some as yet unexplained
way and counteract their poisonous properties. Antitoxins are specific in their reactions, and consequently each toxin must be met with
a specific antitoxin.

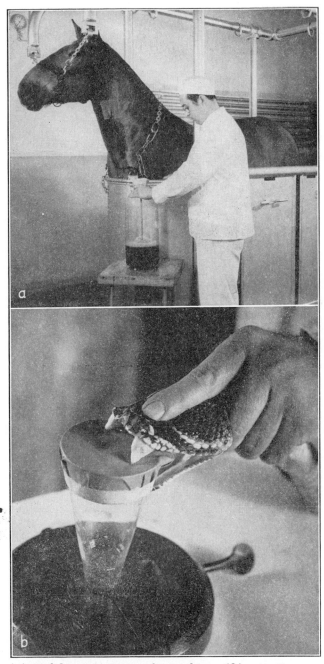

Fig. 49. (*a*) Withdrawing antitoxin from a horse; (*b*) extracting venom from a rattlesnake. (*a*) *By permission of Parke, Davis and Co.;* (*b*) *by permission of Sharpe and Dohme.*

In former years, if a person contracted diphtheria, his recovery depended on whether he could form a sufficient amount of antitoxin. Today, diphtheria antitoxins are prepared commercially from horses. The horse is an excellent animal for the production of large quantities of the antitoxin and builds up antitoxins when injected with the toxin of diphtheria. The serum is then extracted and prepared for the market. Today, thanks to the bacteriologist and the horse, "no child need have diphtheria."

Cobra and rattlesnake venoms are now combated by means of venom antitoxins. The venom is extracted from the snakes, and the antitoxin is built up in the goat in much the same way as in horses. Both bacterial antitoxins and antivenins are now available commercially.

Originally, it was thought that for each specific immunological reaction there had to be present a specific antibody and therefore there had to be many separate, distinct, and independent antibodies. Extensive investigation has added to the knowledge concerning these reactions, and it is now thought that the essential factor common to all manifestations of the union of antigen and antibody, i.e., clumping of cells, formation of precipitates, or lysis of cells, regardless of these ways in which the union can be detected, are caused by the same antibody. This interpretation has been termed by some workers the "unitarian" hypothesis. In all reactions showing the union of antigen and antibody, the antigen must not have been altered chemically and certain environmental conditions—salt content, temperature, hydrogen-ion concentration, etc.—must be present before the maximum reaction takes place.

Immunity. It has often been observed that some people when exposed to certain infectious diseases never become afflicted with them. They are said to be immune. The organisms, for this applies to other animals besides man, may have in their blood stream and tissue certain antibodies which counteract specific antigens. Thus the horse is naturally immune to diphtheria; the negro is more resistant to yellow fever than the white man; man is immune to distemper, a disease of dogs. This resistance is often called **natural immunity** or one phase of **active immunity.**

Man may acquire active immunity in several ways. He may have built up antibodies by having had certain diseases, or by having been protected against them by inoculation with dead bacteria as by typhoid "shots." This type of inoculation brings about reactions similar to those occasioned by living bacteria.

Again, man and certain organisms (particularly domestic cattle) may have a **passive immunity** which is effective over a period of years. In acquiring passive immunity, the antibodies built up in one animal are transferred to another animal. Immunity, in the last analysis, depends on the amount and kind of antibodies in the blood serum, that is, the liquid part of the blood minus the fibrinogen or fibrin.

BLOOD GROUPS

It had been noticed by medical men that in blood transfusions the mixture of the two bloods in the patient often produced harmful instead of helpful results because of the agglutination of the red corpuscles of either the donor or the recipient or both. Death too frequently followed a transfusion. Landsteiner made a study of this condition and found that the action was no random process but that human blood could be classified into four main groups on the basis of the agglutinizing reaction. These four main groups have been designated as AB, A, B, and O, respectively. Incidentally it has since been found that there are subgroups also. The agglutinizing reaction takes place because of the presence of a specific **agglutinin** in the patient's blood which may act with another substance, **agglutinogen,** found in the erythrocytes of the donor. Today, many other factors such as the Rh factor (see page 262), Hr factor, M factor, and N factor are known to exist, and consequently the story of these reactions has become quite complicated.

By simple tests it is possible to find out the type of blood a person has. Accordingly, before a transfusion is given the blood types of both patient and donor are ascertained. This is known as "matching bloods." A study of the accompanying chart will demonstrate the agglutinizing effects of the various types of blood (Fig. 50). Here it will be seen that any type of blood can be injected into a person with type AB. Likewise no serum will agglutinate erythrocytes of group O, which can thus be used for transfusion into blood of any type. However, whenever possible, both donor and recipient should have the same type of blood.

These blood characteristics apparently are hereditary. However, they may not become fully established until sometime after infancy. A comparison of blood types has been used in court to determine the parentage of a child. Although paternity cannot be proved, yet the impossibility of being the father of the child in question may be established.

Blood groups have been detected in other animals besides man. Another interesting application of blood tests has been made by anthropologists in their study of races. By a special technique it has been possible to test mummified tissue. Tests have been made of Peruvian and Egyptian mummies as well as of certain Basket-maker Indians.

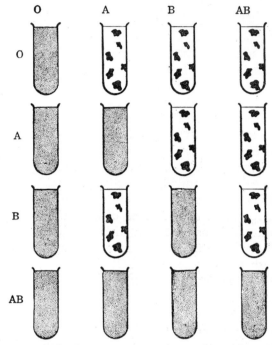

FIG. 50. Reactions of blood groups. Test tubes with stippling show no agglutination; all others show agglutination.

WILLIAM HARVEY AND THE DISCOVERY OF THE CIRCULATION OF THE BLOOD

The early Greek and Roman philosophers were greatly impressed with the various internal movements which they could see in themselves and others. They could feel the beating of the heart and of the pulse and recognized the fact that the body was filled with a red fluid which would flow from a wound. Most of their knowledge about these reactions came from talking about them and not through investigation. They could not examine human bodies because this was contrary to their religion and against their prejudices. They were content to examine the dead body only superficially. Galen considered the heart the source of the body's heat and thought the blood was a sort of oil which burned to furnish the required heat.   In those days it was known that the blood in the right side of the heart was different from that in the left side of the heart, so Galen proposed the theory that the blood was "purified" by a passage through invisible

Fig. 51.   William Harvey (1578–1657), who discovered the circulation of the blood.   *Photograph furnished by Army Medical Museum (negative No. 33740).*

pores in the wall or septum between the right and left ventricles. Another interesting idea held at that time was that the arteries contained air and the blood circulated in the veins.   Gradually the theory gained ground that the heart propelled the blood.   Servetus proved that the blood was oxygenated by the lungs and not by the passage through the interventricular wall.   Eventually it was recognized that the heart did drive the blood through the pulmonary circulatory system, but the idea was held that the systemic circulation was accomplished in some other way.

William Harvey (1578–1657), an English physician, conceived the idea that the heart was responsible for the entire blood circulation and that the blood coursed, as it were, "in a circle." He was fascinated in watching the beating heart of animals and at one time thought that "the motion of the heart was to be comprehended only by God." Continuing his experimentation, he showed that every time the heart contracted there was a pulse in the arteries, and that when the heart ceased to beat the pulse stopped. In this way he showed that the arteries contained blood coming directly from the heart. Later he was able to demonstrate that the flow of blood in the veins was toward the heart. In the course of his study of the arteries and veins, he showed that the valves in the veins would prevent the blood from going backward. He reasoned that, if an arm, for instance, were tightly bound or tied, if the blood were traveling from the heart to the limbs, swelling of the veins would be on the side farthest from the heart, and the swelling of an artery would be nearest the heart. In this way the conclusion was reached that the arteries carried blood away from the heart and that the veins carried it toward the heart.

The work of Harvey illustrates in a striking way the scientific method of approach. For nine years he continued experimental work on the circulation of various animals, and only after that did he publish his treatise on the circulation of the blood. The following statements from his book show this attitude very clearly. "I sought to discover the motions and uses of the heart from actual inspection and not from the writings of others; at length, and by using greater and daily diligence and investigation, making frequent inspection of many and various animals, and collating numerous observations, I thought I had attained to the truth." When in doubt about publishing his findings, he made the following observation, which strikingly expresses the attitude of the scientist toward truth: "Doctrine once sown strikes deep its root, and reaped for antiquity influences all men. Still the die is cast, and my trust is in my love of truth and the candour of cultivated minds."

7

Metabolism
The Release of Energy
Respiration

We have been studying the processes of digestion and absorption of carbohydrates, fats, and proteins and the transportation of these digested foods to each individual cell by the blood. In addition to these energy processes, animals may release energy in the form of heat, movement, light, secretion, nerve-cell activities, and electricity. All these processes represent work of some sort and we have already learned that work always involves transfer or transformation of energy. All organisms in order to live must have a store of potential energy which is continuously being changed to kinetic energy. Further, every living cell of the organism must carry on these energy transformations. The problem before us now is to see how the cells and the organism change this potential energy into kinetic energy.

The work of the cell then involves a transformation, into kinetic energy, of the potential energy stored in its carbohydrates, fats, and proteins. This transformation is accomplished by a series of chemical reactions that break down these complex compounds into simpler forms, thereby releasing their energy content. This liberation of energy, or transformation of potential into kinetic energy, is a fundamental and all-important metabolic process. In all organisms it is accomplished by similar chemical reactions, and the process is known as **respiration** (*respirare*—to breathe).

Nature of respiration. The process of respiration is sometimes compared to the burning of wood. When wood is burned we speak of the process as oxidation because the carbon in the wood combines with oxygen of the air, forming carbon dioxide. The hydrogen of the wood combines with oxygen to form water. In this process of oxidation heat is liberated and light is emitted. In the process of respiration under ordinary conditions, oxygen is consumed, and or-

ganic compounds, such as carbohydrates and fats, are oxidized, forming water and carbon dioxide.

In certain animals a portion of the energy released in respiration
is not heat but a weak light called **bioluminescence** (*bios*—life;
lumen—light). A familiar example is the light released by the firefly.
Perhaps respiration is so frequently thought of as a process of burning
because the ultimate result—the production of carbon dioxide, water,
and kinetic energy—is the same as that obtained from the burning
of organic substances in air. Although this comparison may aid us
in forming some simple conception of the nature of respiration, it
can be relied upon only in the most superficial manner, for respiration in the cell is a very different process from the oxidation of coal
in a furnace.

> The oxidation of coal, as well as that of many other substances, takes place
> only at high temperatures. Likewise, respiration apparently occurs only in the
> protoplasm itself or in close proximity to it, which means that it occurs in the
> presence of water or in water, whereas combustion outside the living organism
> cannot be carried on in water. These differences between respiration and ordinary
> combustion of organic substances may be partly accounted for by the fact that
> the oxidation of organic compounds in respiration involves the action of oxidizing
> enzymes produced by the protoplasm. The enzymes concerned in or associated
> with respiration are: **oxidase, oxygenase, peroxidase,** and **catalase.**

The materials used and the waste products formed in respiration
are clearly defined, but the reactions occurring in the cell by which
the organic compounds are changed into wastes with release of energy
are not so clearly understood. In other words, we know only the
beginning and the end of the process and very little about the intermediate stages. The results of respiration can be comprehended
more easily; e.g., stored foods are used up, and there is a consequent
loss in weight. Respiration also produces heat, which is quite evident in animals.

Influence of external factors. External conditions as well as enzymes tend to accelerate or retard respiratory activity. Respiration
tends to increase with rise of temperature until the heat becomes
injurious to the tissues. The amount of moisture present, within
certain limits, also influences the rate or intensity of respiration.
Wounded parts have a higher respiratory rate than those that are
intact, and young tissues have a much greater respiration intensity
than old ones. The list of factors affecting respiration might be extended considerably, but these statements will suffice to show that
respiration, like all other chemical processes, undergoes marked

changes in response to the influence of various environmental conditions.

Aerobic and anaerobic respiration. Up to this point we have been considering respiration as it occurs when a normal supply of free oxygen is present. Such respiration is known as **aerobic respiration** (*aer*—air; *bios*—life).

Sometimes a respiratory reaction takes place in the absence of free oxygen. This is called **anaerobic respiration** (*an*—without; *aer*). In anaerobic respiration the oxidation of complex compounds is not entirely completed. Instead of the formation of carbon dioxide and water as a direct result of the reaction, intermediate compounds such as alcohol or lactic acid may be formed. This partial oxidation of the organic compounds may be accompanied by a rearrangement of the atoms within the molecule without the presence of any free oxygen; or it may involve the agency of oxygen derived from the breaking down of other compounds of the cell. The energy transformed in the muscular contraction is released by anaerobic respiration.

THE BREATHING MECHANISMS IN MAN

The breathing mechanism. In man, we find that air with 20 per cent of oxygen normally reaches the pharynx through the nose, where it passes over a system of much-folded, bony plates covered by a moist epithelium. At the back of the pharynx the air enters a slitlike opening called the **glottis,** which, in man, is guarded by a cartilaginous fold, the **epiglottis.** The glottis opens into a cartilaginous chamber, the **larynx** or voice box ("Adam's apple"), which contains the **vocal cords.** From the larynx a tubular **trachea** leads down through the neck, dividing in the chest region into the **right** and **left bronchi** (Fig. 52). A succession of small, incomplete rings of cartilage is present in both the trachea and the bronchi, supporting the walls of these tubes and rendering them non-collapsible. The right and left bronchi lead respectively to the right and left **lungs,** where they branch into an intricate system of tubes or **bronchioles** which finally end in tiny, thin-walled sacs called **alveoli.** The walls of the alveoli, bound together by connective tissue, contain countless permeating blood capillaries. Owing to the very large number of alveoli, the lungs have a spongy texture, and the total surface exposed to the air is also very greatly increased—estimated to be approximately 100 square yards. The lungs are located in the **thoracic cavity,** which is bounded laterally by the walls of the thorax supported by the curving ribs. This cavity is sep-

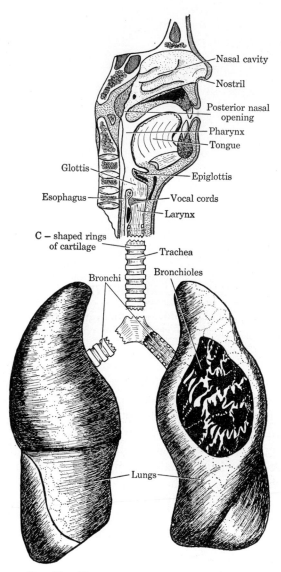

Fig. 52. The respiratory apparatus of man.

arated from the abdominal cavity by a broad sheet of muscular tissue, the **diaphragm.** The membrane lining the thoracic cavity and covering the lungs is called the **pleura.**

The mechanics of breathing. The thoracic cavity is an air-tight compartment enclosing the elastic lungs, which communicate with

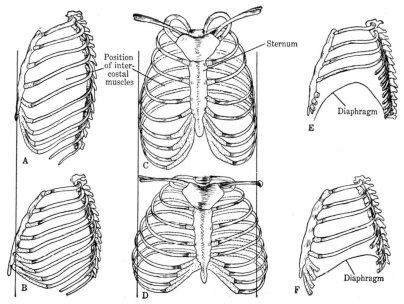

FIG. 53. Diagrams showing the mechanics of breathing. *A* and *C* show position of ribs and sternum at the end of an expiration. *B* and *D* show the ribs raised upward and outward by action of intercostal muscles. This causes an enlargement of the chest cavity, permitting air to rush into the lungs (inspiration). *E* and *F* show the role of the diaphragm in breathing. *E* shows the diaphragm raised, thus decreasing the volume of the chest cavity and aiding in expiration. *F* shows the diaphragm lowered (contracted), thus enlarging the chest cavity and aiding in inspiration.

the outside only through the trachea. In normal breathing, as the chest cavity is enlarged, the pressure of the air in the lungs is reduced below atmospheric pressure and so air passes into the lungs. This is **inspiration** (*in*—into; *spirare*—to breathe). The enlargement of the chest cavity is brought about by the contracting of the **intercostal muscles** (*inter*—between; *costa*—rib), which move the ribs upward and outward on each side and in front, and also by the contracting of the muscular diaphragm, which increases the depth of the chest cavity (Fig. 53). Thus, in normal breathing, both the intercostal and diaphragm muscles function.

When the muscles involved in inspiration relax, the elastic recoil of the expanded lungs, aided by other factors, brings about a decrease in the volume of the chest cavity and increases the pressure of the air in the lungs, causing some of it to be forced out (Fig. 53). This is **expiration** (*ex*—outside; *spirare*). In "forced" expiration, muscles of the abdominal wall and others are involved, effecting more rapid action and expulsion of a larger amount of air.

Exchanging oxygen and carbon dioxide. We have already seen that in diffusion the molecules of liquids, solids, or gases tend to move from regions of high concentration to regions of lower concentration. According to the physical law of diffusion of gases, if a permeable membrane separates two volumes or two solutions of a gas at different pressures, the gas will pass through the membrane from a region of higher to one of lower pressure. Moreover, each gas behaves independently of any other gases that may be present. Now it has been shown that gases will pass through a *moist* membrane according to the principles just stated. The cell membrane is kept constantly moist by secretions from the protoplasm. So if "fresh" air containing oxygen comes into the alveoli of the lungs, and if, in the thin, moist walls of the alveoli, there is a flow of blood with a low pressure of oxygen, oxygen will diffuse to this region of low pressure or into the blood through the capillary walls. Here the oxygen unites in a loose chemical combination with the hemoglobin of the red corpuscle, forming **oxyhemoglobin,** which is carried along with the blood through the body among the cells of the tissues. These tissues, if they have been releasing energy by oxidation, have a low oxygen pressure. The oxyhemoglobin now readily breaks down into hemoglobin and oxygen, which diffuses through the moist cell membranes to these low-pressure regions in the cells (Plate VI).

The same general process holds true for carbon dioxide, which we have seen is the product of oxidation. The blood has a lower carbon dioxide pressure than the cell and the tissue fluid that surrounds it. So the carbon dioxide passes through the moist cell membrane and gets into the tissue fluid, whence it finally reaches the blood where some of it may be carried in the plasma proteins and some in the hemoglobin of the red corpuscles. The carbon dioxide is thus carried to the lungs, where the air in the alveoli has a lower carbon dioxide pressure or density than that of the blood. Consequently, the carbon dioxide passes into the air in the lungs and is expelled during expiration. Since gases behave independently of each other, oxygen may be passing into the blood at the same time that carbon dioxide is leaving the blood; or vice versa, if conditions are changed.

The somewhat generalized description just given is supported by numerous carefully controlled experiments involving accurate quantitative measurements.   The following tables * show the difference in percentage of gaseous content of inspired and expired air and indicate that air in the lungs "loses oxygen and gains carbon dioxide and consequently the blood absorbs oxygen and eliminates carbon dioxide."

	N	O	CO_2
Inspired	79	20.96	0.04
Expired	79	16.02	4.38
		4.94	4.34

The difference in pressure between the oxygen and carbon dioxide in the blood and those in the alveoli of the lungs is shown by the following summary (arrows show direction of gas flow):

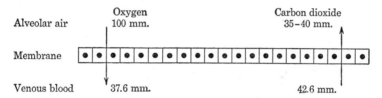

The difference between the gas tensions in the tissues and those in the arterial blood is summarized as follows:

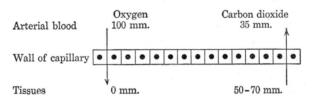

Regulation of the breathing mechanism in man. Regulation of breathing is brought about by nerve impulses sent out from the **respiratory center** located in the brain (medulla).   These impulses go out to the various muscles of the ribs and the diaphragm, initiating movements that cause inspiration and expiration.   For the most part, this rhythmic action is automatically controlled, but we can exercise voluntary control to some extent, as when we hold our breath.   Apparently the impulses sent out from the brain are influenced by the amount of carbon dioxide in the blood.   Thus it can be readily understood that we breathe more rapidly after exercising violently because

* W. H. Howell, *Textbook of Physiology*, pp. 698, 718, 719, W. B. Saunders Company, by permission.

more carbon dioxide has accumulated in the blood from the muscles and other tissues. Lack of oxygen produces no appreciable effect, but an excess amount of carbon dioxide causes an inspiratory or expiratory impulse to be sent out. When the carbon dioxide reaches a sufficiently high concentration in the blood, it is impossible for a person to hold his breath. One cannot commit suicide by holding the breath. Further effects of carbon dioxide on the body action will be discussed later.

THE BREATHING MECHANISM IN OTHER ANIMALS

From the foregoing discussion we can readily see that for the exchange of gases, oxygen, and carbon dioxide, for example, a moist membrane is necessary. Furthermore, the membrane must present an exposed surface sufficient to care for all the oxygen needs of the organism. In the very simplest forms (protozoans and sponges) sufficient body surface is exposed so that no special breathing mechanism is necessary. In the earthworm the oxygen-carbon dioxide problem is solved by a covering of moist skin well supplied with blood capillaries. Some "cousins" of the earthworm have folds of skin, or special thread-like filaments, which are used in oxygen-carbon dioxide exchange. In many aquatic animals breathing is done by the gills. The water containing oxygen flows over the gills, which take up oxygen and release carbon dioxide. The gills of crayfish, lobsters, and crabs are feathery plumelike structures. In most mollusks (oysters, clams, squids, water snails) there are specialized folds known as gills which bring about this same exchange. The mantle, a fold of skin which covers the soft visceral structures of certain mollusks, is also a respiratory organ (Plate V and Fig. 54).

In adult insects and some related animals the air enters the respiratory tract through small pores in the body wall, called **spiracles**. The spiracles lead into a system of tubes called **tracheae** which resemble only superficially the trachea of man. These tubes made of spirally twisted tissue branch, divide, subdivide, and end in very minute vessels which carry the air with its oxygen directly to the tissues. Carbon dioxide is expelled through these same tubes. The air is exhaled and inhaled by contractions of the body wall, and the rate of these contractions is dependent on and varies with the activities of the insect. The blood of such animals has little to do with oxygen and carbon dioxide distribution. Spiders exchange oxygen and carbon dioxide by means of folds of tissue called "book lungs." In some animals, such as insect larvas (dragonflies), the hind gut or cloaca is very vascular and is used in breathing.

In fishes, **gill slits** lead from the pharynx and open to the exterior. The **gill arches** or the walls of the gill slits are supported by either bony or cartilaginous rods and are used for the attachment of very

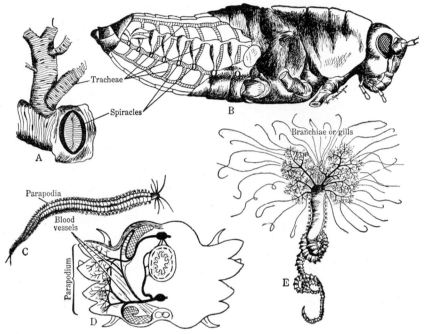

Fig. 54. Breathing mechanisms of other animals. *A* and *B*, insects; *C–E*, worms (annelids). *D, modified from Hegner, "Invertebrate Zoology"; E, redrawn from Parker and Haswell, "Textbook of Zoology," Vol. I. By permission of the publisher, the Macmillan Co.*

delicate, highly vascular gills.   The water containing dissolved oxygen enters the mouth and flows through the gill slits over the gills to the exterior.   Gills of tadpoles and salamanders are usually bushy in type. It is to be noted that one of the main principles in breathing devices is the provision of a maximum amount of moist surface with a minimum of bulkiness (Plate V).

With some modification, the general plan of the breathing mechanism described for man is the same in practically all vertebrates other than fishes.   In frogs there is no diaphragm.   Closing of the nostrils and raising of the floor of the buccal cavity force air from the pharynx into the rather simple saclike lungs.   Thus, in a sense, the air is

swallowed.   The lungs of birds are attached to the ribs.   When the bird
is not flying, inspiration and expiration take place respectively by the
raising and lowering of the chest.   In addition to lungs, birds have
large accessory air sacs located in some of the bones.   These sacs increase the breathing surface to a large degree and function especially
when the bird is flying.   In flight the bird's powerful wing muscles must
have a firm anchorage.   This is furnished by the ribs, which are held
rigid by the contracted rib-muscles which cannot now function effectively in ordinary breathing.   Under such conditions, the air sacs, which
are filled and emptied in flight, serve to bring about inspiration and
expiration through the lungs.   There are no vocal cords in the larynx
of birds, but the sounds are developed by a vibratory membrane in the
syrinx (*syrinx*—a pipe), a special structure located in the trachea just
before it divides to form the bronchi.

REGULATION OF BODY TEMPERATURE

Every chemical reaction is influenced by the temperature of the
environment in which it takes place.   Thus temperature variation will
affect practically every chemical, physical, and biological process.
These combined reactions going on in the living cells and tissues result
in the formation of certain behavior patterns and influence the adjustment mechanism of the whole organism.   The lower animals, including
such backboned forms as fishes, frogs, and snakes, are markedly affected
by environmental temperatures.   In the cold their metabolic processes
slow down and the animals become sluggish.   When the temperature
rises, the animals become more active.   The body temperature of these
animals varies directly with that of the environment.   Such animals are
said to be **"cold blooded"** (**poikilothermal**).   The body temperature
of such animals is usually only a few degrees above that of the environment.   This condition accounts for the cold "feel" of a fish, frog, or
snake; since the temperature of these animals is approximately that of
the environment, the animals feel cold when touched by our "warm-
blooded" hands.

On the other hand, certain animals such as dogs, cats, and men possess certain adaptive mechanisms or make certain adaptations which
maintain a fairly constant body temperature and thus make possible a
"more even tempo" of life activities.   Through the ages the body tissues
of these **"warm-blooded"** (**homiothermal**) animals have become so
adjusted to certain constant temperature that even a relatively minor
shift either to a lower or a higher temperature is injurious and may

even result in death.   Life, then, depends on the maintenance of a fairly constant optimum temperature.   This condition is brought about by various devices.

Increase in heat production by muscular exertion has been observed in man, horses, dogs, and other animals by all of us.   The animal must make an effective adjustment for this increase in heat production.   The two important processes in man which help to regulate excessive heat

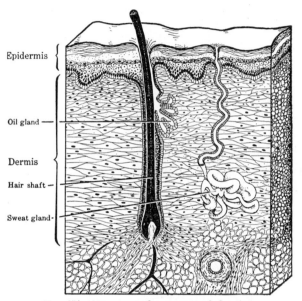

Epidermis

Oil gland —

Dermis

Hair shaft —

Sweat gland ·

FIG. 55.   Diagram of a section of the skin.

are the evaporation of sweat from the skin and the elimination of water vapor from the lungs.

It may be recalled that a moist membrane is necessary for gaseous exchange.   Thus the lining membrane of the lungs must be kept moist. The moisture, supplied by the blood, is constantly diminished by evaporation and is lost with each expiration in the form of vapor.   To bring about this change, just as to change water into steam, heat is required.   In the organism, heat comes from the oxidation of various compounds in the cells, which in turn heats the blood as it courses through the organism.   In the lungs and skin the blood loses some of its heat and water by evaporation.   Thus cooled, the blood, as it circulates, cools the tissues and in a large measure controls the temperature of the organism.   It is estimated that, of the heat loss in man, 85 per cent is lost from skin, 10 per cent in breathing, and 5 per cent in warming food and air.

Water is given off from the skin of various vertebrates in two ways: by the secretion of sweat glands, and by evaporation from the general epithelial surface.   In man, the **sweat glands**—there are over 3,000,000 of them—are tubular glands whose internal, coiled, terminal region is well supplied with blood vessels (Fig. 55).   From the blood in these vessels the gland removes some of the excess moisture, which is excreted as sweat and varies in amount with both the individual and his activities.

Increase in oxidation may be brought about by muscular exertion, which, in turn, causes a greater activity of the sweat glands and more water (sweat) is secreted, which, evaporating, absorbs more heat. Shivering is a type of involuntary muscular exercise.   Dogs may adjust their temperature to some extent by panting.   Excessive cold results in a contraction of the blood vessels of the skin, cutting down the supply of blood to these regions so that less heat is lost.   The temperature of an animal is influenced by other factors, such as the accumulation of an insulating layer of fat under the skin, the development of such protective structures as hair, feathers, and scales, and the wearing of clothes.

EARLY HISTORY OF RESPIRATION

One of the earliest respiration experiments on record was performed by Robert Hooke in 1667.   He demonstrated before the Royal Society that in order to be kept alive a dog must have a "sufficient supply of fresh air."   A little later (1674) John Mayow conceived the idea that air contained a specific substance which was necessary to support combustion and to maintain vital activity.   He wrote as follows: "With respect, then, to the use of respiration, it may be affirmed that an aerial something, whatever it may be, essential to life, passes into the mass of blood.   And thus air driven out of the lungs, these vital particles having been drained from it, is no longer fit for breathing again."   He called this substance the *spiritus nitro aereus,* and of course this was a shrewd guess at what we now recognize as oxygen.   Priestley discovered oxygen a century later (1774), but he called it "dephlogisticated air," i.e., air deprived of **phlogiston,** which, according to this theory, was a specific substance in matter that was liberated by burning.   Priestley's experiment revealed the fact that, after air had been "spoilt" by the respiration of animals, it could be restored by the activity of green plants if exposed to sunlight.   However, it was the brilliant Frenchman

Lavoisier who discovered the real nature of respiration and who gave to the world the correct interpretation of the chemistry of combustion. By carefully weighing his materials he was able to account for changes that had hitherto been unnoticed, and by a series of excellent scientific experiments he ascertained that respiration is a chemical process by which the oxygen of the air is consumed and carbon dioxide produced.

8

Metabolism
Elimination of Waste Materials
The Carbon and Nitrogen
Cycles

We have learned that many and varied chemical changes take place in animal cells; that some of these changes store up energy and that others release this energy in the performance of the different functions necessary to support vital activity. In the course of these changes, especially those involved in catabolism, many compounds are formed which are not used in growth or repair and which do not again enter into the metabolism of the cells. Such substances are usually called waste products. Some of them may be of service to the organism, whereas the accumulation of others would be extremely harmful and might even result in death. Throughout its life, the organism provides, in one way or another, for the elimination of all harmful wastes.

WASTES—EXCRETION

It has already been pointed out that energy is released by the oxidation of stored carbohydrates, fats, and proteins. Even the living tissues may be broken down and their proteins and fats oxidized.

Because of differences in food supply and in the metabolic processes themselves, wastes may vary somewhat from animal to animal and even in the same individual from time to time. Animal wastes such as carbon dioxide or urea may be products of metabolism, or they may be toxic substances formed by the animal body under either normal or diseased conditions. Other cast-off materials termed wastes, but not direct byproducts of metabolic processes, are indigestible substances and unabsorbed food which accumulate in the lower end of the alimentary canal. In many animals, including organisms so different as man and the earthworm, the outer protective covering is continually sloughing away and continually being restored. Dead scaly portions of the skin are worn away and sloughed off daily. The horny covering of the crayfish, the skins of snakes, feathers of birds, antlers of the deer, and the hair and horns of other animals are shed periodically.

The simplest animals have no highly complex excretory organs, and much of the waste is eliminated from each individual cell directly into the environment. However, these wastes are very similar in nature to the wastes of the highest animals. As animals increase in complexity, as will be shown later, they develop a great variety of excretory organs.

Carbon dioxide. It may be recalled that carbon dioxide, together with water, is formed for the most part by oxidation of carbohydrates and fats, although some of these wastes may come from digested protein not used in tissue building. In the lower animals, carbon dioxide is eliminated mostly through the body surface, but in the more complex invertebrates other devices are involved, such as the tracheae of insects and various types of gill-like structures. In the vertebrate animals carbon dioxide is thrown off in greatest amounts by the lungs or gills, and in lesser amounts through the skin. In man very little carbon dioxide is eliminated by the skin.

Water. Although the lungs and skin eliminate water, probably the most important structures involved in water regulation are the kidneys. The relative importance of these mechanisms varies with different animals.

Nitrogen compounds. These, as well as sulphates, phosphates, and other waste products of protein metabolism, are excreted, for the most part, by the kidneys, in the form of a watery solution called **urine.** In man, the kidneys are located in the abdominal region on either side of the backbone at about the level of the lowest ribs. The urine is drained from them by two tubes, the **ureters,** emptying into a muscular reservoir, the **urinary bladder,** which empties through a tube, the **urethra** (Fig. 56). In some animals, such as birds, the urinary bladder is missing and the ureters empty into the cloaca. In frogs, the ureters carry the urine to the cloaca whence it passes through a ventral opening into a urinary bladder. The accumulated urine is later voided through this opening into the cloaca and thence to the outside.

The kidney. To understand more clearly the mechanism of the urinary system, some knowledge of the detailed anatomy of the kidney is necessary. We shall first examine the comparatively simple "kidney" of the earthworm. The coelom of an earthworm is divided into compartments filled with coelomic fluid in which waste material may be found. In most of these compartments are pairs of small, looped tubes called **nephridia** (*nephros*–kidney), which open into the coelom by ciliated funnels (Fig. 57). Beyond the looped region each nephridium empties to the outside through a pore in the body wall. The looped part of each nephridium is closely invested with blood vessels from which waste material may be extracted and discharged to the exterior through the nephridial tube. The waving cilia at the funnel-opening create a current in the coelomic fluid which causes the wastes in this fluid to move into and through the nephridial tubule to the outside.

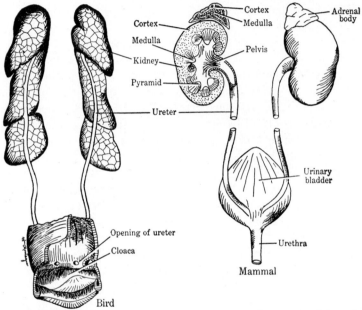

FIG. 56. Urinary systems of a bird (chicken) and a mammal (man).

In the kidneys of reptiles, birds, and mammals the tubules are more localized or closely aggregated than in fishes and amphibians. Two main regions can be distinguished in this kidney—an outer zone called the **cortex,** where most of the secreting structures are located, and an inner **medullary region** made up mostly of **collecting tubules** (Fig. 58). A unit of this secreting mechanism consists of a knot or mesh of blood vessels (arterioles) called a **glomerulus** (*glomus*–ball of yarn) enclosed in a double-walled capsule called **Bowman's capsule.** The glomerulus and capsule form a **Malpighian body** (Fig. 58). Bowman's capsule in a sense is the indented end of a rather complex, looped **secreting tubule.** The many secreting tubules join the collecting tubules in the medullary region of the kidney. The smaller collecting tubules in turn join each other to form larger drainage tubules which discharge the urine into the funnel-shaped end of the **ureter.**

The mechanics of the kidney. The blood enters the glomerulus of the kidney through an **afferent vessel** and leaves by the **efferent vessel.** The smaller diameter of the efferent vessel subjects the blood to increased pressure in the glomerulus so that, as it passes through the

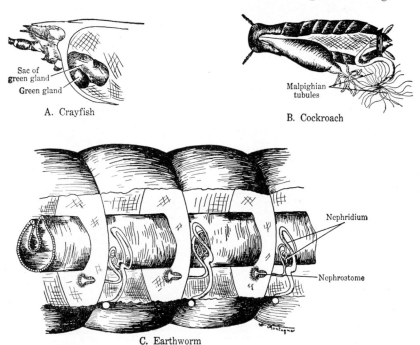

Sac of
green gland
Green gland

A. Crayfish

Malpighian
tubules

B. Cockroach

Nephridium

Nephrostome

C. Earthworm

FIG. 57. Kidneys of invertebrates. *A, after Huxley. B, redrawn from Comstock, "A Manual for the Study of Insects." By permission of the publisher, the Comstock Publishing Co.*

glomerulus, the blood loses water, glucose, urea, and other salts, which make up the urine. Urea, one of the main constituents of the urine, is the result of the complete breakdown (deamination) of excess amino acids in the liver. After leaving the glomerulus, the efferent artery forms a dense network about the secreting parts of the tubule (Fig. 58). The water or urine, as it leaves the glomerulus and enters the secreting tubule, contains glucose, urea, and other salts in a very dilute solution. As the urine passes down the tubule, much of the water is resorbed as well as glucose and some of the other substances previously filtered out in the glomerulus. The result is that the urine entering the urinary bladder is a much more concentrated solution and of a composition different from that of the liquid leaving the glomerulus. For example, bladder urine normally contains no glucose but has a concentration of urea 70 times greater than that existing in the blood.

The experimental work leading to the discovery of the functioning of the kidney described above is quite interesting. By careful manipu-

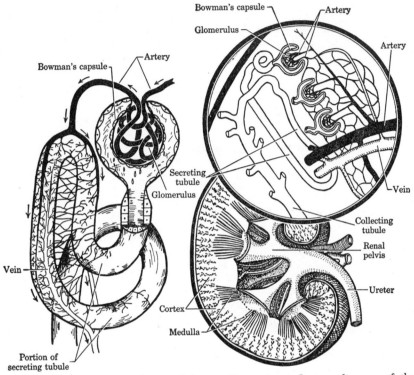

FIG. 58. Anatomy of the human kidney. Shown in circle is a diagram of the structure of the cortex.

lation it was possible to insert a quartz tube of microscopic dimensions into Bowman's capsule and to draw off enough urine for chemical analysis. This analysis showed that the composition of glomerular urine was practically the same as that of the plasma of the blood except that the proteins were missing. The relative concentration and composition of glomerular urine as compared with bladder urine, as already described, was revealed by this analysis. In another experiment, microscopical examination showed that when dyes are injected into the blood they filter out into the glomerular urine, which deepens in color as it trickles down the secreting tubules.

THE CARBON AND NITROGEN CYCLES

The ultimate fate of animal bodies. We have been considering the wastes formed in living organisms and the elimination of these wastes. From what has been said we may infer that dead cells may be disintegrated and eliminated from the organism like other wastes. The question that now arises is what becomes of the material of the animal after it finally dies. The final disposal of wastes and dead matter involve two very important series of events, viz., the **carbon cycle** and the **nitrogen cycle.**

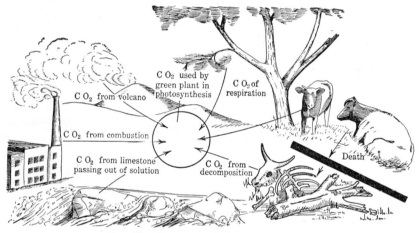

Fig. 59. Diagram of the carbon cycle.

The disintegration of dead organisms. When living organisms die their dead bodies are disintegrated by various plants and animals which feed on them. The digestive and respiratory activities of all animals, including man, bring about a dissolution of plant and animal tissues. The organic material itself is gradually disintegrated, forming increasingly simpler compounds until finally all the carbon is completely oxidized and returned to the atmosphere as carbon dioxide. Two very important groups of plants involved in this work of decomposition are the **bacteria** and **fungi.** When these plants attack tissues, they induce a decomposition commonly spoken of as rotting or decay. One of the end products of decay is carbon dioxide. Thus we see that, by combustion of gas, wood, coal, and other substances, by oxidation in living plants and animals, and by the disintegrating processes of decay carried on by bacteria and fungi, the carbon dioxide supply of the air is constantly being renewed. Green plants use the carbon dioxide and build the carbon into carbohydrates which are the building stones of fats and proteins. When these organic compounds are again completely broken down, carbon dioxide is formed once more, and in this way a perpetual cycle is maintained through which carbon functions as the principal constant. This is known as the **carbon cycle** (Fig. 59).

Since proteins are always present in protoplasm and since all proteins contain nitrogen, it is evident that substances other than carbon

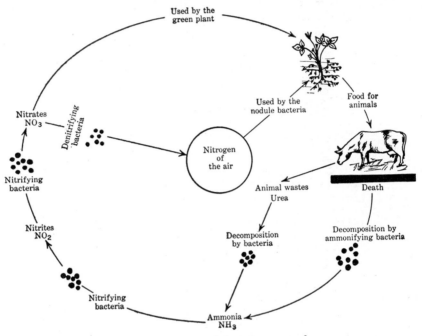

FIG. 60. Diagram of the nitrogen cycle.

dioxide must be formed when dead organisms are disintegrated. The complete decomposition of the proteins is effected by different relays of bacterial organisms. The odor of decaying organic bodies always reveals the presence of ammonia (NH_3). Ammonia is derived from the breaking down of the amino acids by a relay of bacteria known as the ammonifying bacteria. The ammonia is then oxidized by another group of bacteria, forming nitrites (NO_2). The nitrites are oxidized to nitrates (NO_3) by a third group of bacteria. The activities of the various bacteria are essential in providing an available nitrogen supply for all higher plants, which, apparently, can take up nitrogen only in the form of nitrates, and thus, indirectly, this bacterial action is also the source of the nitrogen supply for all animal life.

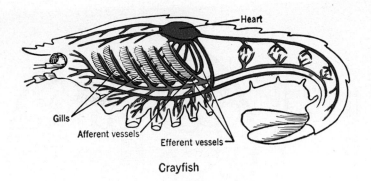

Crayfish

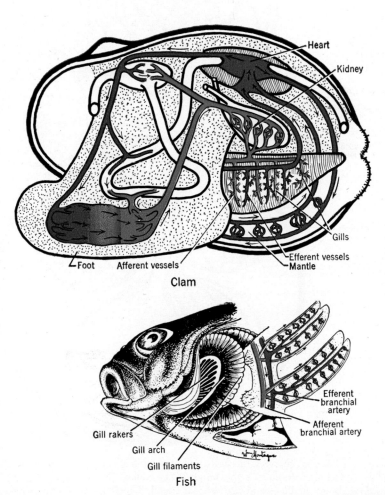

Clam

Fish

PLATE V. Diagrams showing the circulation and oxygenation of the blood in certain aquatic animals. *Clam redrawn, modified from Buchsbaum's "Animals Without Backbones," University of Chicago Press.*

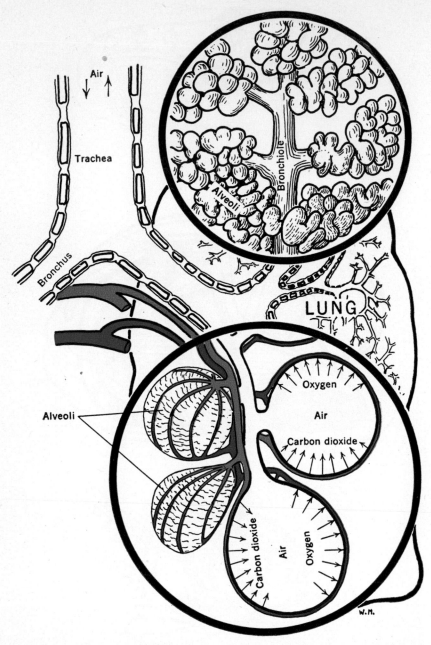

PLATE VI. Diagram showing the exchange of oxygen and carbon dioxide between the blood and the air sacs of the lungs. The venous blood containing carbon dioxide is shown in blue, and the arterial blood, which has lost carbon dioxide and acquired oxygen, is shown in red.

When proteins are broken down by the metabolic activity of animals, nitrogenous wastes such as urea are formed. The wastes are attacked by bacteria, and, as in decay, the nitrogen is returned to the soil in the form of nitrates. Thus we see that nitrogen functions through the **nitrogen cycle** (Fig. 60) like carbon through the carbon cycle. For a proper appreciation of some of the most fundamental biological processes, the importance of these cycles can hardly be overestimated. Were it not for the sequence of events in these cycles, the clock of life would have run down millions of years ago.

9

Coordination and Environmental Adjustment
Chemical Coordination

Sensitivity has been mentioned as one of the characteristics of living protoplasm, and therefore it must be an attribute of all living things. Sensitivity is the capacity of protoplasm and of organisms to respond to environmental influences or stimuli. A **stimulus** has been defined as any change of relation between an organism and its environment, or between different parts of an organism, which brings about a modification in the activities or behavior of the organism, called the **response**. It is by such responses that animals adjust themselves to the constantly changing environment in which they live. By the term adjustment we shall designate the many ways in which animals respond to conditions and changes in their environment. The most obvious adjustments made by organisms are the changes of location or position, such as the flight of a moth toward the light. Other extremely important adjustments, such as the secretion of digestive fluid by a gland as a response to the influence of food, are more obscure and less easily noticed by the casual observer.

In connection with the term environment we must think not only of the external factors that influence an animal but also of the internal conditions likewise capable of inducing reactions within the organism. Each individual cell, whether a unicellular organism or some unit of a multicellular organism, has its own environment. Since sensitivity is a property of all living protoplasm, it follows that each unit of this substance is sensitive, and consequently every living cell makes its own adjustments in the performance of its functions.

In any machine made up of many parts, the working of the parts must be so coordinated that each one contributes to the smooth operation of the machine. In fact, coordination is the fundamental principle underlying all organization. In a football team each player has his particular assignments, but they are so correlated in the various plays

120

that when they are executed successfully the eleven men function as a team, a unit, and not as eleven independent individuals. The same principle underlies the organization of every plant and animal whether made up of a single cell or billions of cells as in man.

Although each cell responds to its own particular environment, the activities of all the cells and groups of cells (tissues and organs) are so regulated and correlated by coordinating agencies that, like the individual performances of the members of an orchestra, they merge and blend into a perfect harmony.

In the living animal two agencies operate to bring about the correlation of activities of the component cells, tissues, and organs. These agencies are the mechanism of **chemical coordination** and the mechanism of **nervous coordination.** Apparently, the first of these two systems is the more primitive, and, in this chapter, we shall confine our attention to the subject of chemical coordination.

In chemical correlation, some parts of an animal may produce a chemical substance which may exert a marked influence on the activity of another part of the same organism. These chemical agents may be effective in the cells in which they are produced, or they may diffuse through the cell membranes and be transported to other parts of the organism by the blood, lymph, and tissue fluids. Such chemical factors differ widely in nature, exert different influences, and determine and control different cell responses—in brief, they aid in coordinating the functions of the different units of the organism. The maintenance of this relationship among component parts existing in both animals and plants is known as **chemical coordination.**

HORMONES

We have already seen that the body has certain glands whose secretions leave the gland by way of a duct. In addition to these glands there are other secreting organs without ducts whose secretions are poured directly into the blood stream, which carries them to the various tissues of the organism. Such glands are known as **ductless** or **endocrine glands** (*endon*—within; *krino*—I separate), or organs of **internal secretion** (Fig. 61). The following statement of Hoskins gives some idea of the importance of these glands, "The evidence is now conclusive that what we are—physically, mentally, sexually and emotionally—depends in no small measure upon the functions of our endocrine glands."

The internal secretion of the endocrine glands is known as a **hormone** (*hormao*—I arouse). Hormones are agents of chemical coordination; they are usually excitatory and specific in their actions. They, together with the nervous system, integrate all the activities of most animals.   Perhaps the best picture of hormone action can be presented by describing the functioning of one of these secretions.   We have

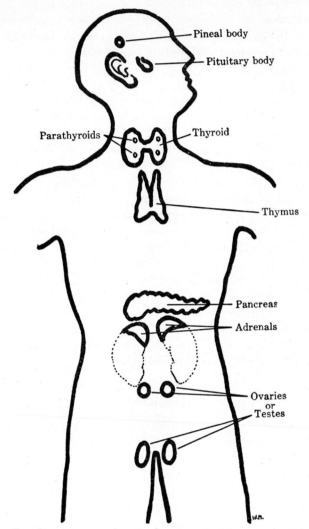

FIG. 61.   Diagram showing location of endocrine glands.

already seen that food is acted on by the pancreatic juice in the small intestines.   Some organs are aroused to secrete through nervous stimulation, and for a long time the pancreas was thought to be such an organ.   However, about 1902, Bayliss and Starling found that, when food passes into the small intestine, certain intestinal glands pour a substance into the blood stream called **secretin.** In a few seconds the secretin is carried by the blood to the pancreas, which at once begins to secrete pancreatic juice. Thus it was found that the secretion of the pancreas is initiated not by nervous impulse but by the stimulation caused by a chemical substance (secretin), a hormone. There is no conclusive evidence as to how these hormones function, but it is thought that they act as catalysts. Hormones are found not only in animals but also in plants.

Hormones are relatively simple compounds but very powerful physiological agents. The summary of a statement by Hoskins brings this out quite vividly. Epinephrin, the active principle of the adrenal medulla, can be readily detected by biological assay in a dilution of 1 part in 300,000,000. In other words, if 1 ounce of this substance were so diluted with water, the diluted solution would fill 9 miles of gasoline trucks apportioned 268 trucks to the mile, and each truck holding 2,000 gallons. Abel has isolated from the pituitary gland a hormone so powerful that 1,560 miles of such trucks would be required to reduce 1 ounce to the undetectable point.

The pancreas and the islets of Langerhans. It had long been suspected that the pancreas was involved in diabetes, an ailment in which the sugar of the blood is lost in the kidneys and voided with the urine. For example, it was observed that ants which feed on sugar were attracted to the urine of dogs whose pancreases had been removed. After years of experimentation Dr. Banting, a Canadian doctor, assisted by several co-workers, finally demonstrated the relation between the pancreas and diabetes. In his experimental work, Banting tied off the pancreatic duct of a dog, thus causing the cells secreting the digestive pancreatic juice to degenerate. He discovered that certain isolated areas, made up of a different kind of cells and called, after the discoverer, islets of Langerhans, were apparently not affected by this tying off of the pancreatic duct, nor was there any evidence of diabetes. He then removed the entire pancreas from another dog, which soon developed diabetes and died. Now this diabetic condition could have been the result of various factors and events incident to the operation, such as the effect of the anesthetic, the rearrangement of tissues, hemorrhages, and like operative disturbances. To eliminate the influences of such factors, a controlled experiment was set up. The same operation was performed upon another dog except that the pancreas was not removed. This dog did not develop diabetes. Evidently the lack of the pancreas was responsible for the disease.

The entire pancreas was extracted and the extract was injected into a diabetic dog whose pancreas had been removed. It was discovered that the extract did not change the condition of the dog. Apparently enzymes of the pancreatic juice destroyed the diabetes-preventing substance.

Meantime Dr. Banting remembered that in embryonic dogs the islet tissue developed earlier than the cells secreting pancreatic juice. So

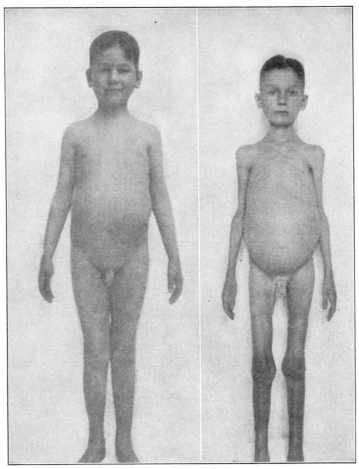

Fig. 62. Effect of insulin. *Right*, August 20, 1922, before insulin treatment. *Left*, June 20, 1923, ten months after insulin treatment. *By permission of Dr. Frederick M. Allen and* Journal of the American Medical Association.

he made an extract from the embryonic pancreas, and injected this into the tissues of a depancreatinized dog dying of diabetes. The dog's blood sugar increased, and in a few days the animal had recovered and was apparently normal. Work on the preparation of a diabetes-preventing extract continued, and finally a carefully prepared extract was tried on a man afflicted with diabetes. It worked! Today, this hormone called **insulin** (*insula*—island) is used as a standard treatment of diabetes (Fig. 62). However, since it does not restore the lost function to the islets of Langerhans, insulin must be given throughout life. Continued biochemical research has now made it possible to use purified extract of insulin from pancreatic tissues of cattle and other domestic animals. Moreover, we see once more that here is another important discovery which was not achieved "overnight" but only after years of careful, scientific experimentation.

The thyroid and thyroxin. **Thyroxin** is an extract of the endocrine gland, the **thyroid,** a two-lobed organ located adjacent to the windpipe, just below the voice box or "Adam's apple" (Fig. 61). For many years, in various Alpine valleys and in the Pyrenees, there lived dwarflike human beings who were only three or four feet tall. The arms and legs of these people were unusually short, and their short legs were so bowed that their walk was an ungainly waddle. The coarse and leathery skin hung in folds in various parts of the body. The teeth were defective, and the hair was sparse and coarse. Not only were their heads misshapen and the tongues entirely too large for their mouths, but also their minds were those of children. This condition was called **cretinism.** About 1891, Dr. Murray tried injecting under the skin of some of these unfortunates an extract of thyroid made from the glands of another animal. The results were positively astounding! Many children in this cretinous condition when thus treated soon became practically normal and remained so as long as the treatment was continued (Fig. 63).

Interesting results of experiments on other animals were obtained from the use of this new extract. Gudernatsch found that frog tadpoles fed dried thyroid matured much earlier. They soon developed legs, lost their tails, and became tiny frogs not much larger than a fly. Later Allen found that, if he removed the thyroids of a frog tadpole, it always remained a tadpole, but became abnormally large. When fed thyroxin it changed into a frog. Other very interesting facts have been discovered about the effects of thyroid extract on other animals.

The thyroid gland regulates the oxidative rate in the animal, that is, heat production and energy liberation in all the organ systems. If thyroid secretion is either deficient or too abundant, abnormal mental and physical effects may be produced. Undersecretion of the thyroid lowers the rate of metabolism and causes the individual to become fat, sluggish in mental reactions, and even feebleminded.

The heart rate is lower and the sex drive decreased. A condition somewhat similar to cretinism may appear in adults having subnormal thyroid glands, but the degree of cretinism is modified by the age of the individual. Thyroid deficiency may stimulate the formation of new gland tissue, resulting in an enlargement of the thyroid known as **simple goiter.** This is a compensatory reaction. When one of a pair of organs such as the kidneys, or part of an organ, is destroyed,

FIG. 63. Effect of thyroxin. *A*, cretinism before treatment. *B*, after treatment with thyroxin. *Photographs furnished by Dr. Edwin C. Kendall.*

the remaining tissue may enlarge or increase its activity to "compensate" for the loss.

On the other hand, if, for some unknown cause, the thyroid is overactive, the symptoms are almost the opposite of those described for thyroid insufficiency. The basal metabolic rate is increased, which calls for more and more food. The individual becomes highly nervous—overactive, so to speak—and irritable. Sometimes a complete derangement follows and **exophthalmic goiter** may develop, characterized by bulging eyeballs, irregular heart action, nervousness, and insomnia.

Man has been able to overcome simple goiter and cretinism. He now knows the chemical nature of thyroxin, which is really an amino acid ($C_{15}H_{11}O_4NI_4$) now prepared synthetically by the biochemist.

Thyroxin is rich in iodine, of which the thyroid gland must have an adequate supply. There is reason to believe that many centuries B.C. the Chinese had learned by trial and error that substances containing iodine had a beneficial effect upon the thyroid. The Greeks (460–370 B.C.) added burnt sponges and sea weeds, substances rich in iodine, to the diet to relieve goiter. A study made of the distribution of simple goiter and cretinism showed that in certain goiter belts 25–60 per cent of the population was affected. These belts were usually in former glaciated regions in which the soil has been leached of its iodine, resulting in iodine deficiency in the soil, water, and plants. Such regions are the Great Lakes country and the St. Lawrence valley in North America, the Andean plateau in South America, and the Alps, Pyrenees, and Carpathian mountain regions in Europe. On the other hand, people living near the sea, where there is an abundance of salts, particularly those containing iodine, are free from goiter. This knowledge suggested the administration of iodine as a remedy for simple goiter, a treatment which has proved largely effective. Advanced cases of goiter, however, require operative treatment.

The parathyroids (*para*—near; thyroid). In man there are usually four parathyroids. They are about the size of peas and are either embedded in the thyroid glands or located close to them (Fig. 61). In many of the early operations for goiter, after removal of the excess thyroid tissue, the patients were afflicted with twitchings, nervousness, and facial spasms. Later it was found that experimental removal of the thyroid of dogs and cats caused a convulsive disorder called **tetany.** The same operation in rabbits did not have this effect. Tetany begins by spasmodic contractions of the muscles leading to convulsions. There is acceleration of the heart beat, and finally death by asphyxiation owing to a spasm of the muscles which closes the glottis. An examination of the blood of these animals shows a marked decrease in calcium content. Gley in 1891 discovered that in rabbits the parathyroids were not embedded in the thyroid gland and that rabbits after removal of the thyroids were not affected. Hence it was apparent that removal of the parathyroids was responsible for the undesirable aftereffects of a "thyroid" operation. Later, it was discovered that these reactions did not occur in dogs, cats, and man if the parathyroids were left intact within the animal.

Today it is known that the parathyroids secrete a hormone, **parathormone,** which regulates the calcium level in the blood, which, in turn, is responsible for normal muscle function, bone growth, and tooth formation. The hormone is destroyed by digestion; consequently in parathyroid deficiency the hormone must be injected. The effects of parathyroid deficiency can also be remedied by the injection or feeding of calcium.

An oversecretion of parathormone causes the calcium and phosphorus to leave the bones and the teeth; carried away by the blood, these elements are lost through the kidneys. The bones become soft, and deformities often result. We have already seen that vitamin D, the antirachitic vitamin, is concerned with calcium metabolism. Apparently, however, there is little connection between the vitamin mechanism and the hormone function. In chronic lead poisoning parathormone extracts have been used to remove lead deposits from the bones. Parathyroid extracts have proved effective in the treatment of children suffering from chronic convulsions, irrationalism, maniac excitation, and similar disorders.

The pineal body. In man this gland, about the size of a pea, is located on the dorsal surface of the brain between the cerebral hemispheres (Fig. 61). The philosopher Descartes thought that it was the seat of the soul! At the present time, finding little evidence of an endocrine function, many scientists are of the opinion that the pineal body is not an endocrine gland.

The thymus gland. This glandular structure is very prominent in young animals. In man, it lies behind the upper part of the breastbone and extends from the heart up into the neck (Fig. 61). It practically disappears in the adult. Like the pineal gland, it is the subject of many conflicting reports and opinions. The suggestion has been made that it speeds up growth and that it produces lymphocytes, a non-endocrine function. Carlson and Johnson conclude that "at present the weight of the evidence seems to be against the hormone interpretation, although the final answer must wait further experimentation."

The preceding discussions of the function of the pineal and thymus are good illustrations of the workings of science. A number of years ago, these glands were considered to be unquestionably endocrine in function. Further experimentation, as well as a more critical repetition of former experiments, have caused earlier conclusions to be scrapped and have reduced the problem to the "I do not know" status. Someone has well said that the path of science is strewn with the wrecks of dead and dying theories. A scientist must have an open mind and be willing and able to adjust or scrap his previous conclusions in the light of new evidence.

The adrenal glands (*ad*–near; *renes*–kidney). In most vertebrates these glands lie close to the kidneys, and in man they cover the anterior ends of the kidneys like little caps (Figs. 56 and 61). An adrenal gland is made up of two distinct regions which have had an entirely different embryological origin. The outer part of the gland is known as the **cortex** and the center as the **medulla**.

The secretion of the medullary region of the adrenal gland is called **adrenalin** or **epinephrin**. The chemist has analyzed adrenalin ($C_9H_{13}NO_3$) and is now able to prepare it synthetically in the laboratory. Unlike most endocrine glands, the medulla is under nervous control. It regulates blood pressure and the tonus of the involuntary muscles. A lack of adrenalin may cause a loss of strength or "nerve." When adrenalin is injected, the heart beat increases, the arteries contract, the hair bristles, the skin becomes "gooseflesh," and the eyeballs tend to protrude and the pupils dilate. Cannon and his co-workers believed that the reactions associated with fear or anger may be caused by an increased secretion of adrenalin into the blood stream, brought about by nervous stimulation.

In this connection the following observation by Turner [*] is worth considering. "Many teachers of general biology and related subjects have dramatized the emergency theory of medullary functions without appreciating that the evidence upon which it is based is unsatisfactory. It is surprising that the theory has been widely accepted merely on the grounds that it seems 'logical' or 'reasonable.' Although it may be that the adrenal medulla is essential for the optimal mobilization of the organism's defenses in emergency situations, the concept has not been proved unequivocally by laboratory experimentation. . . . Although the emergency theory appears reasonable and logical, it should not be accepted fully until more direct evidence is forthcoming to support it." The following observation of Francis Bacon is quite apropos, "Whatever the mind seizes upon with satisfaction is to be held in suspicion."

Apparently the function of the medulla can be taken over by the autonomic nervous system, for the medulla can be removed without affecting the life processes of the animal. It is probable that the adrenal medulla is essential for the optimum functioning of the sympatho-adrenal system.

Since adrenalin causes the dilatation of the bronchioles of the lungs, it is used for the relief of asthma and hay fever. It is applied locally to prevent excessive bleeding from wounds. Sometimes adrenalin has been injected directly into the heart after it has stopped beating, to initiate renewed contractions and thus restore life.

The cortex secretes the hormone **cortin,** which seems to be essential for life since removal of the cortex results in death. Further investigations have shown that cortin is made up of some twenty-five compounds. When the adrenal glands are removed from experimental animals, water and sodium chloride are lost from the blood and tissues, and the basal metabolic rate decreases. The animals lose

[*] C. Donnell Turner, *General Endocrinology*, W. B. Saunders Co., Philadelphia, 1948, pp. 223–224.

their appetite. Muscular weakness ensues, ending in prostration and death. Destruction of the adrenal cortex in man by Addison's disease causes many of the effects just listed, and, in addition, the skin becomes a peculiar bronze color (Fig. 64). Injections of cortin alleviate these conditions and sometimes there is complete recovery.

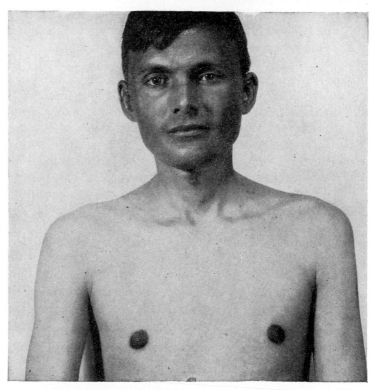

Fig. 64. A case of Addison's disease. Note the bronzing of the skin. *From Grollman, "Essentials of Endocrinology." By permission of the publishers, J. B. Lippincott and Co.*

There is good evidence that the adrenal cortex is closely related in its activities to other endocrine glands. Tumors in the cortex have resulted in abnormal and precocious sexual maturity. This would indicate a relation with the gonads. In women, overactivity of the cortex may result in a change toward masculinity. The reverse is true in the male. Some cases have been recorded where an almost complete sex reversal has taken place. According to Hoskins, "the deep-voiced, coarse-featured, bearded ladies of the circus sideshows are probably victims of this glandular mishap." There may be some relationship between the adrenal cortex and the gonadal secretions. There is conclusive evidence of an interrelation between the pituitary gland and the cortex of the adrenal.

The anterior lobe of the pituitary produces an **adrenocorticotropic** principle which stimulates the production of cortin by the adrenal cortex. This principle called **ACTH** along with **cortisone,** one of the compounds from the adrenal cortex, when given in high concentration has very beneficial effects in such diseases as allergies, rheumatic diseases, leukemia, and others. However, the treatment has not proved to be effective in some cases, and overdoses of these drugs have caused masculinity in women.

The gonads and their hormones. It has been known for a long time that the ovaries of the female and the testes of the male produce eggs and spermatozoa, respectively (Fig. 61). More recently it was discovered that these glands also produce hormones. In the ovaries the egg develops in a fluid-filled vesicle called the Graafian follicle, which apparently is the source of the hormone called **estrogen** (*oistros* —gadfly, frenzy) ($C_{18}H_{22}O_2$). Among other effects, estrogen controls the recovery changes in the wall of the uterus succeeding the menstrual period up to the final stage of preparation when the hormone of the corpus luteum, **progesterone,** becomes active. The **corpus luteum** is a yellow, cellular mass which replaces the Graafian follicle after it has burst to release the egg from the ovary. Progesterone controls the final changes in the uterine wall and helps to bring about the implantation of the embryo in the uterus. It also helps govern the formation of the **placenta,** the organ of nutrition for the developing embryo and fetus. Although both estrogen and progesterone play an essential role in the growth of the nipples, ducts, and secreting portions of the mammary gland, it remains for a specific hormone from the pituitary gland to bring about lactation or secretion of milk. The process of human reproduction will be described in a subsequent chapter, and the action of these hormones and their effect in the human female reproductive cycle will be more fully discussed.

Estrogen is also responsible for the production of **secondary sexual characters** of the female such as the accessory reproductive organs. In female birds the type of plumage and the lack of combs and spurs are the result of the influence of estrogen. Estrogen influences the psychic or behavior reactions of the female in man as well as in birds. If the ovary is removed and later estrogen is injected, the female's physical and behavior characteristics remain normal. When such diseases as cancers and tumors of the genital organs of women make operations necessary, if at all possible, one ovary or some ovarian tissue is not removed.

The hormone of the testis is known as **testosterone** ($C_{19}H_{30}O_2$). It has been synthesized in the chemist's laboratory from cholesterol, a substance present in almost all animal tissues. It is interesting to note that most of the gonadal hormones are sterol derivatives. This hormone is secreted by tissue of the testis other than that which develops into gametes. The hormone is responsible for the formation of the secondary sexual structures of the male such as the accessory

A	B

FIG. 65. Sex reversal in a chicken. A, hen before operation. B, the same bird after operation showing the change from female to male characteristics. *By permission of Dr. L. V. Domm.*

reproductive organs and, in man, the deep voice and distribution of hair. In the males of many varieties of chickens, this hormone induces the development of the comb and spurs. The psychic or behavior patterns peculiar to the male of all animals are evidently influenced by this hormone.

The following experiments have definitely shown that many specific physical and mental characteristics associated with sex are dependent on the secretions of the gonads. For instance, if the ovary of a female guinea pig is transplanted into a male from which the testes have been removed, the hair and the skeleton of this male come to resemble those of the female and the milk glands enlarge to functional size. Again, if the ovary is removed from a young leghorn hen, she will develop a larger comb, spurs, and wattles, because in birds there is but one functional ovary and when it is removed the other, functionless gonad develops into a testis which produces the male hormone responsible for these characteristics. The plumage will become male-like owing to the absence of the female hormone (Fig. 65).

Castration and **ovariectomy** (removal of the ovaries) are regularly practiced by livestock growers and poultrymen. The unsexed animals are usually more docile, develop larger bodies, and take on fat more rapidly. Castrated (testes removed) roosters are known as capons, pigs as barrows, horses as geldings, bulls as steers, and men as eunuchs.

For a long time it has been known to livestock breeders that if, when twin calves are born, one calf is a male and the other a female, the female usually will be sterile. The sterile female is known as a **freemartin.** Lillie, in his study of the problem, showed that the sterility was caused by the fusing of the fetal membranes so that there was a mixture of the male's blood and its hormones with that of the female. Since the male gonads develop more rapidly, the male hormone is being secreted into the circulation for some time before the hormones of the ovary are produced. As a result the female has some male characteristics as well as female and is known as an **intersex.** When frog tadpoles of different sexes are grafted together in pairs, the same result occurs.

One of the most interesting and clever experiments performed in endocrine research was the following: A portion of the uterine wall of an animal was removed and placed in the anterior chamber of the eye of the same animal, and it grew! There were no nerve connections, therefore any change taking place there would have to be brought about by chemicals carried to it by the blood stream. This uterine tissue was found to exhibit the same cycle of changes as those taking place in the walls of the uterus. In monkeys, even the bleeding which occurs in normal uterine tissue at menstruation was observed. The changes which take place in the uterine mucosa as a result of the injection of hormone extracts could be readily observed in the transplant.

The pituitary body. This gland is attached to the midregion of the lower surface of the brain and rests, well protected, in a small cavity in the floor of the skull. In man, it weighs about $\frac{3}{140}$ of an ounce and is about the size of a hazelnut.

The pituitary gland is made up mainly of two lobes of different embryological origin. The anterior lobe arises from a pouch pinched off from the roof of the mouth, and the posterior lobe is derived from the floor of the brain. The two lobes are united and attached to the brain by a stalk (Fig. 61). Each lobe of the gland has its own peculiar secretions. Early anatomists, including Galen (200 A.D.), knew of the location of the pituitary gland but neither they nor Vesalius (1514–1564) had any knowledge of its functions. In fact for many years the pituitary gland was supposed to serve as a filtration apparatus for wastes from the brain! Through countless years of experimentation there has been established the fact that the pituitary gland plays a part in many and varied physiological activities necessary for the life of

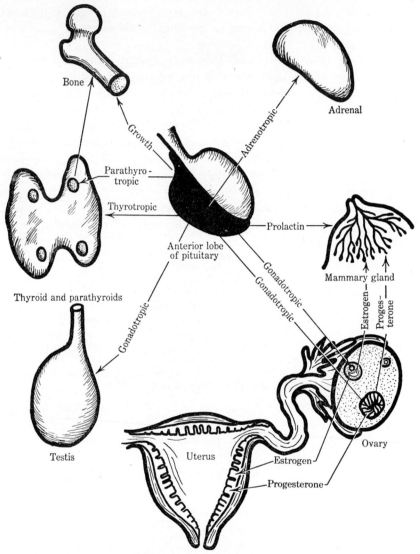

Fig. 66.   Diagram showing the relation of the anterior lobe of the pituitary to various other endocrine glands and structures.

backboned animals.   The reports dealing with the function of the pituitary are voluminous, but it is fairly certain that new research will necessitate the abandonment and the modification of certain current views on the activities of the pituitary. It will be noted that products of the pituitary influence the functions of many other endocrine glands, but Turner does not believe it merits the term "master gland" since it is probable "that all the members of the endocrine system are interdependent and tend to influence each other reciprocally."

The various extracts from the posterior lobe have the general name of **pituitrin.** Abel reports that the chemical salt of the hormone extracted from the posterior lobe is so powerful that a dilution of 1 part in 15,000,000,000 produces a noticeable effect in the uterine muscles of a female guinea pig. The extract of the posterior lobe (Fig. 66) is made up of two hormones: one tends to raise the arterial blood pressure; the other is a powerful stimulant of the uterine muscles and is used by physicians to hasten childbirth. According to some physiologists, pituitrin acts more like a drug than a hormone.

Certain hormones from the anterior lobe influence growth. Rats treated with extract of the anterior lobe have grown to more than *twice* the size of their litter mates. Apparently the same growth effect is produced in man, for, if the gland is enlarged and overactive, giants result (Fig. 67). Goliath, the Philistine, and overlarge individuals of our own times may have had enlarged pituitaries from childhood. Autopsies of many of these "giants" have shown enlarged and tumorous pituitaries. Sometimes the gland does not begin excessive secretion until after maturity is reached, and then, instead of giants, gorillalike men with huge hands and feet, enlarged heads, enlarged bony ridges over the eyes, and protruding lower jaws and tongues are the result. This condition is called **acromegaly** (*akron*— extremity; *mega*—large).

Deficiency of this secretion results in normally proportioned, dwarflike men (Fig. 67). Tom Thumb and other midgets of the circus probably owed their livelihood to the subnormal activity of the anterior lobe of the pituitary. Investigators have found by experimentation that removal of the pituitary in dogs and rats results in retarded growth and development which can be prevented by implanting pieces of fresh pituitary under the skin. If such implants are made on normal rats, gigantism results.

Another hormone of the pituitary affects the functioning of the gonads. If the gland is removed before puberty the gonads never mature. If the operation is performed on adult animals, production of eggs and spermatozoa ceases, and changes take place in the sexual cycles of the female. On the other hand, excess amounts of the hormone hasten the breeding period and the maturing of eggs and spermatozoa. If some of this gland is transplanted under their skin,

Fig. 67.   Extremes in size of the human body, probably the result of abnormal
functioning of the pituitary gland.   The giant, 8 feet, 9 inches, in height, may be
the result of an overactive pituitary; the dwarf by his side may be the result of
an abnormally inactive pituitary.   The woman is of average size.   *Copyrighted
by Underwood and Underwood, New York.   Reproduced by permission.*

frogs, which normally breed once a year in early spring, may be stimulated to lay eggs within a week or ten days.

Research has shown that there is a close interaction between the hormones of the anterior lobe and those of the ovary. The pituitary secretes a hormone called the **follicle-stimulating hormone (F.S.H.),** which causes the production of estrogen. Another pituitary hormone, known as the **luteinizing hormone (L.H.),** assists in the formation of the corpus luteum which secretes progesterone. Progesterone in turn acts on the mucosa lining of the uterus (Figs. 66 and 106).

Another anterior-lobe hormone, **prolactin,** apparently is an important factor in milk secretion by the mammary gland. Removal of the pituitary from lactating rats causes the flow of milk to cease, whereas injection of prolactin causes the animal to lactate. Injection of prolactin into virgin rats stimulates the mothering instinct, and such rats will build nests. Investigators have found that this hormone is intimately concerned with growth and is very important in the maintenance of the corpus luteum and the secretion of progesterone. Perhaps "prolactin" is a misnomer.

Evidence has accumulated which indicates that there is a close relationship between the thyroid and the pituitary. Remove the pituitary, and the animal shows a condition of hypothyroidism; inject the extract of the pituitary into a normal animal, and hyperthyroidism results. This action seems to be independent of the thyroid. The pituitary apparently exerts physiological effects on the adrenal cortex and on the parathyroids. Others of its hormones seem to have some control over insulin production in the pancreas.

Other hormones of vertebrates. We have already pointed out that secretin, a substance secreted by the intestine, is a hormone. There is some evidence that the walls of the stomach may secrete a hormonelike substance called **gastrin** and that certain liver extracts may act like hormones. It has been shown that when fatty foods enter the duodenum the intestinal wall forms the hormone **cholecystokinin,** which, carried by the blood to the liver, causes the gall bladder to contract forcibly, sending the bile into the intestine. The placenta, a structure developed in the higher mammals, secretes a hormone resembling one of those produced by the anterior lobe of the pituitary. It may also secrete estrogen. The Aschheim-Zondek test for pregnancy in women is based upon the presence or absence in the urine of the first-mentioned hormone, the "pituitarylike" one.

Hormones of invertebrates. Experiments have rather clearly demonstrated that there are endocrine glands in invertebrates. In the insects there is present a **growth** and **differentiation hormone**

(GD hormone) which helps to bring about the differentiation of adult characteristics. This hormone is secreted by the so-called **prothoracic glands** or from glands close to the brain. Another hormone, the **juvenile hormone,** is secreted by the **corpora allata,** a gland located

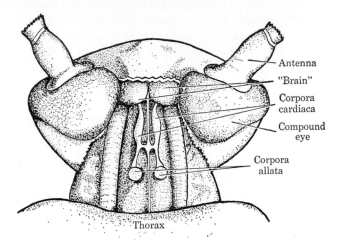

Antenna

"Brain"

Corpora cardiaca

Compound eye

Corpora allata

Thorax

Fig. 68. Hormone-secreting organs of insects. A dissection of a roach's head showing the corpora allata and the corpora cardiaca. *Redrawn from Turner, "General Endocrinology." By permission of the publisher, W. B. Saunders Co.*

near the brain (Fig. 68). This hormone assists in the retention of the nymphal or larval structures of insects while they are undergoing metamorphosis. Ingenious experiments have been devised to determine the action of these hormones. In one specific experiment one insect in the nymphal stage is partially beheaded and united with a

Fig. 69. Diagram to show how decapitated nymphs of the insect (*Rhodnius*) are connected by a fine capillary glass tube through which the hormones can be transmitted. *From Turner, "General Endocrinology." By permission of the publishers, W. B. Saunders Co.*

completely decapitated insect also in the nymphal stage. The two insects are so united by a tiny glass tube that there is possible an exchange of body fluids (Fig. 69). Thus from the insect with intact glands there presumably is carried growth and differentiation hormones into the more immature insect lacking these specific hormones. Under such conditions both insects continue to differentiate.

The arthropod *Dixippus* has a gland in the head which secretes a pigment-activating hormone responsible for the coloring of the animal. Hanström found in the head of certain insects a substance which, if injected into shrimps, tends to concentrate their red and yellow pigments. Destruction of certain gonadal tissue in some crabs often results in partial sex reversal somewhat similar to the phenomenon observed in female chickens when the ovary is removed. In certain arthropods there is some evidence that both metamorphosis and molting are controlled by hormones. In the bug *Rhodnius* the hormone controlling molting seems to be secreted by glands located in the head.

OTHER CHEMICAL CORRELATIONS

We have already pointed out that the amount of carbon dioxide in the blood controls the respiratory center in the brain and is thus the regulator of breathing movements. The force and rate of the heart beat both directly and indirectly are to some extent under the control of carbon dioxide.

Neurohumeralism. Loewi, a German, removed the living beating hearts from two anesthetized frogs and so connected them that an artificial fluid (Ringer's solution) would flow through both hearts. He then stimulated the vagus nerve (part of the autonomic system) of *only one heart* and slowed down its beat. The other heart, though it had no nervous connection, was similarly affected by something in the circulating liquid. Continued experimentation and investigation have shown that there was given off, by the stimulated vagus nerve endings, a substance called **acetylcholine,** which acts on the cardiac muscle as an inhibitor. This inhibitory substance is given off by the **parasympathetic autonomic system.** Another substance, **sympathin,** liberated by the nerve endings of the **sympathetic system,** acts as an accelerator. Sympathin is similar to adrenalin in its effect on muscles. Interestingly enough, the adrenal medulla and the autonomic system have the same common embryological origin. Apparently, the nervous effects of the autonomic nervous system "are not brought about by the nerve impulses themselves, but by chemical substances which the impulses cause to be liberated from the nerve endings." It has been shown that the contraction of skeletal muscle (voluntary) is caused by the liberation of acetylcholine from the voluntary motor nerve endings. These discoveries may lead to research which may revolutionize our concepts of the nervous mechanism. In that event we shall be throwing aside or modifying old theories and hypotheses in the light of new evidence.

10

Adjustment to Environment
Nervous Coordination
Receptors

We have already learned that adjustment of the organism involves responses to stimuli of various kinds. According to the form of energy involved, stimuli may be classified as follows: **mechanical** (contact, pressure, sound); **thermal** (changes in temperature); **osmotic** (changes in osmotic pressure); **chemical** (changes in concentration of chemicals); **electrical** (changes in strength and direction of the electrical current); and **photic** (changes in color intensity or direction of light). The effectiveness of these stimuli depends not only on the nature and extent of the change, its rate or suddenness, but also on the physiological condition of the organism.

Responses may be easily perceptible or quite imperceptible. A response may be gradual and not easily detected, like a slow change in the rate of metabolism or in the form or structure of a cell as the result of a gradual change in pressure, temperature, or chemical composition. However, the striking, easily observed responses, the ones with which we shall be primarily concerned, are so great as to be entirely out of proportion to the stimuli. They may be likened to an explosion brought about by pulling a trigger.

Kinds of response. Some of the general types of responses are: **mechanical,** such as muscle contraction and ameboid movement; **secretion,** the release of stored substances from a cell; **luminescence,** production of light; **color change,** contraction or expansion of pigment cells; **electrical discharge** of considerable strength. The kind of response depends upon the kind of effector involved and not upon the nature or magnitude of the stimulus. Thus a muscle cell (not necessarily the entire muscle) always responds by contraction, no matter what kind of stimulus is applied; and a gland cell always secretes, regardless of the stimulus affecting it. The magnitude of

140

the response is not dependent on the *strength* of the stimulus but upon the *condition* of the cell at the time it is stimulated. At a given time a stimulus of a certain strength will be required to evoke a response. A weaker stimulus will have no effect, and one of greater strength will produce exactly the same response as that induced by the weakest effective stimulus as long as the condition of the cell remains the same.

A cell never makes an incomplete or partial response. If a stimulus evokes a state of excitation in any given cell, such a cell will always respond to the limit of its capacity. In other words, **a cell always responds to the limit of its capacity to any stimulus which is at all effective; there is either a complete response or none at all.** This is known as the **all-or-none law.**

Excitation, transmission, and response. The immediate response of protoplasm when stimulated in any way is called **excitation.** This

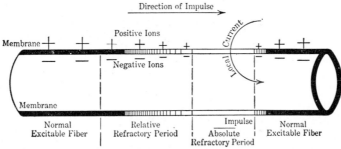

Fig. 70. Diagram showing transmission of impulse along a nerve. Note that the action current is transmitted by a succession of changes in electrical charges along the nerve. *From Boring, Langfeld, and Weld, "Introduction to Psychology." By permission of John Wiley and Sons.*

is a physicochemical change accompanied by an alteration of the permeability of the cell membrane to electrical charges, which gives rise to an electric current known as the **action current** (Fig. 70). Action currents serve as stimuli to excite other cells, and in this way the primary effect of the original stimulus may be propagated from cell to cell until responses are induced in several, often remote, parts of the organism. After excitation, the cell, if not stimulated again, will return to its original condition. However, if a stimulus of any strength is applied within a brief interval after excitation and before the cell has recovered, no excitation will be effected. This period is known as the **refractory period.** A stimulus does not always induce action; sometimes it causes the cessation of some activity of the cell, an effect known as **inhibition.** This may be regarded as a prolongation of the refractory period, since the cell during this time is rendered incapable of normal excitation.

The visible response to a stimulus frequently appears in some part quite remote from that to which the stimulus was applied. In all such responses there are three stages: **reception,** or the setting up of the state of excitation by the initiation of a physicochemical change at the point of contact with the stimulus; **conduction,** that is, transmission of the impulse or wave of excitation to various parts of the organism;

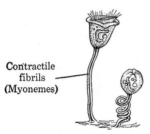

Contractile
fibrils
(Myonemes)

FIG. 71. Contractile fibrils (myonemes) in the simple animal *Vorticella.*

and **response** or **effect,** which is the reaction the organism makes in adjustment to the stimulus. From the place of the application of the stimulus to the point where the effect is noted, there is a progressive movement of the action current set up by the original stimulus. This chain of reactions has been compared to a series of events beginning with the striking of a match (stimulus) that ignites (reception) a fuse of gunpowder along which a wave of combustion travels (conduction) until it reaches a keg of gunpowder and causes a violent explosion (effective response).

In the higher animals there are **receptors,** i.e., sensory cells and their processes, which may be scattered or localized as organs of special sense; **conductors,** which are various types of sensory and motor nerve cells with their processes; and **effectors,** which may be either muscles that react in movement or glands that react by secreting.

The simplest animals have all three functions localized in a single cell; that is, every cell is its own receptor, conductor, and effector. Some parts of the cell may serve as receptors, as the pigment spots of certain simple organisms which may be affected by light. In the epithelium of a simple animal called hydra there are cells whose external, exposed surface acts as a receptor, and on whose inner, basal region are contractile fibrils which are the forerunners of a separate muscular tissue found in the higher animals. In other animals, such as *Vorticella* (Fig. 71), contractile fibrils called **myonemes** (*mys*—muscle; *nema*—thread) may be present, which may bring about the contraction of the animal. Conduction of the impulse takes place through the general protoplasm of the cell. However, as animals increase in complexity, cells and groups of cells are found which may be specialized as receptors, conductors, or effectors. Two of these functions (reception and conduction) result in the formation of some type of **nervous tissue** and **nervous system.**

Receptors are specialized cells, or highly developed cellular structures, which are readily affected by stimuli of various kinds. Most of our knowledge of the functioning of these specialized structures has come from the study of the receptors in man and other higher animals. Although we have little exact information about the actual sensations of the lower animals, we have been able to arrive at some conclusions on the basis of their behavior when subjected to the same general experiments as those in which man is the guinea pig. Receptors may be divided into three general classes: The **interoceptors** (*inter*—inward; *capere*—to take); the **exteroceptors** (*exter*—outward; *capere*); and the **proprioceptors** (*proprius*—one's own; *capere*).

The interoceptors. These are receptors located in the respiratory system, the alimentary tract, and other internal organs of the body. Thus the sensation of hunger is initiated by the stimulation of certain receptors in the stomach walls when the empty stomach contracts producing what are called "hunger pains." Thirst receptors, located in the throat, are apparently stimulated by osmotic changes caused by loss of water. Other interoceptors are involved in pain, fatigue, nausea, and sexual sensations.

The exteroceptors. These are the receptors through which we become aware of our changing relations with the outside world. According to the stimuli which activate them, they may be grouped as chemical receptors (in man, in the nose and tongue); light receptors (in man, in the eye); temperature (in man, in the skin); mechanical (in man, in the ear; pressure in the skin). The eye, ear, and nose have sometimes been called distance receptors because they are stimulated by agents emanating from sources not in contact with the organism.

Proprioceptors. The proprioceptors furnish information about muscular tension and movement which result in body position and locomotion. They are located in the muscles, tendons, and joints, and in certain parts of the ear (utriculus, sacculus, and semicircular canals).

CHEMICAL RECEPTORS

Taste and smell. In man and other vertebrate animals, taste receptors known as **taste buds** are found mostly on the upper surface and sides of the tongue. The taste buds are embedded for the most part in the numerous small projections which cover the tongue and give it a velvety appearance. The taste bud opens upon the surface through a pore (Fig. 72). The dissolved substances entering the pore stimulate the nerve endings in the taste buds, and the impulse set up by the stimulus is conveyed to the brain. These chemical receptors can be stimulated by substances in solution only, and they seem to be receptive only to stimuli which give the sensations of sweet, sour, bitter, and salty. One cannot taste with a dry tongue. Other flavors which we seem to "taste" are really experienced through our smell receptors, or through the joint action of smell receptors and taste buds. As we all know, a severe "head cold" robs us of our taste so that we have a tendency to use more sugar and salt in our food. When we have such a cold, vanilla ice cream seems to us to be just so much frozen sweetened cream. There is no vanilla "taste" because the mucous membrane of the nose is so inflamed and covered with mucus that the sensory endings cannot be stimulated. Oils are unpleasant because of their "feel" rather than their "taste."

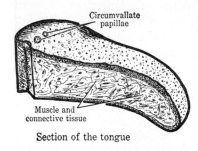

Section of the tongue

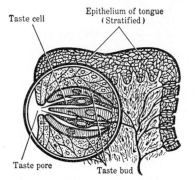

Section through a circumvallate papilla

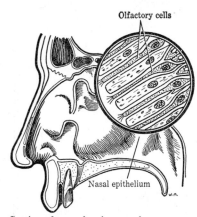

Section of nose showing nasal passage

FIG. 72.   Chemical receptors of taste and smell.

Just as the taste receptors are stimulated by substances in solution, so the olfactory receptors are stimulated by substances which are finely divided or in the form of gases or vapor. It has been said that smell is "taste at a distance." In man these receptors are located in a portion of the **olfactory epithelium** lining the nose. The material which may be smelled does not stimulate the olfactory receptors directly but must be dissolved in the fluid covering the mucous membrane containing the receptors. The olfactory receptors are in functional synaptic contact with the endings of the olfactory nerve, which leads to the brain (Fig. 72). Smell is used by animals not only as a guide when seeking food but also as an aid in avoiding enemies and finding mates during the breeding season.

In insects, the olfactory receptors are in the **antennas,** or "feelers," located on the head. It is also possible that these receptors may be found in other parts of the body. Flies and carrion beetles which feed on, and lay their eggs in, carrion, will find concealed decaying flesh even though it is enclosed in a box and hidden from sight. Aided by their olfactory receptors, ants find their way to the nest and recognize their nest mates. Jordan describes an instance where some female moths (*Promethea*) were enclosed in a box and kept in a building. No males of this particular kind of moth had been seen in the vicinity at the time, yet a few hours after the females were placed in the box, more than forty males were found about the building!

MECHANICAL RECEPTORS

The ear. In backboned animals, the mechano-receptors for hearing and equilibrium are developed for the most part in the ear. The mechanical principles and structures of organs of equilibrium are essentially similar. The general plan of structure calls for a vesicle lined with sensory, hairlike receptors, whose cavity is filled with a liquid in which may be one or many freely movable solid particles (Fig. 73). When an animal changes its position, the liquid with these concretions or particles—sometimes they are grains of sand—shifts about coming in contact with different groups of the lining sensory hairs and stimulating them. The resulting impulse is carried to the brain (in higher animals), and proper adjustments are made. In some animals, such as clams, oysters, and crayfish, these organs are called **statocysts** (*statos*—standing; *kystis*—bladder) (Fig. 73).

In the shrimps, animals which resemble and are related to crayfish, the stato-cyst opens to the outside. When the animal molts, that is, when it loses its hard outer shell, it loses the sand grains from its statocyst as well. Kreidl placed some shrimps, just after they had molted, in a dish with iron filings instead of sand grains, and the shrimp placed iron filings instead of sand grains in the statocyst. He then brought into play an electromagnet which shifted the particles, but not the animals' position, and observed that the animals turned over on their backs, thus accommodating themselves to the stimulus.

In vertebrates, from fishes to man, the balancing organ of the ear consists of two small saclike chambers called the **utriculus** (*utriculus*—little skin bag) and the **sacculus** (Fig. 73). In addition to these structures there are three semicircular canals having both ends of each canal connected with the utriculus. The utriculus and the sacculus contain specialized end organs, each consisting of a group of cells with hairlike processes called **hair cells.** Fastened to the hair cells are concretions of calcium carbonate called ear stones or **otoliths.** The hair cells are well supplied with nerve endings; hence any move-

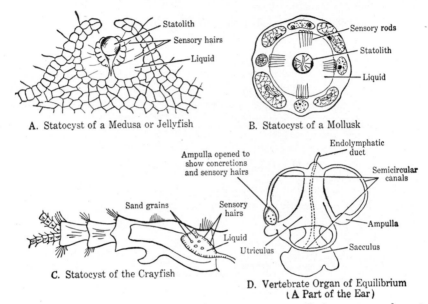

A. Statocyst of a Medusa or Jellyfish

B. Statocyst of a Mollusk

C. Statocyst of the Crayfish

D. Vertebrate Organ of Equilibrium
(A Part of the Ear)

Fig. 73. Organs used in maintaining equilibrium. In all these organs there is the same general structural plan: a cavity lined with sensory hairs and containing a liquid in which there usually are some floating particles. *A and B, redrawn from Dahlgren and Kepner, "Principles of Animal Histology." C and D, by permission of the publisher, the Macmillan Co., modified from Huxley, "The Crayfish."*

ment of the head changes the position of the otoliths and sets up a reflex which may result in a righting reaction on the part of the animal. In man, apparently, the utriculus and sacculus are concerned with the relation of the body to the changes of gravity. In other words, when the eyes cannot assist in orientation, as when a person dives into deep water or an aviator flies blindly, the ear structures tell us which way is up or down. In addition to these mechanisms, the eyes also function in head and body-position adjustments.

The semicircular canals are located in three different planes arranged approximately at right angles to each other (Figs. 73 and 74). The canals contain a fluid. Movement of the head in any plane sets the liquid in motion, thus stimulating certain sensory hairlike structures, and this assists man to a large degree in the maintenance of his equilibrium. This equilibrium mechanism and those equilibrium mechanisms of the invertebrates are really to be considered parts of the proprioceptor system.

An ocean voyage often causes too much change of position and overworks the vertical canals of the equilibrium mechanism, inducing seasickness. In testing the fitness of prospective aviators, one of the most important tests is designed to ascertain whether the semicircular canals are functioning normally. The candidate is placed in a special chair and whirled rapidly in various planes and directions. His adjustment time is then observed and measured.

Hearing is the perception of certain vibrations of bodies which give rise to sound waves. The sound waves spread out from the vibrating body in all directions and may be transmitted to animals through air or water. The organs of hearing of various animals are mechanical devices which receive the sound waves. The sound waves, creating a state of excitation in the form of a nerve impulse, are carried by a nerve (the **auditory**) to the brain, where they are interpreted. The organs for sound perception vary in complexity in different animals and reach their highest degree of complexity and perfection in man and other mammals. In man there is an external appendage, the lobe or **pinna,** in common parlance "the ear," which is useful in collecting sound waves and determining origin of the sound. Leading from the pinna into the head is a small tubular passage, the **auditory meatus** (*meatus*—passage), which ends in a chamber, the **tympanic cavity** or **middle ear** (Fig. 74). The opening of the auditory meatus into the tympanic cavity or middle ear is closed by a partition of tissue, the **tympanum** or **eardrum.** By this arrangement the tympanum is subjected to air pressure through the auditory meatus. Any sudden increase in pressure, like an explosion, might burst the drum. Such an accident is often prevented by the **Eustachian tube,** a passage which leads up from the pharynx to the middle ear, and thus the tympanum may have approximately equal pressure on both sides. This construction permits the eardrum to vibrate more freely.

Pronounced changes in atmospheric pressure, such as are encountered in changes of elevation, often cause an uncomfortable sensation of "deafness." This sensation is sometimes experienced when one is carried upward rapidly in an elevator or rides over a mountain in an automobile. The condition can be relieved by yawning or swallowing, which opens the Eustachian tube and, permitting air to enter the middle ear, equalizes the pressure on the two sides of the eardrum.

The essential organ of hearing is the **cochlea** (*cochlea*—snail), a spiral, fluid-filled sac enclosed in bone. This region of the ear is separated by constriction from the utriculus and the sacculus, the portions of the ear concerned with equilibrium. The semicircular canals, utriculus, sacculus, cochlea, and associated structures make up the **inner ear** (Figs. 74 and 75). The tympanum is connected to the fluid-filled cochlea of the inner ear by a chain of three bones (**malleus, incus,** and **stapes**), which is found in the middle ear (Fig. 74).

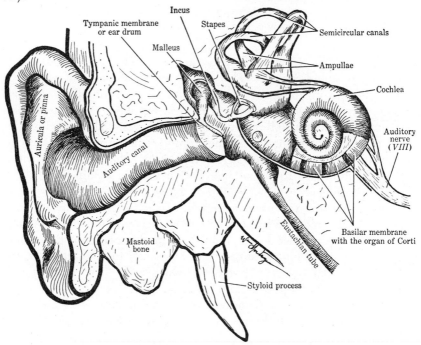

FIG. 74. Diagram of the anatomy of the human ear.

This mechanism works as follows. Sound waves come in through the outer ear and set the tympanum in vibration.

The vibrations of the tympanum, causing vibrations of the chain of these bones, are thus transmitted to the liquid of the cochlea. The diameter of the cochlea decreases as successive coils become increasingly smaller, and a **basilar membrane,** made up of tautly stretched transverse fibers attached at each end to the walls of the cochlea, is suspended in the liquid of the cochlea (Fig. 75). The basilar membrane supports the **organ of Corti,** made up of hair cells which are overhung by a membrane (Fig. 75). These sensory hair cells are connected to the brain by the **auditory nerves.** High notes or tones may affect regions where the fibers are shortest, corresponding to the short strings of the piano; low notes or tones affect the longer fibers corresponding to the long strings of the piano or bass. The vibrating fibers of the membrane, in turn, move the hair cells, which strike the overhanging membrane, bringing about stimulation in the hair cells and setting up an impulse which is carried to the brain.

Apparently when the ear is stimulated by sound vibrations the organ of Corti within the cochlea causes changes in electrical potentials which have the same

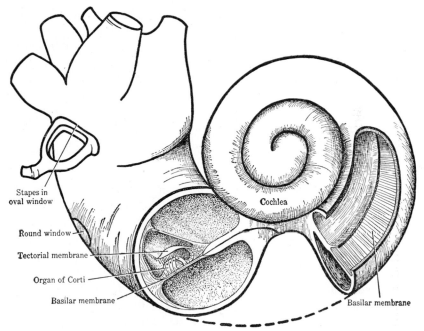

Stapes in
oval window

Round window

Tectorial membrane

Organ of Corti

Basilar membrane

Cochlea

Basilar membrane

Fig. 75.   Diagram showing the auditory apparatus of the inner ear.

frequency as the sound waves. Wever and Bray exposed the auditory nerve of a cat and connected it with a telephone in another room by means of electrodes and a vacuum-tube amplifier. Words and musical notes sounded at the cat's ear could be heard distinctly through the telephone.

Deafness. Deafness may result from several causes. The eardrum may have burst or become hardened so that it is unable to vibrate; hence, sound waves or vibrations fail to reach the inner ear unless they are very intense. To be heard one must shout. Other causes of deafness may be the closure of the outer passage by "wax," defects in the bony chain, defects in the cochlear region, or a degenerating auditory nerve.

"Hearing" in other animals. The lower vertebrate animals have no outer ear, no chain of bones, and no spiral organ of Corti. In the frog, the tympanum is at the surface of the body and connected with the inner ear by a single bone. In some animals, including man to some extent, sound vibrations are carried to the auditory nerve through the bones of the head. Vibratory movements in water are probably imperceptible to us, but the fishes have a system of cutaneous and sub-cutaneous sense organs, called the **lateral line organs,** which respond to these slow vibrations.

It is very difficult to prove that insects hear. Forel believes that they do not hear as we do but that their receptors for sound are more like our tactile organs. However, invertebrates may have some sense of hearing, because they produce "sounds," some so high-pitched that the human ear cannot perceive them. Moreover, some insects have been observed to respond to the call of their mates and to artificial imitation calls. The grasshopper has a pair of external tympana which connect with a vesicle and a nerve. Hearing organs are located on the antennas of some insects and on the legs of others.

LIGHT RECEPTORS

When the word sight is mentioned, we at once think of the human eye, an organ which can function only by the aid of light. However, light perception or reception, and consequent stimulation, does not necessarily mean image projection. This has been shown in the studies of the so-called "eyes" of simple animals, properly called **photorecep-tors.** In many of the one-celled animals, the photoreceptor consists of an "eye spot" or pigment spot which is sensitive only to changes in light intensity. In fact, all protoplasm is more or less sensitive to light. In many animals there is material in the surface epithelium which registers changes in light intensity. The earthworm has specialized sensory cells for light perception and responds quite readily to a beam of light flashed upon it. The anterior or head end is more sensitive than the posterior. Similar evidence seems to indicate that photo-receptor cells are present in oysters, clams, and other animals.

The eye. A true eye is concerned with form and color percep-tion as well as with change in light intensity. It is an organ which consists of a photosensitive surface like the plate or film of a camera and a mechanism, a **lens,** that focuses the light on this sensory sur-face. Further, a true eye has nervous connection with the brain which interprets these photographed images.

In its structure and working the eye has often been compared to a photographic camera. The outer tough **sclera** or "white" of the eye is the box of the camera. The **cornea** is a transparent region of the

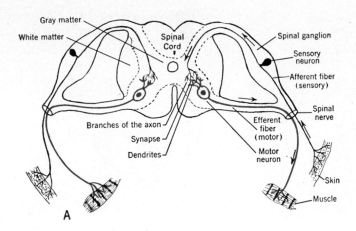

A

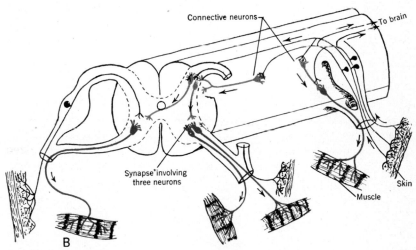

B

PLATE VII. Reflexes. The functioning of the nervous mechanism. A, diagrammatic cross section of the spinal cord with a pair of spinal nerves showing relation of the neurons and the mechanism of a simple reflex arc. Arrows indicate the path of a nervous impulse. B, diagram of the adjustor mechanism involved in a more complicated nervous reaction. *Modified from Curtis and Guthrie, "Textbook of General Zoology." By permission of the authors and of the publisher, John Wiley & Sons.*

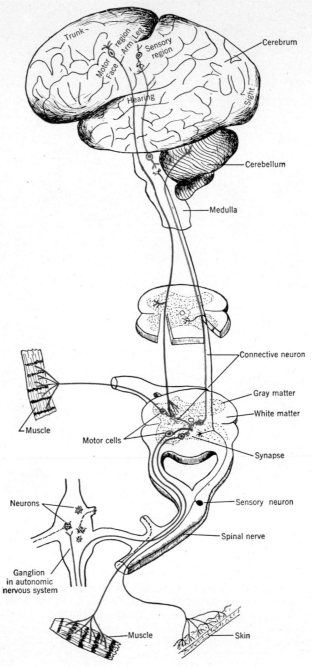

PLATE VIII. Diagram showing the functioning of the brain and spinal cord.

sclera, which may be compared to the opening in the box through
which light enters (Fig. 76). Under the sclera lies the choroid coat,
containing many blood vessels. This coat is darkly pigmented and
may be likened to the dark lining of the camera. The portion of the
choroid seen through the cornea is the colored curtain, the **iris**. The
round opening in the iris is the **pupil** of the eye, which admits light to

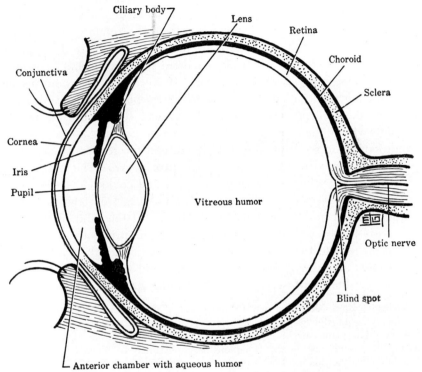

FIG. 76. Diagram of a section of the human eye.

the **lens** lying immediately behind the iris. The inner lining of the
eye is the **retina** (*rete*—net), which contains photoreceptor cells; it is
comparable to the sensitive film or plate of the camera. The eye is
kept rigid and turgid by the **aqueous humor** (*aqua*—water; *humor*—
moisture) and the **vitreous body** (*vitreus*—glassy; *humor*). The
watery aqueous humor fills the chamber between the cornea and the
lens, and the more jellylike vitreous body fills the space between the
lens and the retina.

How the Eye Photographs. The eye is "pointed" toward the object
to be photographed by muscles which rotate the eyeball in the socket;
also the animal may turn its head. The light rays are brought to a

focus on the retina principally by the cornea and the lens. In some animals the lens may change its position; in others, its shape. The change in shape of the lens is brought about mainly by the **ciliary muscles** lying in the middle coat of the eye. Thus, the closer an object is held to the eyes, the thicker the lens becomes. This is called **accommodation.** To bring out the image more clearly, just as in the camera or microscope, the amount of light must be regulated. This is done by the iris, which acts like a diaphragm to change the size of the pupil. The object is now clearly focused on the retina, upside down as in a camera. In the retina there are millions of specialized receptors called **rods** and **cones.** The rods are more sensitive in dim light and dark; the cones are sensitive to color. If we saw only by means of the rods, our world about us would appear in black, white, and gray. We owe the perception of color to the cones. Rods are used mostly for night vision, the cones becoming quite functionless. Under normal conditions these receptors are stimulated, and the resultant nerve impulses are carried to the brain by the **optic nerve.** The brain then constructs the image in its true proportions and colors.

The surface of the eye is kept moist by tears from the **lacrimal gland,** located in the upper and outer region of the orbit of the eye. The tears flow down across the eyeball and drain into the tear duct, which opens into the nose. Tears serve to lubricate the eyeball and the eyelids and also to keep the delicate outer covering of the front of the eye, the **conjunctiva,** from becoming dry and inflamed.

Vision Defects. Blindness may be the result of derangements of various parts of the eye. In this respect, Clendening continues the camera comparison as follows: "The plate may be fogged or broken; the retina may be diseased. The lens of the camera may be dirty; the lens of the eye may be blurred by cataract." Blindness may be due to atrophy of the optic nerve, as a result of the hardening of the arteries, Bright's disease, or diabetes. Cataract may be the result of an infection or malnutrition. This condition can be remedied by removing the lens, "a simple operation in competent hands." The lens of the eye glass takes the functional place of the one removed.

Among other causes of defective vision is the lack of adjustments in the lens of the eye, which results in improper focusing. If the image is to be brought out clearly and not to appear blurred, it must be formed sharply on the retina. Some people are said to be farsighted (**hyperopia**) which means that, with the lens in a "normal" state, the image is formed behind the retina. In other persons, said to be nearsighted (**myopia**) the image is formed in front of the retina (Fig. 77). Farsightedness can be corrected by wearing glasses with convex lenses, and nearsightedness, by glasses with concave lenses (Fig. 77).

Eyes of Invertebrates. Some eyes of invertebrate animals resemble superficially the general plan of structure just described, but most invertebrate eyes are used mainly for light perception and, in many invertebrates, for the detection of motion. There is usually a tough covering corresponding to the **sclera,** and the eye proper has a **lens** and a sensory retinalike structure (Fig. 78). Eyes of this type are found in certain mollusks, annelids, and spiders, and in the **simple eyes** or **ocelli** of insects. The focal length of such eyes is very short. The

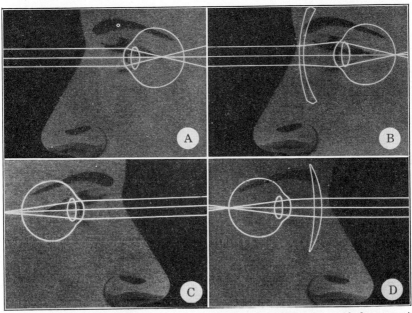

FIG. 77. *A*, condition found in myopia (image formed in front of the retina). *B*, condition corrected by a lens. *C*, condition existing in hyperopia (image formed back of the retina). *D*, condition corrected by a lens. *Courtesy of the Bausch and Lomb Optical Co.*

invertebrate eye which most closely resembles the "camera eye" of man is that of the squid, in which the arrangement of the layers of retinal cells is just the reverse of that in the vertebrate eye.

Crabs and insects have what is known as a **compound eye,** consisting of a number of small simple eyes called **ommatidia** (*omma—* eye); the number of simple eyes in a single compound eye may vary from 7 to 27,000.

Each **ommatidium** or **simple eye** has a lenslike organ and a group of **photosensory cells** or **retinula** which corresponds to a retina (Fig. 78). Each ommatidium is isolated from adjacent ones by cells containing black pigment. The **retinulas** of the compound eye are connected to the brain by nerve fibers.

The compound eye is supposed to produce **mosaic vision.** Each ommatidium forms a separate and different image of a small specific portion of the object. Thus there is no overlapping of image, and the

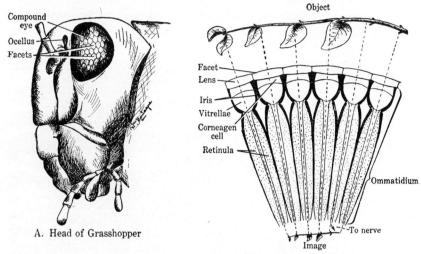

A. Head of Grasshopper

B. Diagrammatic Section of a Compound Eye

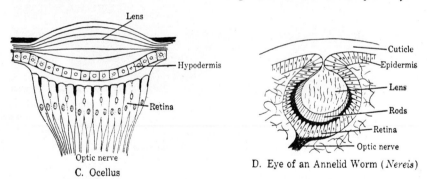

C. Ocellus

D. Eye of an Annelid Worm (*Nereis*)

FIG. 78. Compound eye of insects, mosaic vision, and eyes of other invertebrates. *C, redrawn from Comstock, "A Manual for the Study of Insects." By permission of the Comstock Publishing Co. D, redrawn from Hegner, "Invertebrate Zoology," after Andrews. By permission of the publisher, the Macmillan Co.*

sum total of all these images gives a complete picture of the object observed. Hegner suggests that this method of image formation "may be well adapted for recording motion, since any change in position of large objects affects the entire 2,500 ommatidia" in a crayfish (Fig. 78). Compound eyes can see objects at a distance of 7 to 10 feet. It is probable that the image "photographed" by the compound eye is more blurred than that taken by the eye of man.

Apparently, insect eyes differ from those of man in more respects than structure. In an interesting series of experiments Lutz has shown that ultraviolet
light rays which are invisible to human eyes are visible to insects. On the other
hand, insects are color blind to red, which appears gray to them. Lubbock
confined some ants in a box, into one region of which ultraviolet light entered
through a prism. Another part was illuminated by red light. To human eyes
the ultraviolet end would appear dark, and the red end, light. The ants hurried
into the region illuminated by the red rays. Flowers of different plants which
seem to man to be alike in color may have a different color pattern to an insect
if one flower reflects ultraviolet light and the other does not. To the insect, even
the color patterns of other insects are different from those seen by man. At least
they appear different in photographs made of objects which reflect only the ultraviolet. Lutz concluded that there is a possibility that this reaction is "not vision
in the usual sense of the word" but may be "a complicated physiological phenomenon."

OTHER RECEPTORS

Touch. The mechanical receptors responsible for touch are found
on the free surfaces of almost all organisms. As pointed out, the touch

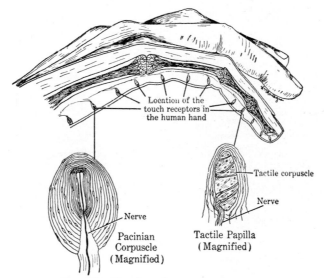

Fig. 79. Touch and pressure receptors.

receptors are located in the protoplasm of all external cells. In some
lower animals, certain structures such as the antennas of insects and
crayfish have specialized tactile organs in the form of stiff, tactile hairs
or bristles. In the higher forms we find various types of tactile mechanisms. The cat's "whiskers" are supposedly tactile in function. In
man, sensitivity in touch is not uniformly distributed but is restricted

to certain areas which can be mapped out.   In these areas are found specialized end organs called **tactile corpuscles** (Fig. 79).   The sensation of pressure is very similar to that of touch but is perceived by the stimulation of different receptors (**Pacinian corpuscles**).

Temperature and pain receptors.   In addition to the receptors for touch and pressure there are in the skin other receptors for warmth, cold, and pain.   These receptors are grouped in special spots.   Pain spots contain no special receptor—just free nerve endings.   The warmth and cold receptors are scattered over the body in different areas.   Thus in the skin of the face there are few cold spots but many warm spots; on the other hand, there are few warm spots in the mucous lining of the mouth and pharynx, an arrangement which enables us to drink extremely hot tea and coffee.   So far as is known these thermal receptors occur only in warm-blooded animals.

11

Adjustment to Environment
Nervous Coordination
The Adjustment Mechanism
Effectors

We have seen that various agents, such as chemicals, light, and heat, may act as stimuli to arouse and excite various specialized receptors in an organism. Further, certain tissues, especially nervous tissue, are adapted not only for excitation or reception of stimuli but also for transmission. We have just studied various specialized adaptations of the nervous system for the reception of stimuli, such as the eye, taste buds, ear, and tactile corpuscles. From these special sensory regions a state of excitation, set up by stimuli, is transmitted along the nerve fibers as a **nerve impulse.** In the sensory structures, the nerve impulse travels toward the **central nervous system,** which is made up of the **brain** and **spinal cord.** In the central nervous system, various necessary adjustments and coordinations are usually made as a result of the stimuli, and a fitting response in the form of a nerve impulse is sent out to the effectors, which are muscles and glands.

Nervous tissue. The structural unit of nervous tissue is called a **neuron** (*neuron*—nerve). A neuron consists of the **cell body** and its processes, of which there are usually two kinds, **dendrites** and **axons** (Fig. 80). Dendrites (*dendron*—tree) may be either long fibers with much-branched endings or short processes branching close to the cell body. They serve to conduct nerve impulses, induced by stimuli, toward the cell body. Axons (*axon*—axis) are usually fairly long fibers which branch at the free end at quite a distance from the cell body. They may reach a length of several feet and may carry the nerve impulse to the next neuron in a chain of neurons or, if terminal, may discharge the impulse into a muscle or gland. They usually conduct impulses away from the cell body.

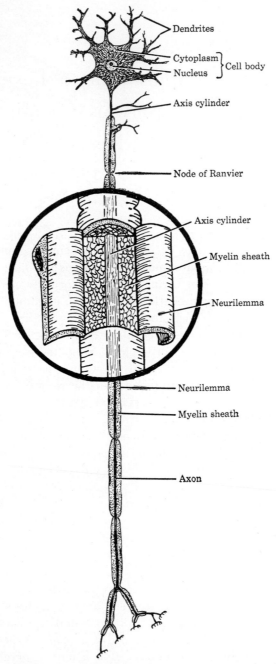

Dendrites

Cytoplasm
Nucleus } Cell body

Axis cylinder

Node of Ranvier

Axis cylinder

Myelin sheath

Neurilemma

Neurilemma

Myelin sheath

Axon

FIG. 80.   Diagrammatic sketch of a typical neuron.

The axons of certain neurons may be invested by sheaths. The inner sheath or **myelin sheath** (*myelos*—marrow) is made up of white, fatty material surrounded by a transparent cellular outer sheath, the **neurilemma** (*neuron; lemma*—skin). These coverings are supposed to insulate the nerve fibers and increase the speed of conduction. The myelin sheath is interrupted at intervals by the **nodes of Ranvier.** Neurons are held together by supporting tissue. They receive their nourishment and lose their wastes through the blood. The neurilemma is necessary for the regeneration of nerve fibers (Fig. 80).

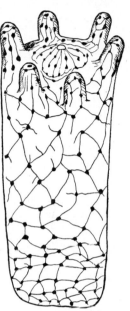

FIG. 81. Nerve net of hydra. *Redrawn from Curtis and Guthrie, "Textbook of General Zoology." (After Hadzi.)*

Nervous systems in general. In some of the simpler animals (hydras, corals, and their relatives), the nerve cells are found mostly under the outer body layer, or outer epithelium, where they form a diffuse, netlike meshwork of nerve tissue which has been designated a **nerve net** (Fig. 81). Investigation has shown that the nerve cells of this meshwork are separate units in contact with each other only. This type of nervous system transmits in all directions equally well, for there are no definite paths of transmission and no centralization.

In certain jellyfishes there is a nerve ring around the circumference. This construction results in a diffuse transmission of impulses and usually a very general response which involves large regions of the organism. Connected zigzag strips cut from the body wall of the sea anemone are affected by the stimulation of only one strip. The basal region of a sea anemone from which most of the animal has been removed will continue to creep about.

In most of the higher animals, beginning with the worms, the nervous tissue becomes more localized, or centralized, to form linear cords called **nerve cords.** In certain regions of these cords nerve-cell bodies are often grouped to form a **ganglion.** From the ganglia the processes of the nerve cells may be grouped into a sort of cable called a **nerve,** usually leading off to various parts of the animal. In insects, the development of specialized structures such as mouth parts, wings, and legs may involve a shift in the position of the ganglia and often a fusion of them. In worms, insects, crayfish, and their close relatives, the nerve cord is made up of two longitudinal cords. In vertebrate animals there is one central, tubular nerve cord called the **spinal cord,** which is enlarged at its anterior end forming the **brain.**

Reflexes. The operation of the nervous system depends on the way the neurons are connected and grouped into systems, which involves the relative position and endings of the dendrites and the axons. The foundation for the understanding of the nervous system and its functioning is the **reflex arc.** Theoretically, in a vertebrate animal, at least two neurons are necessary in a simple reflex arc involving the spinal cord. However, it is probable that in the higher animals at least three neurons are involved. One of these, called the **sensory neuron,** receives the stimulus from the fine-branched endings of its process among the cells of the skin. The cell body of this sensory neuron is located in a ganglion with other sensory neurons, near the spinal cord. This ganglion is called a **spinal ganglion** (Plate VII).

For purpose of illustration we shall consider the simplest form of a reflex arc, made up of two neurons. The axon of the sensory cell ends in the spinal cord, where it comes in functional contact with the dendrites of another neuron, the **motor neuron,** which is in the ventral horn of the cord. This region of functional contact is known as a **synapse.** The axon of the **motor neuron** extends from the spinal cord to a muscle or a gland and may be enclosed in the same bundle or nerve with the sensory fibers of the sensory neurons, as well as other motor axons. This nerve is a **spinal nerve** (Plate VII).

How neurons function. A nerve impulse, or state of excitation caused by a stimulus, is transmitted by the process of the sensory neuron to the cell body. The impulse passes through the cell body, out the axon, and across the synapse to the dendrite of the motor cell. It then passes through the motor cell body, and along the axon to the muscle which is stimulated to contract. If the ending is in a gland, the effect of the stimulus may be the discharge of glandular secretions. Thus we may say that impulses are carried to the spinal cord by **afferent** or **sensory fibers,** and that they leave by the **efferent** or **motor fibers.** An action brought about by an impulse that travels around a reflex arc is called a **reflex action.** Since reflex actions are known to occur in animals having no central nervous system, it follows that a reflex arc need not involve a central nerve cord. It is probable that most reflex actions involve many neurons instead of two as in the simple reflex arc just described.

In man and other higher animals, this receptor-conductor-effector mechanism reaches a degree of complexity, of specialization, of such delicate balance that one can only with difficulty appreciate its workings. To this system man owes much of the coordination of his bodily movements and the extraordinary development of his intellect and emotions which, rather than his other systems, sets him apart from other animals. An understanding of man as a social and spiritual being as well as a biological organism involves some knowledge of his nervous system. An understanding of the life and behavior of other organisms, high or low in the scale of complexity, rests upon the study of the adjusting mechanism. We have seen and analyzed the simplest of these responses, and we shall now attempt further analysis by a more detailed study of **receptors, conductors** including the adjustment mechanism, and **effectors.**

THE NERVOUS MECHANISM

The nervous mechanism in man and other vertebrates is made up of three systems: the **central,** the **peripheral,** and the **autonomic nervous systems.** The central nervous system consists of the spinal cord and brain. The peripheral nervous system consists of the nerves which leave the spinal cord, the **spinal nerves,** and the nerves which leave the brain, the **cranial nerves.** The autonomic nervous system (*auto*—self; *nomos*—province or self-governing) is an auxiliary system of ganglia and nerves regulating and controlling most of the internal organs, such as those of the alimentary tract, the heart, and the arteries, which are not under the control of the will.

The central and peripheral nervous systems. The **spinal cord** in vertebrates is enclosed in a canal in the backbone of the animal. The paired spinal nerves leave it at regular intervals along its length. Each nerve has two roots in the cord, a **dorsal root** and a **ventral root** (Plates VII and VIII). The dorsal root is made up of **afferent, sensory fibers** which arise in the cell bodies of **sensory neurons** in the spinal ganglion close to the nerve cord where the sensory root emerges. The ventral root is made up of efferent fibers coming from cell bodies of neurons found in the nerve cord. The fibers from these two roots enter the same sheath. In man it is estimated that there are approximately 630,000 nerve fibers in the dorsal root, and 200,000 fibers in the ventral root, of a spinal nerve.

There are two main regions of the spinal cord: an outer one called the **white matter,** made up of nerve fibers some of which are surrounded by myelin sheaths; and an inner one, made up mostly of nerve cell bodies and dendrites, called the **gray matter.** The nerve cells in the gray matter of the spinal cord are either motor neurons or connective neurons. The myelinated fibers of the white matter are: afferent fibers of sensory nerves, which may run lengthwise through the cord and end in the brain; axons of connective neurons of the gray matter of the cord or the brain; and efferent fibers running to the spinal nerves. These regions and relations are brought out in Plates VII and VIII, which should be carefully studied.

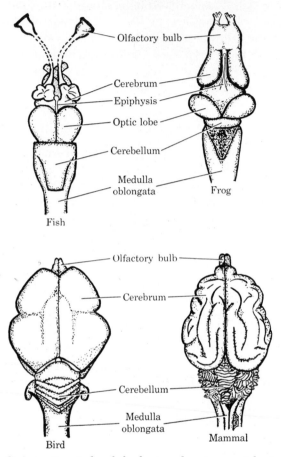

Fig. 82. Comparative study of the brains of various vertebrate animals.

The brain is the highly differentiated region at the anterior end of the spinal cord. In vertebrate animals, five general divisions are recognized, only three of which will be considered here: the **cerebrum,** which is most anterior; the more posterior **cerebellum;** and the most posterior **medulla oblongata,** which merges into the spinal cord (Plate VIII and Fig. 82).

The five general regions recognized in the vertebrate brain are: the **telencephalon** (*tele*–far; *enkephalon*–brain); **diencephalon** (*di*–second); **mesencephalon** (*mesos*—middle); **metencephalon** (*meta*—after); **myelencephalon** (*myelos*—marrow). Figure 82 shows the general relationship of these brain regions in various vertebrates.

The Cerebrum (Telencephalon). Plate VIII and Fig. 82 show that the cerebrum is made up of two hemispheres which become much enlarged and more pronounced from fishes to man. In man, where it covers and dwarfs the other regions, it is much folded. There is an outer layer of **gray matter,** the **cerebral cortex,** which conforms to these folds and covers the underlying **white matter.** There is an essential similarity between man and the lower animals in the function of the various brain regions except the cerebrum. A frog whose cerebrum has been removed behaves quite like the normal unoperated animal. There is little loss in vital function in birds and dogs after removal of the cerebrum except that the dog loses what he has learned. The animal will eat only when food is placed in the mouth. The development and differentiation of the cerebral cortex to a large extent make man what he is. Failure of this structure to develop means idiocy. The cerebrum is the region of thinking, memory, volition, consciousness, and mental life generally. These activities are carried on by the estimated 10,000,000,000 neurons of the cortex. Experimental studies have shown that certain areas of the brain may control certain specific activities. These regions were mapped as shown in Plate VIII. The areas not so marked are called the **association areas,** and it is here that such processes as learning, recall, imagination, and reasoning take place. However, Lashley has demonstrated that, in rats, the functional areas are not absolutely fixed, but that if one region of the cerebrum is destroyed another will take over its functions. He found that some rats, when he destroyed as much as 80 per cent of the cerebrum, could continue to learn. However, certain regions such as the auditory and visual seemed to be specific.

The brain pattern of man seems to be more fixed than that of a rat. In 1848, a quarryman named Gage was tamping a blast which exploded suddenly and drove a crowbar through the left side of his jaw and out through the top of his head in the frontal region. He lived for 12 years after this and could hear, see, taste, smell, and perform voluntary movements. However, his temperament and disposition were affected. He would go into fits of rage and wander away. He would not work, and he became dishonest. After he died in convulsions, an autopsy showed that the left prefrontal portion of his brain was destroyed. Probably some of the adjacent areas had been injured also. Theoretically, this region is responsible for the qualities that were impaired.

The functions of other areas have been discovered by the ingenious method of opening the skull and stimulating certain areas of the brain with an electric needle. For example, one small area stimulated will cause an animal's thumb to twitch, and if a wider area is stimulated the entire arm comes into action. Other areas stimulated give specific reactions of other body regions. Not only have these functional areas been determined by destruction and stimulation, but post-mortem examinations of the brains of handicapped individuals, including the mentally sick (insane), have shown tumors and various other defects in certain regions. Some indication of the brain pattern is thus ascertained from the behavior of these unfortunates. By electrical devices, it has been possible to trace the path of nerve impulses from the various sense organs to certain brain regions.

The Cerebellum (Metencephalon). This division of the brain is the center for reflex coordination, equilibrium, motor coordination, and muscular tone—in other words, an organ of motor control. Destruction of this region of the brain results in jerky, ineffective, uncoordinated muscular movements. It is almost impossible for the hand to pick up anything, and the affected person "reels drunkenly" when he tries to walk. No function of "consciousness" seems to exist in the cerebellum. In man, stimulation of the cerebellum is not felt. Its cortical region or gray matter is estimated to contain 1,000,000,000 neurons. Into it come the relay fibers from the skin, the joints, the eyes, the ears, the muscles, and from the cerebrum itself. The following illustration adapted from Clendening brings out the function of the cerebellum more clearly. A golfer is urged to keep his eye on the ball when he is trying to hit it. His eyes are 6 feet from the ball and his hand 3. Why should his looking at the ball help him to place one tiny space on the face of his club within $\frac{1}{164}$ of an inch of the spot on the ball which will send it farthest and straightest? Because of his cerebellum, which receives fibers from the center of vision in the cerebrum, from the semicircular canals, and from his muscles and joints. All these together give him a sense of space, distance, and muscular steadiness. The cerebellum makes connections with the motor centers sending fibers to his muscles; the result is a motor sense of "placement." Thus the functions of sight, equilibrium, feeling, and motion are brought together and integrated. A good athlete needs a good cerebellum.

It will be noted, from a study of Fig. 82, that size and complexity of the cerebellum vary with the motor activity and structure of the animal. In frogs and salamanders, rather sluggish animals having poorly developed powers of locomotion, the cerebellum is very small; in the much more active birds, it is relatively very large and well developed.

The Medulla Oblongata (Myelencephalon). This posterior division of the brain gradually merges into the spinal cord (Plate VIII and Fig. 82). The medulla receives stimuli from the viscera through the autonomic system. It is the center that regulates such automatic or unconscious, yet vitally important, functions as the heart beat, blood pressure, and movements of the lungs in breathing. It controls body temperature, the involuntary movements of the intestinal tract, and the action of various glands. A frog with all the brain cut away except the medulla continues to breathe normally and to swallow pieces of food placed in its mouth. The animal may even continue to live for a long time with all the brain missing except the medulla.

THE AUTONOMIC NERVOUS SYSTEM

The autonomic nervous system regulates the internal organs of the animal, such as the alimentary tract, lungs, heart, blood vessels, bladder, and glands. In general, we might say that it regulates those structures having involuntary muscles. In man it is beyond the direct control of the will and takes care of the "routine drudgery of life." In other words, one cannot deliberately cause the heart to beat faster or change the rate of intestinal peristalsis. Stimuli that result in emotional reactions also affect the autonomic nervous system and glands of internal secretion. We have already seen that emotional stimuli, such as fear and anger, often add to adrenal activity, which results in increase in blood pressure. Stage fright is usually accompanied by dryness of the mouth and throat. Emotional stress may interfere with digestion because the flow of gastric juices tends to be diminished as a result of the cutting off of the normal blood supply to the alimentary tract. It is well known that many digestive disturbances can be traced directly to worry or excitement.

This system is sometimes known as the involuntary nervous system. Anatomically it consists of two divisions, the **parasympathetic division** centered in the sacral region of the cord and parts of the brain (medulla and midbrain) and the **sympathetic division** made up of two chains of connected ganglia extending along each side of the spinal cord in the thoracic and lumbar regions (Fig. 83). Sensory neurons of the autonomic system are found in the spinal ganglia, and motor neurons are located in the spinal cord. Fibers from these neurons are found in the dorsal and ventral roots of the spinal nerves. In addition, fibers originating from ganglia of the autonomic system may be present in the roots of the spinal nerves (Fig. 83). Thus it is seen that, by this arrangement, the autonomic system is connected

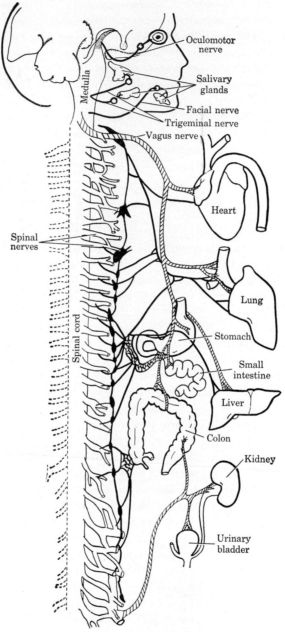

FIG. 83. The autonomic nervous system of man. Note the branches of the vagus nerve which is an important component of the parasympathetic division.

with the central nervous system. Nerve fibers of the autonomic system extending from neurons in the central nervous system to the autonomic ganglia are called **preganglionic fibers,** and those fibers whose neurons are in the autonomic ganglia are known as **postganglionic fibers.** Numerous autonomic fibers as well as ganglia often unite to form a **plexus.** The one most commonly known in man is the **solar plexus,** which lies in the abdominal cavity. Branches extend from this plexus to the various abdominal organs.

Most of the organs supplied by the autonomic system receive a double set of nerve fibers. One set stimulates or accelerates and the other inhibits or retards a reaction. Many structures, such as the intestines, heart, iris of the eye, and the salivary glands, receive fibers from both the sympathetic and the parasympathetic systems. Usually the actions of the two systems are antagonistic. For example, the heart rate is slowed down by impulses transmitted by the vagus nerve (parasympathetic system, cranial region) and accelerated by impulses from the sympathetic division. The iris of the eye contracts under impulses delivered by the parasympathetic division and dilates when it receives impulses from the sympathetic.

Research has demonstrated that nerve impulses of the parasympathetic system bring about the liberation by the nerve endings of a substance called **acetylcholine,** which, when secreted by branches of the vagus nerve in the heart, causes a slowing of the rate of heart beat. On the other hand the endings of the nerves of the sympathetic system release a substance, sometimes called **sympathin,** which has an effect somewhat similar to adrenalin; i.e., it accelerates muscular contraction. The effects of acetylcholine and sympathin are examples of the action of neurohumors.

EFFECTORS

The skeleton. In our bodies, and also in the bodies of other backboned animals, there are bones—round bones, long bones, flat bones, and others, which collectively make up the **skeleton** (*skeletos*—dried) (Fig. 84). This is such a commonplace fact that it is doubtful that we have ever given much thought to the real purpose of bones. We know they are there and that under normal conditions they function.

The skeleton serves various functions. It is responsible in a large measure for the shape of the animal; without it, many animals would be shapeless, jellylike affairs. Even the lowly sponges have supporting structures of some sort, as we shall see later. Skeletal structures serve for protection. The average observer knows how effectively a turtle

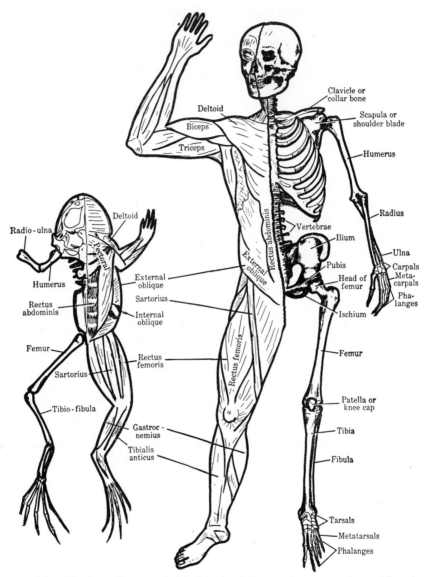

Fig. 84. The bony framework (skeleton) of frog and man together with some muscles that effect movement.

is protected within its shell, a type of structure known as an **exoskeleton** (*exo*—outside). Other familiar examples of exoskeletons are the shells of clams, oysters, and other shellfish, and the tough, horny, outer coverings of insects, crabs, and their relatives. Vertebrates have an inner skeleton called an **endoskeleton** (*endon*—within). Although not so effective from the standpoint of protection, this endoskeleton

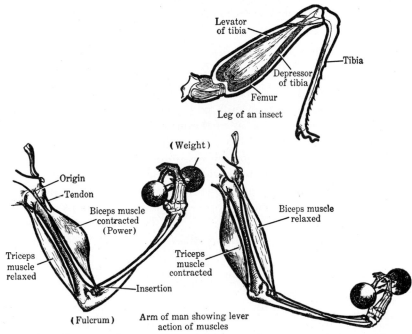

Levator of tibia

Tibia

Depressor of tibia

Femur

Leg of an insect

(Weight)

Origin

Tendon

Biceps muscle contracted (Power)

Biceps muscle relaxed

Triceps muscle relaxed

Triceps muscle contracted

Insertion

(Fulcrum)   Arm of man showing lever action of muscles

FIG. 85.   Effector mechanisms.   Note the antagonistic action of the muscles arranged in pairs.

permits more agility, a more varied response, and better possibilities for animal adjustment. The skeleton, whether exoskeleton or endoskeleton, is an integral and important cog in the **effecting mechanism,** the tool and machine of the directing nervous system.

Skeletons of insects, crabs, and vertebrates make up a system of levers, workable by various types of joints (Fig. 85). Attached to these levers at strategic points are muscles which move them, and this mechanism is responsible for the movement of the animal organism in whole or in part. In vertebrates three main types of joints are present: **hinge joints,** found in the elbow and knee; **ball-and-socket joints,** in the shoulder and hip; and **gliding joints,** in the ankle and wrist. At the joints the bones have enlarged ends which afford more surface for articulation. These ends are covered by a smooth layer of cartilage. The whole mechanism is held in place largely by lashings of connective tissue called **ligaments** (*ligare*— to bind). The joint is lubricated by a fluid secreted by the **synovial membrane** which encloses the joint. The joints of insects, crabs, and their relatives are of the hinged type. In the movement of the exoskeletal coverings of the abdomen, the edge of one segment slides over the edge of the adjacent one—a sort of modified gliding joint.

Muscles and Movement—Effectors in Action

Arrangement. Muscles work by contracting. When a muscle shortens it changes its shape but not its volume. The shortening or contraction results in a pull and consequent movement of the part to which it is attached, as in the arms and legs, or the region of which it is a part, as in the intestine. After the contraction comes a **relaxation,** or the restoration of the muscle to its original length. No work is done during the period of relaxation. Muscles always work by *pull.* They never *push.* Consequently, in arrangement, muscles are usually found in opposing pairs or groups. Certain muscles, the **flexors,** bend a limb at the joint, and others, the **extensors,** straighten it. Often more than one muscle is concerned in the movement of bones in joints such as the hip and shoulder. Frequently the muscles of opposing groups differ in size and strength. Thus the alligator has relatively weak muscles for opening the jaws but more powerful ones for closing them. A man has relatively little trouble in keeping an alligator's jaws closed but is in real difficulty when trying to keep them open. The same general muscle arrangement occurs in the large claw (chela) of a lobster.

Muscles at work. Under normal conditions, the skeletal muscles depend entirely on the nerve impulse to initiate their activities. If the nerve to a muscle is cut, the muscle relaxes completely and will not respond. The nerve impulse is sent through the efferent nerve fibers to each muscle fiber, which receives it through the **myoneural junction** (*mys*—muscle; *neuron*) (Fig. 86). The muscle fiber responds by a single, short contraction and then relaxes. Analyzed, this reaction of the muscle fiber consists of a **latent period,** that is, the time elapsing between the reception of the stimulus and beginning of contraction; the **contraction period;** and the **relaxation period,** which merges into the **recovery period.** A very simplified explanation of the working of the muscle fibers and, of course, of the muscle is somewhat as follows: apparently, the nerve impulse initiates a chemical reaction in the muscle, as a result of which energy is released and revealed in the form of external work such as lifting weights and movement.

Fig. 86. Photomicrograph showing region of contact between nerve and muscle (myoneural junction). *Copyright by the General Biological Supply House, Chicago.*

Contrary to popular belief, muscles will contract in the absence of free oxygen. This energy is furnished by the explosive breakdown, without the use of free oxygen, of an organic phosphate compound into an inorganic phosphate. The glycogen in the muscle then breaks down, forming lactic acid and releasing e..ergy. This energy is used to change the inorganic phosphate back to the organic phosphate necessary for additional contractions. This breakdown of both the organic phosphate compound and the glycogen are anaerobic reactions similar in a way to fermentation, where sugar breaks down into alcohol and carbon dioxide and releases energy as heat. According to some authors the energy released in the anaerobic phase is transformed into muscular contraction; then in the second phase oxygen supplied by the blood is consumed—aerobic respiration—which releases additional energy in the form of heat. Thus we see that oxygen brought by the blood stream is not used directly in muscular contraction. True, rapid and deep breathing brings additional supplies of oxygen to the muscles, but the amount is never sufficient to supply all oxygen needs of the contracting muscles.

Then how does the oxygen function? As the muscles continue their contraction, more and more phosphate change takes place, and more and more glycogen is broken down into lactic acid. Now the oxygen's role is to convert the lactic acid back into glycogen. In so doing it consumes or oxidizes one-fifth of the lactic acid, and carbon dioxide and water are released as waste products.

We see that the athlete doing the hundred-yard dash uses more energy than he had free oxygen to produce, but the glycogen loaned it to him. Thus he built up an **oxygen debt** which is repaid after the race by the continued faster and deeper breathing for a period.

Only 20–30 per cent of the available energy of glycogen of the muscle is manifested in movement. The rest is lost in heat, which is used to maintain a body temperature at which necessary physiological processes can proceed.

The chemical changes involved in muscular action may be represented as follows:

CONTRACTION

Organic phosphates → Phosphate + Organic compounds + Energy (used in contraction)

RECOVERY

Phosphate + Organic compounds + Energy from glycogen breakdown → Organic phosphates

Glycogen → Lactic acid + Energy (resynthesis of organic phosphates)

Lactic acid $\begin{cases} \frac{4}{5} \to \text{Glycogen} \\ \frac{1}{5} + O_2 \to CO_2 + H_2O + \text{Energy (used to resynthesize glycogen)} \end{cases}$

Each skeletal muscle is composed of bundles of muscle fibers. When stimulated, each individual fiber making up the muscle receives a separate impulse which does not spread beyond the fiber receiving it. The result is separate reaction by each fiber. The voluntary muscles can be made to undergo various degrees of contraction by stimulating only certain groups of fibers at a time. Thus the arm can be raised partially or completely, depending on the number of fibers stimulated. This mechanism makes possible the various adaptations of the organism to each situation which confronts it.

The preceding discussion has concerned skeletal muscle, whose structure was previously described under tissues as **voluntary** or **striated muscle.** Two other types of muscle, **smooth muscle** and **cardiac** or **heart muscle,** were described. These two types of muscle are involuntary. In smooth muscle there is a transmission of the contraction from muscle cell to muscle cell, resulting in a wave of contraction which spreads along the structure. This is seen in the contraction waves in the esophagus when food is swallowed. In cardiac muscles there are no distinct cell boundaries but the tissue is made up of continuous protoplasm. Thus a wave of contraction in this tissue is transmitted very rapidly, and, as a consequence, the entire heart contracts almost simultaneously in an **all-or-none** reaction. The contraction of heart muscle is automatic. The heart of a turtle can be removed and suspended in a vessel containing a solution somewhat like the body lymph and it will continue beating for days despite the fact that the rest of the turtle has long since died. Even small isolated pieces of the heart will show contraction outside the body. Smooth muscle may be directly stimulated by stretching, to which it responds by contracting.

Other effectors. Cilia and **flagella** are types of effectors found on some of the simplest animals as well as on various structures of higher animals. The gills of clams are covered with cilia whose beating brings fresh water with oxygen and food to the organism and carries various wastes away. The trachea of man and other higher animals is lined with cilia whose movement expels the dust-laden mucus. In some of the lower organisms, instead of cilia, there are present one or more whiplike structures called **flagella** (*flagellum* —whip) which are essentially similar to cilia in structure and in the mechanism of movement.

We have already discussed various types of glands which are also effectors and have pointed out their function and reactions. There is now set up an adjusting mechanism for the organism. This mechanism is a receptor-adjustor-effector system on whose perfect functioning the life of the individual and of the race depends.

12

Adjustment to Environment
Nervous Coordination
The Nervous System in Action

We shall examine more closely but in a general way the manner in which the central nervous system functions in bringing about adjustments of animals. This involves a study of the transmission of, and the paths taken by, the nerve impulses or states of excitation. We recall that the neuron normally exhibits polarity in that the impulse enters through the dendrites, passes through the cell body, and out the axon. The terminal branches of the axon may be in functional contact with the dendrites of another neuron or of many neurons. Such a place of functional contact or junction between dendrites and axons, for usually many neurons are involved, is known as a **synapse** (Plates VII and VIII). The nerve impulse passes from one neuron to another *only across the synapse*. A somewhat similar junctional relationship exists where the axon comes in contact with the muscle. This is known as the **myoneural junction** (Fig. 86).

The synapse. The nature and peculiarity of the synaptic junctions influence, in a marked way, much of the behavior of the higher animals. In the first place, a nerve impulse will pass across a synapse only in one direction. The synapse has polarity. Thus it is seen that there is "one-way traffic only" through the nerve cells and across the synapse. Experimental evidence indicates that nerve impulses may be slowed up or even blocked at the synapse. The extent of this block may vary under different physiological conditions and in different parts of the same animal. Thus synapses may be affected by certain glandular secretions as well as by toxins formed in the process of metabolism. Loss of oxygen may cause a synapse to lose all capacity for conduction. This is the reason a person may become unconscious when strangled or "half drowned." Certain drugs, among them nicotine and alcohol, may lower the conductivity of the synapse, thus slowing up the time of response and dulling the feeling. On the other hand

174

some drugs increase the conductivity of the synapse so that the slightest stimulus will cause an exaggerated response. An animal in this condition in common parlance is often said to be "nervous."

We have previously pointed out that reflex arcs almost always involve more than just one sensory and one motor neuron. Thus very complicated reflexes result from the combinations of many sensory, connective, and motor neurons. Some of the possible combinations are suggested below:

1. The axon of one sensory neuron may be in contact with two or more motor neurons.

2. The axons of two or more sensory neurons may be in contact with one motor neuron.

3. The axons of two or more sensory neurons may transmit the impulse to two or more motor neurons.

4. Connecting neurons may be present, connecting two or more sensory cells or two or more motor cells in the same or different levels in the spinal cord.

Some fishes have a pair of enormous nerve cells on whose dendrites the axons of no less than twelve sensory cells end. In all probability every neuron in the animal body is connected in some way by the synapses with every other neuron. Thus it may be assumed that a nervous impulse starting at one point could spread all over the body, provided that the same conditions held in all the nerve cells and synapses of the organism.

According to one view this does not happen, for usually the transmission of neural impulses is more or less channeled. Thus the stimulation of one group of receptors results in a response from only a certain group or groups of effectors. The problem before us, then, is the determination of the path followed by the nerve impulse. Dashiell * suggests certain physical possibilities as an explanation of this problem. In this connection we must study Fig. 87, in which diagram the neurons are pictured as removed from the spinal cord and arranged end to end in one plane. "For illustration, assume that a stream of impulses is excited at the receptive point R_2. What direction through the nervous system will it take: (1) over the synaptic junctions c and b to E_1, (2) over synapses c and d to E_2, (3) over c and f to E_3 or (4) over c and h to E_4? What are the relations between each neuron and the succeeding one that are the determining factors?"

* John F. Dashiell, *Fundamentals of General Psychology*, Houghton Mifflin Company, Boston, pp. 266–267.

Several theories are offered to explain the pattern of the pathway. One theory is that the resistance of different synapses differs greatly in degree and the impulse will follow the path of least resistance. In other words, the behavior of an animal in a given situation will depend on the differences of resistance at the synapses. This theory, however, has been much criticized. Another theory offered is that the impulse will follow nerve fibers which have the same rhythm of "refractory (inactive) period or frequency." Still another theory holds that the impulse follows those fibers which have the same **chronaxies,** that is, nerves which have the same excitation period.

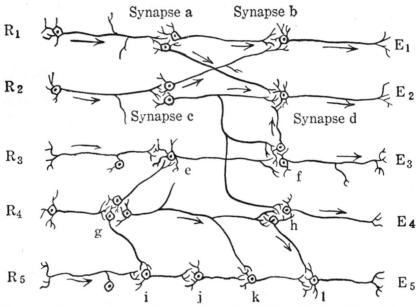

Fig. 87. Diagram showing the possible paths which might be followed by a nerve impulse. *Redrawn from Dashiell, "Fundamentals of General Psychology," by permission of the author and publishers, Houghton Mifflin Co.*

It has been demonstrated that the degree of conductivity over the synapses may be raised by repeating the stimulus at frequent intervals until a response is made. This may be the result of repeated stimuli on the receptor nerve endings; it is known as **summation.** Something of the same mechanism may be responsible for the transmission of an impulse across the synapses. To illustrate, one might not withdraw his hand if pricked gently by a pin only once, but repeated gentle pricks might result in muscular action and withdrawal, or the appropriate reflex. Sometimes repeated stimulation will result in failure to respond, owing to **fatigue** of the neuromuscular mechanism. Sometimes, while response is being made to one stimulus, another stimulus may enter the "circuit," either from within (from the cerebrum) or by the action of another stimulus from without. Such interference inhibits the initial reaction. This inhibition probably means that some synapses in the usual path of a nerve impulse have been blocked. For example, if the skin is punctured by a needle, the hand is automatically jerked away—a purely reflex response. However, if the cerebrum had intervened, such a reaction might be inhibited or the entire body, instead of just the hand, might have been moved from the region of irritation. Concentration on a problem or in carrying out a definite activity involves certain inhibitions or responses. The soldier in the midst of battle may be so "intent" on his objective that he fails to notice his wounds.

The reaction or adjustment in the nervous system opposed to inhibition is known as **facilitation.** For example, if, when a person is so seated that the legs hang freely, a sharp tap is administered just below the knee cap, a prompt kick (knee jerk) will be the response. If, at the time the blow is struck, a startling sound is made, the knee jerk will become more pronounced. Thus the second stimulus produces an augmented response, as a result of facilitation. The cerebrum also may play a part in facilitation of certain responses.

Transmission paths. The following statements may serve to give a clearer picture of the general facts just presented and the part they play in the nervous system. If a boy's foot is pricked by a needle and there results a movement of the leg only, then just the lower portion of the spinal cord has been involved. Because of blocking at other synapses, the nerve impulse has not been transmitted upward to higher levels of the spinal cord. However, if the conductivity of the synapses is increased, the impulse may now go on to a higher level of the cord or into the cerebellum. Other reflex paths of this level are opened and, in addition to the jerk of the foot, there may be head movements, an outcry, and perhaps increased respiration and pulse rate. These reactions are more complex and likely to be more varied. It is possible, if the stimulus is strong enough both in intensity and summation, that the nerve impulse may reach the cortex of the **cerebrum** or highest level where there is a complicated arrangement of neurons. Actions initiated by impulses from the cerebrum are thus **conscious activities.** As a follow-up of the reactions just described, the injured foot may be treated with mercurochrome or iodine. Only when the impulse reaches the cerebrum is the pain perceived. If the cerebrum were absent, the individual could not know the pin had pricked him. Nevertheless, the reactions governed by the spinal cord and the cerebellum would take place.

SOME GENERAL ASPECTS OF ANIMAL BEHAVIOR

We have already seen that simple reflexes are automatic adjustments by the whole or parts of an organism reacting to a stimulus or change in its environment. The question is often asked, "Do animals, other than man, think?" "Do they have intelligence, or merely 'instinctive' behavior?" To answer these questions and to approach the problem of animal behavior with understanding, it would seem necessary to attempt to distinguish between "instinctive response" or "behavior" and intelligent response.

Tropisms. An adjustment involving the movement of an organism or some part of an organism in some direction, determined at least

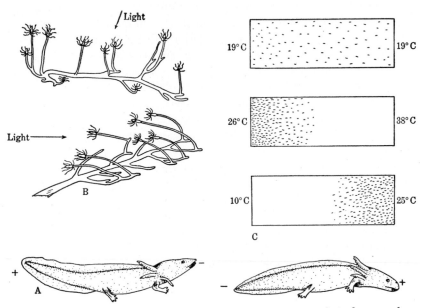

Fig. 88. Tropisms in animals. *A*, electrotropism; reaction of *Ambystoma* larva to electric current. Note the change in position when the current is reversed. *B*, phototropism; reaction of polyps of *Eudendrium* (animal) to changes in source of light. *C*, thermotropism; reaction of *Paramecium* to changes in temperature. Note that the animals react positively to optimum temperature. *A and B, from Loeb, "Forced Movements, Tropisms, and Animal Conduct." By permission of the publisher, J. B. Lippincott Co. C, after Mendelssohn and Jennings.*

to some extent by the direction of the stimulus, is called a **tropism** (*tropa*—a turning). Many insects will be attracted to a light at night. This is a characteristic tropism or tropistic response. Several kinds of tropisms are recognized. In naming them the prefix indicates the stimulus involved. The more common tropisms are:

Phototropism, reaction to light (*photos*—light).
Thigmotropism, reaction to contact (*thigma*—touch).
Hydrotropism, reaction to water (*hydor*—water).
Thermotropism, reaction to heat (*therme*—heat).
Chemotropism, reaction to chemical reagents.
Rheotropism, reaction to currents (*rheos*—stream).
Chromotropism, reaction to color (*chroma*—color).
Heliotropism, reaction to the sun (*helios*—sun).

For free motile organisms the word **taxis** is sometimes used instead of tropism, and the terms then become chemotaxis, phototaxis, rheotaxis, etc. (Fig. 88).

An organism such as the ameba, that can move freely in any direction, exhibits tropistic reactions. When touched at some point with a glass rod the ameba exhibits **negative thigmotropism;** i.e., it moves away from the rod. On the other hand, if it comes in contact with a solid body and remains in close contact with it, it may be exhibiting **positive thigmotropism,** or **positive chemotropism** if the substance is food. Amebas are **negatively phototropic;** i.e., they move away from the light. If heat is applied at some point, an ameba moves in the opposite direction, exhibiting **negative thermotropism. Negative chemotropic** reactions are observed when a reagent like hydrochloric acid or methylene blue is added to the water at some point near the ameba.

Tropisms of one kind or another are manifested by practically every type of living organism, both plant and animal, from the lowest form to the highest. The mechanisms of response and the general behavior exhibit an increasing specialization and complexity, reaching a climax in the highly specialized muscular and nervous tissues whose reactions are responsible for self-determined behavior as well as that of a merely tropistic nature.

The problem of "instincts." In the preceding pages we have seen that the scientist attempts to analyze bodily activities such as digestion and circulation by obtaining experimental evidence based upon the working of actual structures which he can see and, to some extent, manipulate. It has been pointed out that, in the days before the application of scientific method and advancement of scientific knowledge, there was supposed to be some "vital principle" which was necessary for the functioning of the stomach and for the circulation of the blood. In fact, all matter which was found in the organism was set apart as organic matter, something different from the inorganic matter found outside the organism. When an investigator could no longer explain an activity in terms of its demonstrable mechanical workings he resorted to this vital-principle idea. Today, psychologists are attempting to employ the scientific method of assembling objective evidence based on observation and experimentation, to explain all animal behavior including human behavior. In times past, and even today, when certain traits of animal behavior reach a point where they are no longer analyzable, there is a tendency to say that they are "instinctive," that is, that they are one of the peculiar properties of the animal. One psychologist collected reports of more than 5,000 of these supposedly instinctive patterns! The term instinct thus came to be regarded as the refuge of the psychologist when he could no longer explain behavior on the basis of observed mechanisms.

In the language of science today, the term instinct with its unscientific connotations is being viewed most critically, and it may soon be decisively discarded. The observable basis of unlearned behavior is designated as "unlearned trends" or "innate traits." Those who are opposed to the instinct idea and who believe that they are using the scientific method for the study of behavior are inclined to stress the reflexes, which can be more easily analyzed in terms of behavior. They maintain that unlearned trends must spring from an inherited bodily structure and are automatic. The activities of the organism represent the functioning of those physical structures. Given the appropriate stimulus, the animal automatically carries on the specific pattern of behavior.

However, as we shall see below, such automatic acts may be modified. It has been claimed that these so-called instincts, which are probably complex reflexes, are or have been useful in the preservation of the individual animal or the race at some time in its individual or racial history. This statement does not mean that the animal "knew" that any particular reaction was useful. It reacted because its reflex patterns were so blocked out. Confronted with an apparent old situation in a new environment, it makes the inherent response, even though this response may result in its death. Thus moths and many insects fly at night—the moths to get food from the light-colored or white flowers which are so conspicuous in the darkness. The eyes, nervous system, and wing muscles are so constructed that anything of a light color forces a movement toward it. If it is a flower, food is secured; if it is a light or a flame, death is the result.

Learning. Learning might be defined as a modification of behavior because of experience. The amount or degree of learning possible will depend on the complexity of the nervous mechanism. We have pointed out that the nervous system reaches its highest degree of complexity in man. It would logically follow that, if we find the most complex nervous system in man, here we will likewise find the most complex behavior pattern. By the same reasoning we should expect to find in the simplest animals the simplest adjustment mechanism and the simplest behavior patterns. For the lower animals and also for the higher animals, including man, two fundamental

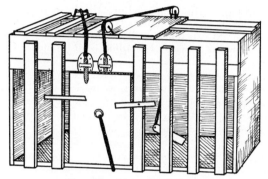

FIG. 89.   Thorndike's box.

learning processes are recognized. They have been designated learning by **trial and error** and learning by **conditioned response.**

Trial and Error. When an ameba, one of the simplest animal organisms, comes in contact with a drop of acid, it withdraws the pseudopodium; then on the same side of the body it puts out another pseudopodium which may come in contact with the same acid drop, only to withdraw the new pseudopodium. This behavior may be repeated several times. Finally pseudopodia project from another region of the animal, and it sets out on a new course that leads away from the irritating medium. However, there is no evidence showing that the ameba ever learns to avoid acid or to make its adjustment by fewer random movements.

In one of his classic experiments devised to investigate the trial-and-error type of learning, Thorndike made use of what was known as the problem box (Fig. 89). In this box he would confine a hungry cat or dog, and outside the box he placed some food. The box was so constructed that the animal could escape from it by pressing a lever, pulling a loop of cord, or stepping on a platform. When put into the

box, the animal naturally would attempt to escape. It would claw
and beat at the bars, or thrust its paws through any opening it could
reach. It would continue this thrashing about, striking anything loose
and movable. In the course of this vigorous, persistent action, eventually and accidentally, the animal would strike the lever, or pull the
loop of cord, or tip the platform, opening the way for its escape. This
first release, as we see, was accomplished by **trial and error.** After
the same animal had been subjected to the same set of conditions for
a number of days, involving many trials, it would immediately claw
the button or loop, thus securing a prompt release. It had learned.
It is interesting to note that even after the loop had been removed
the animal would paw the space where the loop had been.

The following selected experiment will emphasize trial-and-error learning and
will show how widely the process of learning is distributed in the animal kingdom. Herrick describes the following interesting experiments by Yerkes with
earthworms. Yerkes devised a "T-shaped passage with the entrance at the stem
of the T and exit at the right hand turn. At the left turn he placed a piece of
rough sandpaper, beyond which was a device for giving the worm a painful
electric shock. After 20 to 100 experiences the worms **learned** to avoid the left
turn and to go directly to the right and so escape." Heck later repeated the
experiments and found that, if the front end of the "learned" worm containing
the brain was removed, the worms, after growing a new head and brain, reacted
as before. "Removal of the brain did not destroy the habit."

Another method common in trial-and-error experiments is the maze method,
in which an animal is placed in a complicated system of unobstructed pathways
and blind alleys through which it must learn to find its way from the starting
point to the goal where food is placed to induce motivation. After a number
of trials, the animal learns to make the right turns and to avoid blind alleys so
that it reaches the food in a shorter period of time. Incidentally, this maze
running is a habit-forming process. Alterations in the maze have caused the
animal to change the habit. Consequently, we might say that a **habit** is a
"mode of adjustment" capable of certain modifications to fit circumstances.
Adaptations of the problem box and the maze have been used for human subjects as well as for rats, cats, and dogs.

Conditioned Response. It is known that, whenever food is taken
into the "mouth" or buccal cavity, the saliva begins to flow. Apparently this is a natural reflex. About 1900, the Russian physiologist,
Pavlov, measured the flow of saliva from the salivary gland of a dog
by leading a salivary duct to the outside of the cheek and collecting
the saliva there as fast as it was secreted. Pavlov noticed that the
flow of saliva would begin, not when the dog had the food placed in
its mouth, but when he saw the food or his food dish. The sight of
the man who usually fed the dog would also start the secretion of
saliva. Pavlov designated this response a **conditioned reflex;** by the

elaboration of experimental procedures for the investigation of this type of response, he made a real contribution to our study of animal learning.

Since, in a strict sense, this is not a reflex, it has been called more properly a **conditioned response**. In hopes of making further discoveries concerning such responses, Pavlov set up an experiment to "condition" the salivary response by more artificial stimulation. A hungry dog had food placed in his mouth at the time an electric bell began to ring. This procedure was repeated a number of times. Then the bell was rung before the food was offered, and it was found that the saliva began to flow at the sound of the bell. It was likewise discovered that, just as it was possible to develop a conditioned response by training, so was it also possible to eliminate it. Apparently it is safe to say that the nervous system is modified in some way in the conditioning just as it is in other kinds of learning.

When a minnow is thrown into an aquarium with a hungry perch it is promptly seized and devoured. A perch was confined in one end of a glass tank separated by a glass partition from the other end where there were some minnows. The perch tried repeatedly to get these minnows, only to dash vainly against the glass. After a time the attempts were abandoned. Later when the glass partition was removed the perch would swim freely around among the minnows and not attempt to eat them. This experiment not only illustrates **learning** and **memory** but shows us what is meant by a **conditioned response** and **association** as well. Another interesting feature of this experiment is the fact that the cerebrum of these fishes has no cerebral cortex, which in man is the supposed center of intelligence.

There are differences between the learning process of man and that of the other animals. Woodworth,[*] a psychologist, thus summarizes these main points of human superiority:

"1. Man is a better observer; he observes many characteristics of things, people and situations that lie beyond the animal's scope.

"2. Man uses more deliberation, management and control in attacking a problem.

"3. Man makes great use of names, numbers and in general of language in learning.

"4. Partly by aid of language, man is able to think about problems even when the materials are not before him. After struggling vainly with a puzzle, a subject has been known to reach a solution while lying in bed the next morning. Ideation, the thinking of things that are not present to the senses at the moment, is doubtless much more highly developed in man than in any other animal."

[*] Robert F. Woodworth, *Psychology*, Henry Holt and Company, New York, Fourth Edition, p. 318.

For a more complete and detailed analysis of the behavior of man and the higher vertebrates the reader is referred to various books on the related science of psychology.

Popular Misconceptions About the Nervous System

Phrenology. One of the "pseudopsychological gold bricks" which is still sold by "readers" is what is known as **phrenology,** or the reading of a person's character by feeling the bumps on his head. These fakers have mapped out the cranium into various regions where are supposed to be localized such traits as benevolence, destructiveness, firmness, and self-esteem. The right bump in the proper region shows a particularly strong characteristic for the trait located at that place. Today we know that the skull is no true indicator of the shape or size of the brain. Some heads have more bone than others. Further, as Lashley has shown, there is no definite localization of function in the cerebrum except those cases involving "the functioning of definite sensory or motor areas in the body."

Brain size. Phrenologists also stress size of the brain as an index of intelligence, but intelligence depends on the quality rather than the quantity of gray matter. By actual determination, the brains of prominent people were found to weigh an average of but 2 to 4 per cent more than those of inmates of the workhouses. Nor is the difference in brain weight any indication that in intelligence men are superior to women.

Convolutions and learning. Another popular mistaken notion is that as learning progresses there is a deepening of the grooves in the brain resulting in more curves and more convolutions. This morphological change does not take place.

13

Growth and Reproduction

In our study of living animals we have now become familiar with the fact that living protoplasm exhibits certain characteristics. These characteristics are revealed in the various activities of the organism and are responsible for its form, structure, and behavior. Thus we observe that all animals, according to the species, present a rather uniform pattern or shape, develop a particular type of organization, carry on metabolism, eliminate waste, are sensitive and capable of response or adjustment. We shall see that the same general similarity among various animals is also manifested in their growth and reproduction.

GROWTH

In the living organism growth may take place by increase in the volume of the individual cells. The increase in the volume of the cell may be the direct result of an overabundant supply of food plus certain metabolic processes within the cells. We realize that life is a puzzling complex of physical and chemical processes by which the protoplasm and its components are being continually changed. Theoretically these changes result in the formation of increasingly complex substances that, being less active chemically, accumulate within the cell and so increase its volume.

One of the most obvious phases of growth is enlargement, which is a result of the increase either in volume of individual cells or in number of cells or in both. If we observe an individual cell under favorable conditions we may see it undergo a division, forming two new cells. Various explanations have been suggested to explain growth and the ultimate limit in size attained by various animals. Some biologists have pointed out that there must be maintained an optimum ratio between cell surface and cell volume. Other investigators are of the opinion that the ratio of the volume of the nucleus to that of the cytoplasm is a deciding factor in the growth of individual cells. We do know that usually animals attain a rather well-defined size characteristic of the particular species.

Cell division. Mitosis. The separation of an actively growing cell into two daughter cells generally takes place by an indirect cell division called **mitosis.** Since mitosis is involved in the growth and reproduction of all animals, we should become familiar with it. There are numerous variations in the details of mitotic cell division, but no attempt will be made to present them here. However, a general picture of the process will enable us to appreciate its significance in cell multiplication, reproduction, and inheritance (Fig. 90).

We recall that embedded in the cytoplasm of the cell lies the nucleus surrounded by a nuclear membrane. When the cell is in the resting state, i.e., when it is not involved in preparations for division, the chromosomes with the chromatin material are difficult to see (Fig. 13). Within the cytoplasm, lying close to the nuclear membrane, is a very small protoplasmic entity called the **centrosome** (Figs. 13 and 90). In the activity preparatory for division, the central body divides, and each one of the new bodies formed becomes surrounded by a group of radiating fibers called collectively an **aster** (*aster*—star) (Fig. 90). These new central bodies, with their asters, now move apart until they come to lie at opposite poles of the nucleus. At the same time, the nuclear membrane gradually disappears and a **spindle** made up of fibers connects the two asters. Toward the close of this first stage (**prophase**) of mitotic activity the **chromosomes** make their appearance as definite nuclear bodies in the form of "double" chromosomes (*chromos*—color; *soma*—body). The two longitudinal halves of a chromosome are called **chromatids.** The number of chromosomes in the body cells of any particular species is constant. Thus in the cells of man and tobacco there are 48 chromosomes.

In the next stage (**metaphase**), these double chromosomes come to lie at least in part at the central region of the spindle, where they are assembled in a plane, lying perpendicular to the long axis of the spindle, known as the **equatorial plate.** During the **metaphase,** which is of very short duration, the "double" chromosomes become completely separated into longitudinal halves (**chromatids**) that are precisely alike both quantitatively and qualitatively. The halves of each chromosome (chromatids) now begin to move apart and finally come to lie at opposite ends of the spindle. This stage is known as **anaphase** (*ana*—up). As a result of this migration of the chromosomes, each central body is now associated with a complete set of chromosomes, the two sets being exactly alike.

The organization of two new nuclei constitutes the final mitotic stage known as **telophase** (*telos*—end). The chromosomes become vacuolated, and their chromatin material is so arranged that the

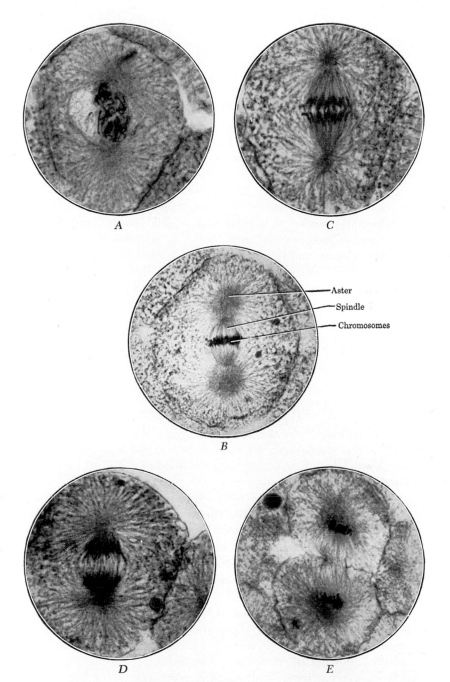

FIG. 90. Photomicrographs showing stages in mitosis. *A*, late prophase. *B*, metaphase. *C*, early anaphase. *D*, later anaphase. *E*, telophase. *Photomicrographs furnished by the General Biological Supply House.*

187

characteristic resting nucleus again appears within a new nuclear membrane. About the time the daughter chromosomes arrive at the ends of the spindle, a change takes place in the region of the equatorial plane which results in the complete division of cytoplasm of the original cell so that two new cells are formed. These new cells may now undergo further structural changes that will build them into working units of the particular tissue of which they form a part.

Thus we see that in all growth certain initial steps are involved. A cell ordinarily grows until it reaches a certain size, when it divides and gives rise to new cells. Finally, after a new cell is formed, it undergoes such changes as are inherently necessary in adapting it for its own peculiar work. Cell enlargement, cell division, and cell differentiation are therefore the initial steps in all growth.

Cancer. Cancer and tumors have been known since ancient times, and they are widely distributed throughout the animal and plant kingdoms and among all races of men. Cancer now claims over 180,000 persons annually in the United States. Cancer and tumors are abnormal growths initiated by a single abnormal cell or group of such cells which, for some unknown reason, grow and multiply at a tremendous rate. The abnormal growths may affect any part of the body. They are of no use to the organism, are beyond its control, and apparently have no stopping point. Of the growths mentioned there are two types, known respectively as benign and malignant. Benign tumors never spread and are restricted in their growth by a limiting membrane. In the malignant type, usually thought of as "cancer," the abnormal cells are carried through the body by the blood stream, by the lymph channels, by growth from tissue to tissue, and by distribution through the coelom.

The actual cause of cancer is not known, but chronic irritations such as those caused by a pipe on the lip, irritation of the cheek from a broken or rough tooth, and chronic irritations from chemicals and from physical agents such as light and X-rays seem to be predisposing factors. There is no evidence that cancer is a germ disease or that it is contagious, nor has it been demonstrated that diet will tend either to initiate or to cure cancer.

Cancer can be cured if treatment is begun at an early stage. Medical authorities urge that periodic physical "check-ups" be made and that there should be an immediate visit to a reputable physician when any of the following symptoms are observed:

1. Any persistent lump or thickening, especially of the breast.

2. Any irregular bleeding or discharge from any of the body openings.

3. Any sore that does not heal, particularly about the tongue, mouth, or lips.

4. Persistent indigestion, especially when accompanied by distaste for meat.

5. Persistent hoarseness which lasts for a month or longer.

6. Sudden changes in the form or rate of growth of a mole or wart.

7. Pain is usually a late symptom—do not wait for it.

The cures for cancer are radium and X-ray, either alone or in combination, or surgery. People are urged to beware of "sure fire" cancer cures by "secret methods."

Asexual Reproduction

Asexual reproduction requires but one parent for the production of new generations. By this method offspring may arise by fission, by budding, and by sporulation.

Fission. In fission the body of an animal divides into two parts, each of which in time forms an animal like the parent (Fig. 91). The

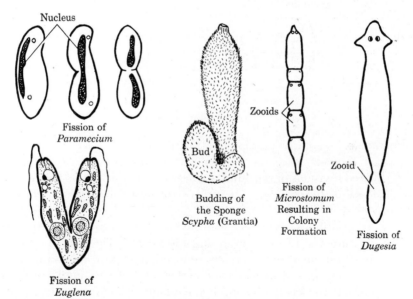

FIG. 91. Asexual reproduction in animals.

ameba apparently pulls apart by constriction, as does also the paramecium. In the little flatworm *Dugesia*, the posterior region of the animal constricts off; this is **transverse fission**. Some animals may split lengthwise in **longitudinal fission**.

Budding. A protuberance (bud) grows out of the parent animal and comes to resemble the parent in form and, in some instances, even in size. Usually this bud eventually separates from the parent animal and takes up a free existence. Sometimes "home ties" are too strong, and quite a few of the buds, with their buds, may remain attached to the parent. Thus a **colony** is formed. Various protozoans, sponges, hydras, and other animals higher in the scale show budding. Some animals produce internal buds, which in sponges are called **gemmules** (*gemmula*—little bud). If the parent sponge dies, the gemmules remain where their parents were attached. Sometimes they are picked up with mud on the feet or the beaks of water birds and transported to new watery fields. Whether in the new habitat or in the old, when favorable conditions of temperature and moisture come, they grow into new sponges.

Spores and cysts. Spores are often formed by animals, particularly the Protozoa. In fact one large group of these animals employs spore

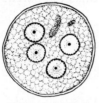 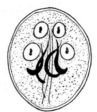

Endameba histolytica   *Giardia lamblia*

Fig. 92.   Cysts of protozoan parasites.

formation so regularly in reproduction that it has been named the *Sporozoa* (*sporos*—seed; *zoon*—animal). Spores are often formed by the repeated divisions of the adult animal and somewhat less frequently by divisions of the zygote. The process of cyst formation or **encystment** consists in the production by the animal of an enveloping, somewhat hard gelatinous case which is protective against ordinary extremes of temperature and resistant to drying (Fig. 92). The animal's metabolic rate or rate of living is greatly reduced, and thus life can remain in the dormant animal over a long period of time, or until environmental conditions become favorable once more for normal animal life. When ponds and brooks dry up many of the microscopic organisms form cysts and live through the adverse conditions. When such environmental conditions as water and temperature once more become favorable the cyst wall breaks and the animal again takes up its active existence. This process undoubtedly had much to do with the belief in the theory of spontaneous generation.

Regeneration

Some animals have the capacity to replace lost parts, a process called **regeneration** (*re*—again; *generare*—to beget). Some years ago oyster fishermen began to collect the starfish from their oyster beds, for they had found that man was not the only animal fond of oysters. They attempted to kill the starfish by chopping them into pieces. Then they shoveled the pieces overboard, where many of them grew into new starfish by regenerating the missing parts. This may be regarded

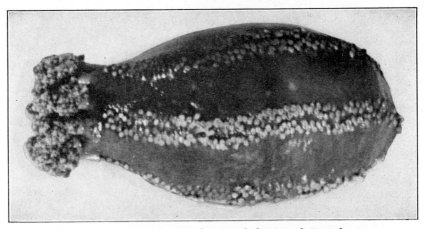

Fig. 93.   Sea cucumber.   *Photograph by David Huntsberger.*

as reproduction by fragmentation. A relative of the starfish, the sea cucumber (Fig. 93), when attacked by an enemy, will often extrude some of its internal organs. In some species there is also extruded a substance which swells up in sea water forming a mass of tough threads in which the enemy may be entangled. "A lobster has been rendered perfectly helpless as a consequence of rashly interfering with a sea cucumber." When danger is past, the animal withdraws its mutilated organs into the body cavity and replaces the loss by regeneration. If the posterior end of the earthworm is lost, the animal replaces it. Pieces of hydras and planarians will likewise form new animals (Fig. 94). Perhaps the most interesting exhibition of regeneration is put on by sponges. If these animals are squeezed through cloth into sea water, the small unicellular fragments or groups of cells collect in little clumps and grow into new sponges. This power of regeneration is found in varying degrees throughout the animal kingdom. In man, when portions of the liver are lost through operations

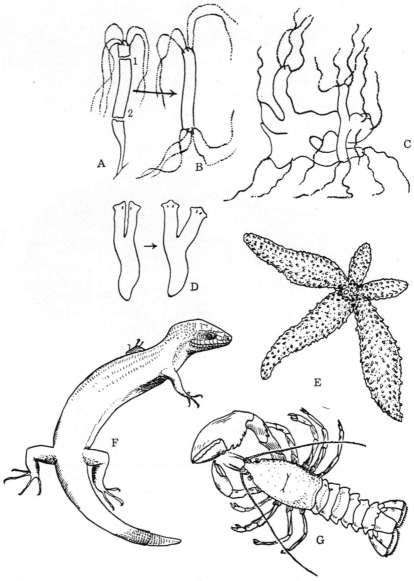

Fig. 94. Regeneration. *A, B,* and *C,* regeneration of *Hydra. B,* section 1–2 may develop into two-headed animals. *C,* reconstitution of a mass of approximately 125 pieces of *Hydra. D,* divided anterior end of a planarian (flatworm), develops two heads. *E,* starfish regenerating two arms. *F,* lizard regenerating new tail. *G,* crayfish developing new claw.

or otherwise, new liver cells regenerate replacements for those lost. Likewise there is some regeneration of nervous tissue and bone.

Some animals possess not only the power of regeneration but also a capacity to lose or to break off appendages at certain places called "breaking joints." This power of automatic surgery is called **autotomy** (*autos*—self; *tome*—cutting). Some crabs throw off their legs or pincers quite readily when handled, and often the captor of a lizard is left with a writhing tail in his hand while the lizard makes its escape. These animals eventually regenerate the parts lost or broken off.

Sexual Reproduction

Sexual reproduction takes place in practically all animals. It is much more prevalent than asexual reproduction, and in most animals

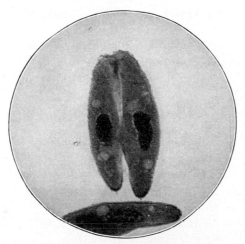

FIG. 95. Paramecia conjugating. *Photomicrograph by the General Biological Supply House.*

it is the only type of reproduction. In a one-celled paramecium, two animals may unite, exchange nuclear material, and then separate (Fig. 95). This process is called **conjugation** (*cum*—together with; *jugare*—to yoke). However, in almost all animals, sexual reproduction involves the union of a small, usually motile, microscopic male gamete or **spermatozoon** (*sperma*—seed; *zoon*—animal) with a larger, nonmotile, food-laden gamete, called the **ovum** or **egg**. The gametes are found in specialized structures called **gonads** (*gone*—that which generates). The male gonads are the **testes,** and the female the **ovaries.**

The sex mechanism. The essential organs involved in sexual reproduction are the ovaries of the female and the testes of the male, together with their ducts by which the gametes can be released from the animal. The ovaries and testes are made up of germinal tissue and supporting tissue. The germinal tissue contains the primordial germ cells which later become mature ova or spermatozoa. Other structures associated with these organs may be regarded as accessories or special devices to assist in bringing about the union of egg and spermatozoon, to protect the zygote, and to furnish nourishment for the developing embryo.

The female reproductive system with its accessories is constructed according to the following general plan (Fig. 96). Most of the higher animals have two ovaries, suspended from the body wall into the coelom by mesenteries. Birds have only one functional ovary. Opening near the ovary is a tube, the **oviduct** (*ovum*—egg; *ducere*— to lead), which is rather slender at the ovarian end but which may become enlarged at its lower end to form a region called the **uterus** (*uterus*—womb). The frog and some other animals have two uteri, but in man the oviducts lead to one common, roughly triangular-shaped uterus. In some animals the uteri may open into the cloaca, but in man and related animals there is a new structure, the **vagina,** which leads to the outside. The eggs burst from the ovary and are collected by the oviducts, down which they pass. In some animals accessory material is added to the egg. Thus in the bird the "white" of the egg, the various membranes, and the shell with its pigments are formed around the egg as it comes down the oviduct. In other animals nutritive material is added from **nidamental glands** (*nidus*— nest). In certain animals the eggs are retained in the uterus, where they develop into offspring.

The male reproductive systems of most animals have many points of resemblance. As previously pointed out the essential organs are the testes together with their ducts that convey the mature spermatozoa to the outside of the body. Testes vary in shape and number among the lower animals, but in the higher forms there are usually two testes together with various accessory organs and glands. In the backboned animals the testes are paired, ovoid bodies which may be either suspended in the body cavity or borne outside the body cavity in a sac called the **scrotum** (Figs. 96 and 104).

The testis is made up of germinal tissue, from which the spermatozoa form, connective tissue, and nutritive tissue to provide for the developing spermatozoa. Other tissues are present which secrete the hormones of the testis. Small convoluted tubules convey the sperma-

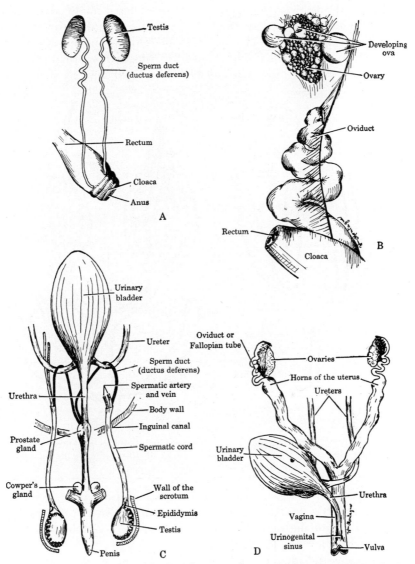

Fig. 96.   Genital systems of bird and mammal.   *A*, chicken (male); *B*, chicken (female); *C*, cat (male); *D*, cat (female).

tozoa into a duct known as the **sperm duct (ductus deferens)** which leads from the testis. The sperm ducts often have modified saccular regions for the storage of spermatozoa, called **seminal vesicles.** The sperm ducts in some animals open into the **cloaca** and in others into the **urethra,** a duct which, in the male, carries both spermatozoa and urine to the exterior. In man and closely related animals there may

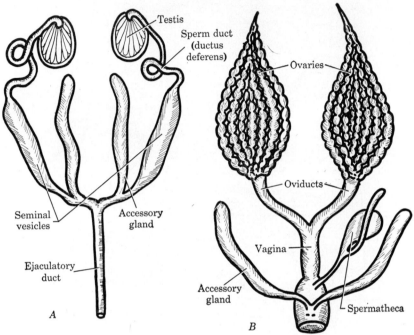

Fig. 97. Genital systems of the male (*A*) and the female (*B*) honeybee. *Redrawn from Comstock, "A Manual for the Study of Insects." By permission of the Comstock Publishing Company.*

be present **Cowper's gland** and the **prostate gland** whose secretions contribute to the fluid in which the spermatozoa swim. Study Fig. 97, and compare the reproductive systems of an invertebrate animal with those of the vertebrates.

Hermaphroditism. In most animals only one kind of sex organ is present, ovaries or testes. Such animals are **dioecious.** However, there are other animals which normally have both ovaries and testes present and functional. These are called **hermaphrodites** (*hermaphroditos*—combining both sexes) or **monoecious** animals. Very few vertebrates are true hermaphrodites, but hermaphroditic invertebrates, such as tapeworms and the common earthworm, are numerous.

In true hermaphroditic forms functional spermatozoa and eggs are produced by each individual. Sometimes the spermatozoa and eggs of the same animal unite, but most often cross-fertilization is insured by the position of the sex glands and accessories so that it is impossible for self-fertilization to take place. In some hermaphroditic animals eggs and spermatozoa do not mature at the same time. In fact the individual may first be a male and later change to a female, or vice versa. In some animals including the vertebrates many individuals are found which have some of the behavior characteristics and the sex organs of both sexes; as a rule only one set of organs is functional, and quite often the animal is sterile. Such animals are not true hermaphrodites but are usually spoken of as **intersexes** (*inter* —between; sex), although dubbed "morphidites" by the man in the street.

Parthenogenesis. One of the supposed functions of the spermatozoon when it enters the egg is the activation of the egg to cause development. Many people have the notion that an egg will not develop without fertilization. In many insects eggs develop into new individuals like the parent without any assistance of the male. In fact there are some species of invertebrates where only females are to be found for long periods of time. In the bees, as is well known, there are queens and workers which are females, and drones which are males. The queen in her marriage flight receives, from the male, spermatozoa which are stored in her body in seminal receptacles. When she returns to the colony and lays eggs, she lays some eggs which are fertilized; these develop into queens and workers. But some eggs are unfertilized, and they give rise to drones. The development of an egg without fertilization is called **parthenogenesis.** Some animals during the summer produce parthenogenetic eggs, which develop into females. In the fall, males as well as females are produced and the eggs are fertilized. Such zygotes have hard, fairly thick shells around them, which enable them to resist cold winter temperature.

Parthenogenesis not only will take place under natural conditions but also can be induced artificially. Frog eggs will start development after being pricked with a needle. Eggs of some animals, such as the sea urchin, require only a vigorous shaking to initiate development. Some of the other artificial means of initiating parthenogenesis are application of various acids to the eggs and even changing the eggs from sea water to fresh water.

Breeding activities and fertilization. The behavior and actions of animals during the periods preceding and following the release of the germ cells are usually called **breeding activities.** They vary widely but are concerned with the common purpose of bringing the ova and spermatozoa into close proximity and insuring fertilization. **Fertilization,** in the strict sense of the term, is the union of a male gamete with a female gamete to form a zygote.

In animals, the actual release of eggs and spermatozoa may be brought about by change in metabolic conditions which in turn are

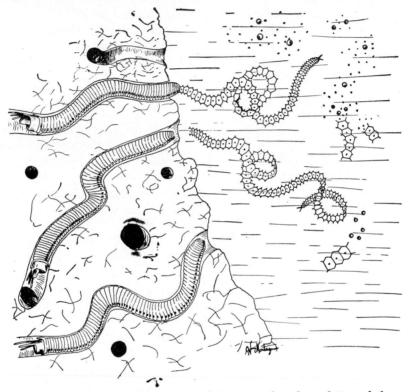

FIG. 98. Swarming of palolo worm. (*After Woodworth, and Borradaile and Potts.*)

the result of stimuli. Thus, in some of the aquatic worms, animals of either sex appear to give off substances into the water which stimulate members of the other sex to sexual activity. The change in the physiological activities appears to occur in rhythmic cycles. One of the classic examples of rhythmic activity is offered by the palolo worm (Fig. 98). When the day of the last quarter of the October-November moon dawns in the southern Pacific, fragments of these worms containing the sex organs break off and come to the surface in such numbers that the water "writhes with worms" and later becomes milky with shed eggs and sperms. This wedding day of the worms is the feast day of the South Sea Islander, who holds the palolo worm in high esteem as a delicacy. In one of the sea urchins the eggs and spermatozoa are shed at the period of the full moon of the breeding season. It is common knowledge that frogs and toads take to the ponds and streams in the spring of the year to lay their eggs and that fishes spawn at regular intervals. In many of the mammals, such as cats, dogs, horses, pigs, and cattle, there are cyclic periods of sexual excitement when the female will receive the male. This periodic condition is known as "heat," "rut," or **estrus** (*oistros*—gadfly, frenzy). At these periods the eggs are released from the ovary, a process known as **ovulation.** In the human female, ovulation occurs at regular intervals of approximately every twenty-eight days.

It has been pointed out that the egg of most animals is large and non-motile and that the spermatozoon is microscopic and motile. The difference in size is largely cytoplasmic, for the nuclei of both mature eggs and spermatozoa usually contain the same number of chromosomes. The spermatozoon is commonly equipped with a tail whose lashing propels it forward. The motility of the spermatozoa and the fact that they are produced in so much greater numbers than the non-motile eggs increase the chances of fertilization. Another factor that assists in bringing about fertilization in some aquatic animals is a substance given off by the eggs called **fertilizin** which attracts and aggregates spermatozoa. In addition to the factors just mentioned for insuring fertilization, some animals lay or produce enormous numbers of eggs. The female oyster, for example, "lays" between 16,000,000 and 60,000,000 eggs, and a sea urchin releases about 10,000,000 eggs.

It is estimated that if all the eggs of the oyster were to be fertilized and developed and this progeny multiplied, the great-great-grandchildren would number 66,000,000,000,000,000,000,000,000,000,000,000,000 (Fig. 99). The shells of a generation would make a mountain eight times the size of the earth. This prodigality of production seems necessary, for, since the eggs are thrown out into the sea, fertilization is a matter of chance. Moreover, many of the eggs are eaten by other animals, and even during development millions of them perish as the result of hungry enemies and adverse environmental conditions. The following from Tennyson seems quite applicable to the situation:

> So careful of the type—
> So careless of the single life.

In toads, frogs, and other animals, the male attaches himself to the female, and, as the eggs pass from the body, the milt or spermatic fluid is poured over them, thus to a large extent insuring fertilization. In the higher animals the spermatozoa are deposited by the male in the cloaca or the vagina of the female, and the eggs are fertilized while in the body of the female. In some animals the eggs are laid later and develop outside the body; in others the eggs develop inside the body.

Fig. 99. Oyster laying eggs. The eggs appear as a cloudy mass extending from the edge of the shell. *Photograph furnished by Fish and Wildlife Service, U. S. Department of the Interior (Paul S. Galtsoff).*

Care of the eggs and young. Animals like the birds, frogs, and many reptiles whose young develop from eggs outside the body are called **oviparous** (*ovum*—egg; *parere*—to bring forth); and those animals like cats, dogs, and man whose young develop from eggs retained in the body are said to be **viviparous** (*vivus*—alive; *parere*). There is little variation in the method of caring for the eggs in viviparous animals since the eggs are retained in the uterus where they develop into young animals. However, among the oviparous animals there is a wide variation in the method and detail of egg disposal and of the care of the young.

The eggs of the bizarre little fish, the sea horse, are placed in a brood pouch which is found on the male! Perhaps the most interesting adaptation for the care of the young is found in the Surinam toad (Fig. 100). The male places the eggs on the back of the female where "a little lidded pouch arises for each of them." Here the egg develops into the adult form.

Certain animals lay their eggs and leave them virtually unprotected. The young have to shift for themselves. The cowbird is extremely callous maternally. She lays an egg in the nest of some other bird, such as a chipping sparrow or a warbler. The egg is larger than those of the owner of the nest, and, when it hatches, the young cowbird

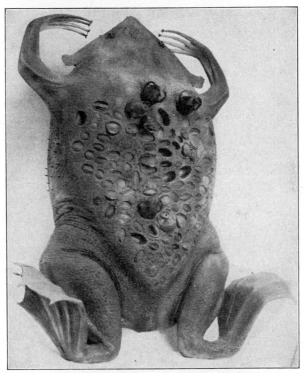

Fig. 100. Surinam toad. Note the small toads developing in pouches on the back of the female. *Photograph furnished by the American Museum of Natural History, New York.*

is larger than the rightful heirs. It gets more than its share of food, and sometimes even pushes the rightful heirs out of the nest. Perhaps the other extreme among birds as far as parental care is concerned is exemplified by the rhinocerous hornbill (Fig. 101). The eggs are laid in a hollow tree and incubated by the female. The male walls her in with a layer of mud, in which there is an opening large enough for her bill to be extruded. The male bird stands by, gets food, and feeds the female during the period of incubation.

The alligator makes a nest of decaying vegetation and depends on the heat of decay to incubate the eggs. Both alligator eggs and snake eggs can be incubated in boxes of sawdust or other suitable material. Some snakes and lizards remain with their eggs. For instance, the python coils around its eggs and assists in incubation. In some animals the eggs are not even put in a guarded nest

FIG. 101. Parental care. Note the male hornbill feeding the female shut in by a wall of mud while incubating the eggs. *Photograph furnished by the Victor Animatograph Corporation.*

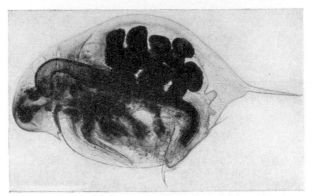

FIG. 102. Parental care. *Daphnia* the water flea, with young in brood pouch. *Photograph furnished by Albert E. Galigher.*

but carried around by the parent. The female crayfish attaches the eggs to the appendages under the abdomen and here after hatching even the young crayfish may be found clinging.

Some of the wasps make a nest or tube of mud in which the eggs are laid. The wasp provisions the nest by stinging and paralyzing a caterpillar so that when the egg hatches there will be plenty of food for the young.

FIG. 103. Parental care. *Above,* pine snake with eggs. *Below,* kangaroo with young in pouch. *Photograph above, by National Zoological Society, Washington, D. C.; below, New York Zoological Society.*

The care of the young by the kangaroo and opossum is well known. The young are born in a rather immature condition and are transferred to the brood pouch in which the mammary glands (milk glands) open by the teats, to which the young are anchored by their mouths. The young animal which requires the longest period of parental care is man. There are numerous other intensely interesting and almost unbelievable examples of both care and lack of care of eggs and young to be found in the animal kingdom. The few examples just cited serve to show some interesting phases of breeding behavior.

Reproduction in man. We have already discussed the reproductive activities of animals in general. We shall now study this process more specifically as it occurs in man. The human reproductive systems are quite similar in many respects to those of other animals,

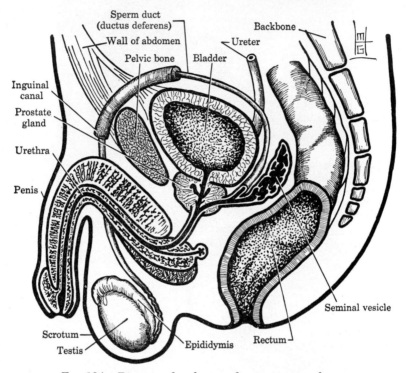

Sperm duct
(ductus deferens)
Backbone
Wall of abdomen
Ureter
Pelvic bone
Bladder
Inguinal
canal
Prostate
gland
Urethra
Penis
Seminal vesicle
Scrotum
Testis
Epididymis
Rectum

Fig. 104. Diagram of male reproductive system of man.

particularly other mammals. In the male, the spermatozoa are formed in the two testes which are located outside the body in a sac known as the **scrotum.** The spermatozoa are formed in the minute, much-twisted tubules of the testes and finally leave the testes by the sperm ducts, two tubes which enter the abdominal cavity through the **inguinal canals** and lead to the urethra, into which they open (Fig. 104). Near the region where a sperm duct enters the urethra there opens into it a small pouch or sac known as a **seminal vesicle.** The seminal vesicles secrete a fluid, but it is doubtful that spermatozoa are stored here as was formerly thought. Where the sperm ducts enter the urethra there is a gland about the size and shape of a

chestnut, the **prostate gland.** The secretions of the prostate gland
and seminal vesicles, in which the spermatozoa swim, make up the
bulk of the **semen** (*semen*—seed). The semen is discharged through
the urethra, which courses through the very vascular, spongy, intromit-
tent organ, the **penis.**

The female reproductive system consists of the two ovaries in
which ova as well as hormones are formed. The ovaries are almond-
shaped organs suspended in the body cavity by mesenteries. Near

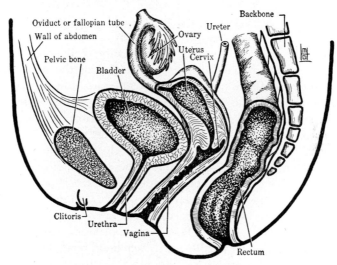

Fig. 105.   Diagram of female reproductive system in man.

each ovary is the expanded funnellike opening of the **oviduct (Fal-
lopian tube)** which extends to one of the two upper corners of the
somewhat pear-shaped, very muscular **uterus** or **womb** (Fig. 105).
The tapering end (**cervix**) of the "pear" extends a short distance into
the tubular **vagina,** which opens to the exterior (Fig. 105). Thus
there is a continuous passage from the vagina through the uterus, up
through the oviduct to the ovaries. Near the entrance to the vagina
are glands, homologous to the prostate gland in man. There is also
a structure homologous to the penis and called the **clitoris.**

We have already called attention to the rhythmic or cyclic reproductive activities of other animals and pointed out that, about the time
of ovulation, that is, discharge of the egg from the ovary, there occurs
a condition known as estrus. In the human female there is a somewhat similar rhythm of ovulation accompanied by certain changes in
the mucosa or lining of the uterus. This series of changes is usually
known as the **menstrual cycle** (*mensis*—month).

Usually one egg is released from either one or the other ovary every twenty-eight days. During the years of sexual activity some four hundred eggs are released. The egg develops in a liquid-filled vesicle, the **Graafian follicle.** As the follicle grows, it forms a bulge on the ovary and finally bursts, freeing the egg. Under normal conditions the egg enters the oviduct. Here it may be fertilized. The cleaving and developing zygote passes down the oviduct and after about three days reaches the uterus. The former Graafian follicle is now succeeded by a growth of endocrine tissue called the **corpus luteum.**

We have already discussed briefly the relation between the hormones of the ovary and the pituitary body and their effect on the uterus. On the average, fourteen days before ovulation takes place in the non-pregnant female, the mucosal lining of the uterus sloughs off. Not only do the mucosal cells degenerate, but there may be slight hemorrhage of the smaller uterine blood vessels as well. This process of sloughing off is known as **menstruation,** which may take place over a period of four to six days. The uterine mucosa now undergoes replacement and repair, apparently under the influence of the estrogen hormone from the ovary. The production of estrogen is under the influence of the pituitary hormone, the F.S.H. (follicle-stimulating hormone), and to some extent the L.H. (luteinizing hormone) (Fig. 106). The uterine lining becomes thicker and softer, better supplied with blood and glands. This is the optimum condition for the reception of a developing zygote and is reached about the time of ovulation or about the fourteenth or fifteenth day after the onset of menstruation. The cells of the corpus luteum, formed apparently under the influence of the L.H. (luteinizing hormone) of the pituitary gland, secrete the hormone progesterone. Progesterone, as well as estrogen, now apparently regulate the formation of the uterine mucosa. Study carefully Fig. 106. If the egg is not fertilized, the uterine mucosa sloughs off usually at the end of twenty-eight days from the onset of the last menstruation, and the menstrual cycle begins again.

If the egg has been fertilized, the developing zygote comes in contact with the uterine wall and embeds itself. The more basal region of contact develops small, branched projections called **chorionic villi** which embed themselves in the uterine wall, the two regions making up the organ of nutrition called the **placenta.** The chorionic villi erode away the maternal tissue of the mother until they are bathed by maternal blood, but usually there is no mixing of the blood of the mother and the fetus. Each has a separate circulation. The blood of the fetus circulates through the chorionic villi, which projects into spaces in the uterine wall filled with maternal blood. Here dissolved

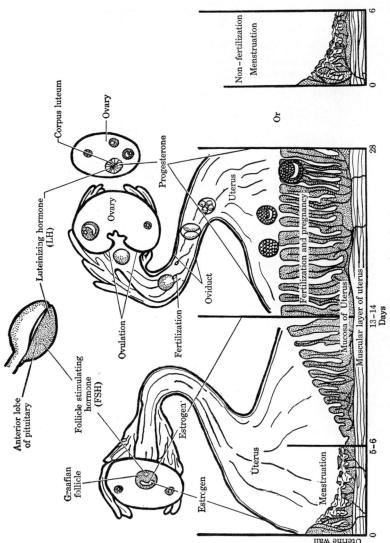

Fig. 106. Diagram showing the menstrual cycle and the most important hormones concerned.

food is absorbed, and gaseous and liquid wastes are thrown off. Consequently, any exchange which takes place between mother and fetus is between the respective blood streams which are separated by cellular membranes. As the embryo grows, it completely fills the cavity of the uterus, and normally after ten lunar months of development a child is born.

In birth, the muscular walls of the uterus contract and the amnion bursts releasing the amniotic fluid. The fetus is expelled, and after breathing and circulation are well established the umbilical cord is severed. The embryonic membranes and the placenta are likewise expelled, making up what is known as the "afterbirth."

14

Development of the Individual
Embryology

We have now described the initial stages in the origin of the individual animal. Mature gametes, i.e., eggs and spermatozoa, are produced, and the union of the two germ cells is brought about to form a zygote, often erroneously called a "fertilized egg." We shall now observe the development of the individual from the zygote.

Cleavage. The zygote, although the result of the union of two sex cells, is nevertheless a single cell. This single cell by mitosis now divides into two cells called **blastomeres** (*blastos*—bud; *mere*—part). These divide into four blastomeres, the four into eight, and so on until eventually by this process of cell multiplication, or **cleavage,** there is formed a single-layered hollow ball of cells known as a **blastula** (*blastos*—bud; *ula*—little). The space or cavity inside the blastula is called the **blastocoele** (*blastos; koilos*—hollow) (Fig. 107). If the yolk is fairly evenly distributed the entire zygote will divide and the cells will be approximately equal in size.

Some eggs, like those of the bird, have an abundance of yolk unequally distributed to one pole of the egg. Here cleavage is restricted to one region or pole of the egg, and a little disk of cells is formed which is often seen on the yolk of the chicken egg. The pole of the egg where the cells are smaller and more numerous is known as the **animal pole,** and the region where the bulk of the yolk is located is called the **vegetal pole.**

As the cells continue to multiply, the blastula undergoes a transformation whereby the blastocoel is practically obliterated and there is formed a two-layered saclike structure enclosing a new cavity. This developing organism or embryo is known as a **gastrula** (little stomach). The outer cell layer is the **ectoderm** (*ektos*—outside; *derma*—skin); the inner the **endoderm** (*endon*—within; *derma*). The sac formed by the endoderm is the **archenteron** (*arche*—beginning; *enteron*—gut) which opens to the outside through the **blastopore** (*blastos; poros*—passage). Soon a third layer of cells forms between

209

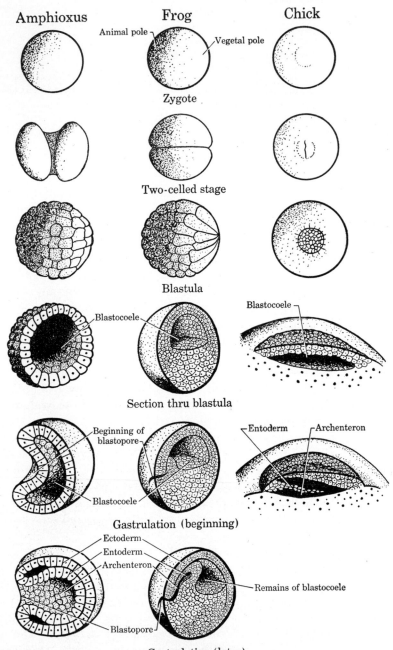

FIG. 107. Cleavage of the zygotes of *Amphioxus*, frog, and chick.

the ectoderm and endoderm called the **mesoderm** (*mesos*—middle; *derma*) (Fig. 107). Mesoderm is not found in animals like sponges and hydras.

When yolk is evenly distributed through the egg, as in the **isolecithal eggs** (*isos*—equal; *lecithos*—yolk), the entire zygote will divide and the blastomeres will be relatively equal in size. This is called **holoblastic cleavage** (*holos*—whole; *blastos*); but in **telolecithal eggs** (*telos*—end; *lecithos*), such as the frog's, the yolk is more abundant at the vegetal pole and cleavage progresses more slowly in that region. The result is unequal cleavage in both cell number and cell size. The cells formed at the animal pole are smaller and much more numerous. Gastrulation is brought about by an overgrowth of the ectoderm over the endoderm. Where cleavage is confined to a disklike region on the yolk, as in the bird and reptile egg, it is known as **discoidal cleavage**, a form of **meroblastic** cleavage (*meros*—part; *blastos*). Insect eggs are known as **centrolecithal eggs**, for the yolk is collected in the center. The nucleus in the center of the yolk mass divides, and the daughter nuclei migrate to the surface of the egg. Cell walls form around them, and eventually the central mass is surrounded by cells. This type of cleavage is called **superficial**. The flatworms, annelids, and most mollusks exhibit what is known as **spiral cleavage**.

The ectoderm, the endoderm, and the mesoderm are the **primary germ layers,** and from them come all the tissues and organs of an adult animal. The ectoderm gives rise to nervous and sensory structures such as the brain, spinal cord, nerves, retina, ear, and taste buds. The epidermis and such structures as hair, nails, reptile scales, and the enamel of the teeth are also derived from ectoderm. The mesoderm gives rise to the supporting tissues of the body (muscle, bone, and connective tissue), the heart, blood, and kidneys. From endoderm is derived the epithelium of the pharynx, thymus, thyroid, respiratory tract including lungs, trachea, digestive tract, and associated glands. This general outline will provide a basis for the study of the further development of the embryo.

Formation of the embryo. The gastrula elongates as a result of the rapid multiplication of the cells of its primary germ layers, especially those of the ectoderm and endoderm. As the embryo elongates, the ectoderm of the dorsal region thickens along the midline to form the **neural plate,** which sinks slightly below the surface of the embryo. Owing to more rapid growth, the sides of the neural plate push up above the general surface of the embryo, forming the **neural folds,** between which is a long depression called the **neural groove** (Plate IX). The two folds diverge at the anterior end of the groove. The parallel neural folds rise higher and higher, grow together, and eventually fuse to form an ectodermal tube, the **neural tube,** which is now completely sunk below the general surface of the embryo and covered by the surface ectoderm. The narrow region of the neural tube eventually becomes the spinal cord, and the broader, expanded region forms the brain.

Simultaneously with the formation of the neural plate and its differentiation into the spinal cord and brain, other changes are taking place. Under the neural plate a long axial rod of cells called the **notochord** has already formed. The mesoderm has developed between the ectoderm and the endoderm. The mesoderm first appeared as two sheets of tissue extending laterally from the region of the notochord and neural tube toward the ventral region. Eventually the mesodermal sheets split into an inner layer of **splanchnic** mesoderm, which is closely applied to the endoderm of the enteron to form the **splanchnopleure** (*splanchnon*—gut; *pleura*—side), and an outer layer of somatic mesoderm applied to the ectoderm to form the **somatopleure** (*soma*—body; *pleura*). The space between these two layers is the **coelom** or **body cavity** (Plate IX).

It should be noted that many organs or body structures are derived from more than one primary germ layer. Thus in the intestine the digestive epithelium or mucosa with its goblet cells is derived from endoderm, but the connective tissue, muscles, blood vessels, and peritoneal layer are derivatives of the splanchnic mesoderm. In the eye the retina and lens are ectodermal structures, but the sclera, choroid coats, and muscles which move the eye are derived from mesoderm. The study of the development of tissues in the formation of the body structures is one of the most interesting phases of biology.

The building of organs. The archenteron which originally was in communication with the outside world by the blastopore soon becomes a closed sac or tube. The mouth and anus form later when inpushings of the ectoderm to the endoderm make pouches which later break through the archenteron. In the early stages of embryonic vertebrates there push out from the walls of the pharynx paired pockets called **gill pouches** (Plate X). In fishes and some amphibians these may break through to the exterior. In most of the higher vertebrates under normal conditions they do not break through. In man, the first gill pouch remains as the Eustachian tube. The closed end of this pouch, which in fishes breaks through to the outside, becomes the tympanum or eardrum. In the fishes, **gills** develop on the walls or **gill arches** which separate the gill slits. The tonsils, the parathyroids, and the thymus are other remnants of the gill pouches of a fish ancestry (Plate X).

The liver is an outpushing from the primitive enteron. Just back of the liver is another outpushing which forms the pancreas. The connective tissue for these organs is furnished by the surrounding splanchnic mesoderm. Farther toward the mouth the lungs arise as an outpushing from the floor of the pharynx. As the animal grows, this tubular structure elongates and divides at the posterior end into two equal branches which differentiate into the bronchi and lungs, and the tube itself becomes the trachea. The end of the trachea, near its opening into the pharynx, appropriates some remnants of the now useless gill arches for supporting cartilages and forms the larynx. The region of the primitive gut just anterior to the liver differentiates into the stomach. The more posterior regions develop into the much-coiled small intestine, large intestine, and urinary bladder.

The ear arises as a thickened patch of ectoderm along the side of the head. This thickened area pushes in to form a pear-shaped sac which undergoes a series of changes that convert it into the ear. The auditory nerve grows out from the brain to supply the ear. The bones of the ear are derived from mesoderm and are remnants of former gill arches which in the earlier ancestors may have supported gills. The Eustachian tube is a made-over gill pouch. The lining of the nostrils arises in somewhat the same manner as the ear, from pockets of thickened ectoderm.

It has already been pointed out that the spinal cord and brain are formed from the neural folds and neural plate. The formation of the eye is an interesting phenomenon. A hollow outgrowth called an **optic vesicle** pushes out from the brain and becomes invaginated at its free end to form a sort of double-walled cup called the **optic cup,** the inner layer of which is the retina. The connection of the optic vesicle with the brain is known as the **optic stalk** which later differentiates into the optic nerve (Fig. 108). When the optic vesicle touches the outer ectoderm, the region it touches thickens and pushes below the surface to form a hollow vesicle that becomes the **crystalline lens.** Apparently the optic vesicle acts as a stimulus on the ectoderm, resulting in lens formation, for, if a piece of the optic vesicle of certain amphibians is transplanted beneath the ectoderm in some other part of the embryo, a lens will form. If, however, the optic vesicle is prevented from touching the ectoderm, no lens is formed. We have already pointed out in a general way the origin of other structures of the eye.

From the foregoing we see that in general the development of the embryo is brought about by thickening and thinning of various regions; by inpushings and outpushings; by splitting and fusions; by cell multiplication; and, finally, by specialization of generalized cells from the primary germ layers.

What has just been said about the development of vertebrates is also true in general of the development of invertebrates. However,

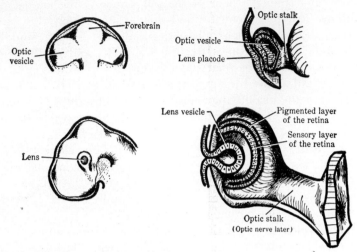

FIG. 108.   Development of the eye.   *Redrawn from Arey, "Developmental Anatomy."   By permission of the publisher, W. B. Saunders Co.*

certain variations occur in mode of cleavage and gastrulation. In the invertebrates there are some interesting modifications of mesoderm and coelom formation. Thus sponges and coelenterates (jellyfish,

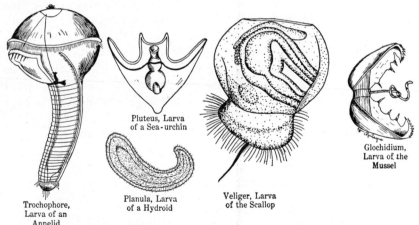

FIG. 109.   Various types of invertebrate larvas.

hydras, corals, and others) are not much more than gastrulas when fully developed.

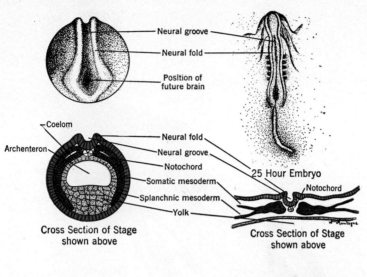

Neural groove

Neural fold

Position of
future brain

25 Hour Embryo

Coelom

Archenteron

Neural fold

Neural groove

Notochord

Somatic mesoderm

Splanchnic mesoderm

Yolk

Notochord

Cross Section of Stage
shown above

Cross Section of Stage
shown above

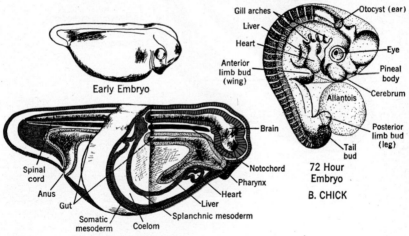

Early Embryo

Gill arches

Liver

Heart

Anterior
limb bud
(wing)

Otocyst (ear)

Eye

Pineal
body

Cerebrum

Allantois

Posterior
limb bud
(leg)

Tail
bud

Brain

72 Hour
Embryo

B. CHICK

Spinal
cord

Anus

Gut

Somatic
mesoderm

Coelom

Notochord

Pharynx

Heart

Liver

Splanchnic mesoderm

Section of an Embryo

A. FROG

LATE IX. Early development of frog (A) and of chick (B). Endoderm shown
in yellow, ectoderm in blue, and mesoderm in red.

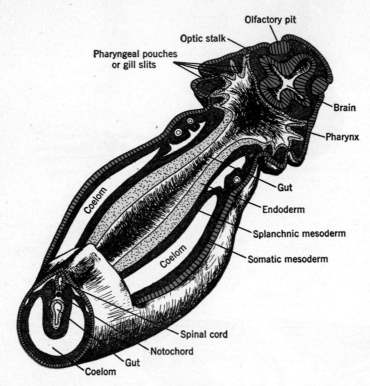

Olfactory pit

Optic stalk

Pharyngeal pouches
or gill slits

Brain

Pharynx

Coelom

Gut

Endoderm

Splanchnic mesoderm

Somatic mesoderm

Coelom

Spinal cord

Notochord

Gut

Coelom

PLATE X. Diagram of the frog embryo with a part of the dorsal half of the body
removed.

In the starfish the mesoderm is derived from two pouches that push out and pinch off from the enteron. These hollow pouches grow down between the endoderm and ectoderm, coalesce ventrally, and their cavity becomes the coelom. Again, in the earthworm we find that the mesoderm is derived from two primitive cells which originate from one of the large cells formed during cleavage. Other interesting invertebrate developmental processes might be described as well as various interesting and bizarre larval forms which later transform into adults (Fig. 109).

Homology and analogy. Just as the preceding general description of early development holds true for the vertebrates, so are the

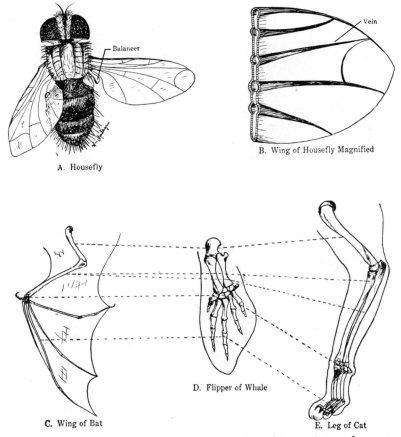

A. Housefly

B. Wing of Housefly Magnified

C. Wing of Bat

D. Flipper of Whale

E. Leg of Cat

FIG. 110. Homology and analogy. *C, D, E* are homologous; *C* is analogous to *B*.

later phases of differentiation likewise quite similar. If we study the foreleg and foot, the arm and hand, and the wing of a bird in the earliest embryonic stages, they are all seen to be budlike outgrowths on the side of the embryo. In fact they are called **limb buds.** As the embryo develops and metamorphoses into the adult, the limb buds change into the structures already mentioned. However, a study of the bones and muscles shows a structural likeness as well as a similar embryonic origin. Such structures, irrespective of function, are said to be **homologous** (Fig. 110). The wings of a butterfly, bee, or other flying insect do not have the same origin and structural similarities as those of a bird or a bat, yet the function, flying, is the same for all

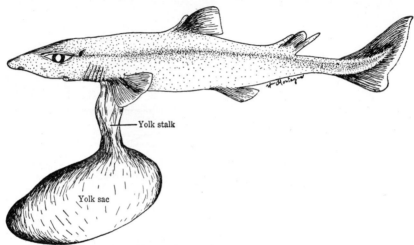

Yolk stalk

Yolk sac

Fig. 111. Embryonic shark.

these animals. Structures, then, which have the same function but whose origin is different are said to be **analogous.** Different types of homologous structures may be found in both the vertebrates and invertebrates, as will be brought out later.

Nourishing and protecting the young embryo. It has already been pointed out that in some eggs there is a much greater amount of yolk than in others and that cleavage is confined to a protoplasmic disk at the animal pole. Here the embryo develops. As the embryo develops, the splanchnopleure, i.e., the endodermal cells with the accompanying splanchnic mesoderm grows down over and completely envelops the mass of yolk in a **yolk sac** (Fig. 111 and Plate XI). The yolk is thus enclosed, in a sense, in the primitive alimentary tract. The embryo continues to grow and becomes almost separated from the yolk, which is being slowly absorbed by blood vessels that have developed in the walls of the yolk sac. However, the embryo still remains attached to the yolk sac by a narrow **yolk stalk** which communicates with the intestine in the **umbilical region** (*umbilicus—*

navel).   As the animal grows, the yolk is absorbed, the yolk sac
shrinks, and its layers are used to close the intestine.

In fishes and amphibians, the eggs are laid in the water where there
is not only plenty of buoyancy for shock absorption but also ample
provision for oxygen supply and waste elimination.   And these embryos require plenty of oxygen, because young organisms and young
tissues have been shown to have a higher metabolic rate than old
ones.   They "live" faster.   Since reptiles, birds, and mammals do not
lay their eggs in the water, provision has to be made to replace this
medium functionally.   This is done by the development of **embryonic
membranes,** which are used for protection, nutrition, respiration, and
excretion.   In all these animals there are formed a yolk sac and stalk,
which function in somewhat the same way as those of fishes and
amphibia.   However, the egg of some mammals, such as man, has
little yolk, and the yolk apparatus is very rudimentary.

In reptiles and birds, folds of the somatopleure grow up over the
sides, head, and tail of the embryo, meet, fuse, and enclose the embryo in a sac called the **amnion.**   The outer layer of the fold forms
the **chorion** (*chorion*—a skin).   (Study carefully Plate XI.)   The
amniotic cavity is filled with the watery amniotic fluid—the substitute
for the pond or the brook of the embryonic fish and frog.   To take
care of respiration and waste, a pouch called the **allantois** (*allas*—
sausage) pushes out from the floor of the gut just back of the yolk
stalk.   The allantois pushes on out between the chorion and the
amnion.   Thus it is close to the shell and, being well supplied with
blood vessels, solves the oxygen and carbon dioxide problems of the
embryo.   At birth these embryonic membranes remain with the shell.

In the majority of mammals, nourishment and waste elimination
of the embryo present a somewhat different problem, solved in a
somewhat different way.   In the first place the mammalian egg is
usually microscopic in size and contains little yolk.   The tiny egg is
fertilized in the oviduct.   The zygote passes down and embeds itself
in the uterine wall.   Here the developing embryo or fetus forms a
yolk stalk, amnion, allantois, and chorion.   However, the outer vascular wall of the allantois is fused with the chorion.   Eventually, the
amnion increases in size until its walls are in contact with the chorion.
In man and many mammals, branching fingerlike processes called
chorionic villi grow out from the chorion at one restricted disklike
region.   The villi erode close-fitting pits in the wall of the uterus.
This uterine-chorionic organ is known as the **placenta.**   The embryo
is attached to the placenta by a rather long, twisted cord of tissues
called the **umbilicus,** in which are found the rudimentary remnants

of the yolk stalk and allantois, as well as two arteries and a vein which carry the fetal blood to and from the placenta (Plate XI).

Some factors modifying development. In the preceding paragraphs, we have tried to outline how the animal organism normally originates and develops under relatively stable conditions in a uniform environment. Through experimentation, biologists have brought about interesting structural modifications and discovered certain factors governing development. Some of these discoveries are almost unbelievable. For instance, it has been found that, if the blastomeres of *Amphioxus* are separated at the two-cell stage, they will develop into two perfect little animals—twins. Sometimes twin frogs may arise in a similar manner. In some jellyfishes each blastomere in the sixteen-cell stage of cleavage will develop into a perfect embryo. On the other hand, separation of blastomeres, or even groups of blastomeres, of other animals in the early stages of development results in the formation of only those particular structures or regions of the animal which would have been produced if the cells had remained grouped together. Motile structures of the embryos of some animals will develop and move around without any other parts of the embryo attached, apparently indicating that very early in development each blastomere becomes restricted as to the variety of structures it can produce. Cleavage of this type is called **mosaic cleavage.** Not only are the potentialities of the blastomeres of some animals fixed early in development but also the tissues which develop from the primary germ layers are determined. Thus bits of mesoderm differentiated for muscles, or ectoderm differentiated for nerves, may be removed from the embryo and grown in artificial cultures outside the body, where they will develop into muscle and nerve.

Spemann and other biologists have found that double-headed monsters can be formed from the gastrula of a newt (a tailed amphibian) by tying a hair around the middle of the gastrula in such a way as to divide the dorsal lip of the blastopore. In another experiment, a gastrula was divided into halves by cutting through the middle of the dorsal lip of the blastopore. One half of the mass was rotated 180 degrees, with the result that there developed two half-embryos facing in opposite directions. By transplanting a portion of the dorsal lip of the blastopore into the side of a young embryo, there was formed a head region indicative of the new axis of an embryo at right angles to the embryo receiving the transplant. Spemann accounted for such unusual developments as the result of an "organizer" which is located in the dorsal lip of the blastopore.

By adding magnesium salts to the water at a particular stage in the development of certain young fish, Stockard has been able to grow fish having a single median eye. Other abnormal fish have been produced by lowering their metabolic rate at certain stages of their development by such methods as reducing the oxygen content of the water and by means of various narcotics (Fig. 112).

Other methods have been found to control the pattern of various animals. *Tubularia* is a simple marine animal which resembles *Hydra*. Its apical region is an enlargement of the stem containing a mouth surrounded by "lips" or

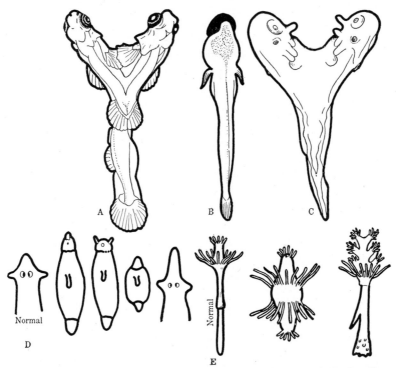

FIG. 112. Modifications of development. *A*, Siamese twins of the brook trout caused by low oxygen supply before gastrulation. *B*, Cyclopia (one eye) induced in the minnow (*Fundulus*) by treatment with magnesium chloride. *C*, partial twinning in the animal *Triton*, an amphibian, caused by constricting the early gastrula. *D*, normal head of the flatworm, *Dugesia* (*Planaria*), and bizarre heads induced by keeping regenerating pieces of the animal in various solutions. *E*, normal hydroid of the animal *Corymorpha* and abnormal forms induced under experimental conditions. *A, redrawn from Stockard, American Journal of Anatomy, XXVIII, No. 2, 1921. B, redrawn from Stockard. C, redrawn from Spemann, Archiv für Entwicklungsmechanik der Organismen, XVI, 1903. D and E, redrawn from Child, "Physiological Foundations of Behavior," by permission of the publisher, Henry Holt and Co.*

peristome, around which are tentacles. These structures make up the hydranth. If the hydranth is removed, the animal will regenerate a new one. If, however, you remove both the hydranth and "foot" (basal) region and then stick the apical region in the sand, a new hydranth forms where the foot formerly was. The former apical region develops into a foot. If neither cut end is put in the sand, a hydranth develops on each cut end. By cutting short pieces transverse to the long axis of such animals as hydras, the little flatworm *Dugesia* (*Planaria*), and others, two-headed animals will regenerate.

Twins and twinning. The phenomenon of twinning is familiar to almost everyone. It is rather well known that some twins may be as "much alike as two peas"; they are of the same sex, look alike, and behave alike. Such twins are known as **identical** or **duplicate twins.** They are supposed to be the result of the breaking apart of the two blastomeres in the two-cell stage, or perhaps of a later division of the embryonic cell mass into two parts. On the other hand, there are twins who do not resemble each other so much either physically or mentally. Such twins, known as **fraternal twins,** probably came from two different zygotes. Triplets, quadruplets, and quintuplets develop from a single zygote or different zygotes. The nine-banded armadillo normally bears four offspring which are alike, and a study of this interesting animal has shown conclusively that the quadruplets are from a single zygote. There are certain wasps which lay their eggs in the eggs of butterflies. Very early the embryo wasp divides into hundreds of separate parts, each of which forms a grublike parasite in the body of the caterpillar. Finally these grubs or larvas form adult wasps, all of which owe their origin to a single egg.

Perhaps the most famous instance of multiple human births of all time is the Dionne quintuplets. Moreover, apparently all are "identical." An intensive study of them apparently indicates that three of the quintuplets have more similarities in common than the other two. Thus it is believed that the Dionnes originally came from one developing group of cells which divided, forming four separate groups. One of these four groups divided. The development of these last two groups gave rise to two very similar individuals that are different from those developing from the other three groups.

Prenatal influence and malformations. Doubtless everyone has seen or read about certain peculiar, abnormal, or malformed animals commonly called monsters or freaks, such as Siamese twins, armless babes, headless babes, two-headed calves, and five-footed sheep (Fig. 113). In man it is estimated that 1 out of every 165 children born is malformed in some noticeable way. There is a tendency on the part of the average individual to explain these monsters and deformities as a result of the influence of the mother on the unborn babe. Thus a child born minus an arm is the result of the mother's seeing, reading about, or even hearing of an accident in which some unfortunate individual lost an arm. Reasons can be manufactured to account for all these occurrences. Further, according to this belief, if the pregnant mother listens to good music, the child will be musically inclined. If she reads good literature, the child will have literary inclinations, and so the story goes.

Modern medical men and biologists do not accept such explanations because there is no nervous connection between parent and offspring. The two nervous systems are separate and distinct. It has already been shown that the blood of the mother and that of the fetus usually do not mix, for the circulatory systems are separate. The anatomical relationship between offspring and parent is one of contact only. The real explanation is that such malformations may be

FIG. 113.   Monstrosities as they occur in nature.   Outline drawings of human double monsters. *From Dodds, "Essentials of Human Embryology." By permission of the author and of the publisher, John Wiley and Sons.*

caused by certain abnormal conditions similar to those set up experimentally, which, as we have seen, produce change in patterns. Birthmarks belong in the same category as these other malformations.

The development of embryology. Embryology, as we have seen, is the study of the developing animal from its origin in the germ cells. It began, as did so many other sciences, with Aristotle about 384 B.C. Aristotle, without the aid of hand lens or microscope, studied and described the daily development of the chick and was much interested in the beating of the embryonic heart. Harvey and Malpighi made some studies on the chick embryo with simple lenses, and in 1677 Leeuwenhoek believed that the embryo existed as a fully formed miniature animal in the egg and that the entrance of the sperm into the egg furnished the stimulus for growth and unfolding. Followers of this school of thought were called **ovists.** Others, called **spermists,** even reported that they could see a minute human form in the spermatozoon. These ideas of the ovists and the spermists constituted what is known as the **doctrine of preformation.** According to a variation of this theory all future generations are incased in the gametes of the present generation—a sort of box-in-box arrangement. Quite serious computations were made of the probable number of descendants present in Mother Eve's ovary, "at the exhaustion of which the human race would end."

Wolff (1759) opposed this doctrine and maintained that the organs of the chick embryo gradually took form from unspecialized living protoplasm. This is the **doctrine of epigenesis,** which, in a slightly modified form, is held today. Today, it is recognized that certain regions of the egg may correspond to definite parts of the embryo, as in mosaic cleavage. Later, in 1827, von Baer, a German biologist, discovered the mammalian egg and the formation and differentiation of the primary germ layers. Von Baer is known as "the father of modern embryology." Hertwig in 1875 observed fertilization and reported the real meaning of the process. Modern embryologists have cleared up much of the mystery of development and are now busily attacking the problem of the mechanics of the process.

15

The Mechanism of Heredity

We have already seen how living organisms are constructed, how they carry on life processes, and how the new individual originates either asexually or sexually by the union of the gametes. Man has recognized from very early times that offspring have a tendency to resemble their parents and even their grandparents. The ancient Egyptians and Babylonians evidently knew something of this principle called heredity for they left us tangible proofs in improved breeds of domestic plants and animals. The old proverb that "like begets like" does not seem to hold in every detail, since it has been discovered that two white rabbits may produce jet-black offspring. In spite of this fact and many others like it, we can still subscribe to the doctrine that "man does not gather grapes of thorns or figs of thistles," but we must also recognize that "like does not produce like, but only somewhat like." Offspring are never exactly like the parents but differ in various physical and mental characters. These differences, generally called **variations,** may be the result of ancestral inheritance, or they may be caused by differences in environment.

Sir Francis Galton, an Englishman, gathered from various sources a mass of accumulated observations on heredity and variation dealing mostly with man. Some of this material came from biologists, some from farmers and breeders, and some from general sources. This material he attempted to systematize and treat statistically. Galton's studies served mostly to focus attention on heredity and to outline the problem but did little toward solving it. His evidence lacked controlled experimental treatment and came from mere random observations. His studies lumped all like characteristics together, whether they were the result of heredity or of environment. Tallness or shortness of stature may be, in some measure, the result of either heredity or malnutrition, yet under Galton's method variations resulting from both heredity and environment received the same interpretation. Much of his study was made on general populations rather than individuals. As we shall see, it was only when an intensive systematic experimental study of individuals was made that the real causes and the mechanism of heredity were revealed. However, credit must be given to Galton for initiating the statistical study of heredity.

Gregor Mendel. Gregor Mendel was an Austrian monk who lived in a monastery in central Europe. This son of a farmer, at great sacrifice on the part of his family, was educated for the priesthood. In his training he also studied mathematics and science and proved to be a very good student. His church work was his vocation, but his hobby was science and mathematics, and particularly the study of heredity. In his monastery garden he experimented with plants and bees, and he published several papers on new varieties of bees which he had been able to produce through breeding experiments. Today he is best known for his breeding experiments with plants, experiments which laid the foundation of the modern science of heredity.

Instead of choosing large groups of plants and animals for study, he picked out one which he knew quite well. Further, he limited each study to one peculiarity or characteristic, did his own crossing or mating, and reared the resulting population through several generations. His epoch-making discoveries were the result of experiments on the common garden pea. It is well worth while to call attention here to the fact that many of our greatest scientific discoveries have been made with ordinary apparatus and commonplace materials in the hands of non-professional experimenters.

Mendel published his experiments in the *Proceedings* of the Natural History Society of Brünn in 1865 and 1866. However, no one understood or appreciated his work until it was rediscovered by three biologists, Correns, De Vries, and Tschermak, working independently. As for Mendel, he rose to the position of abbot of his monastery and became so absorbed in his new duties that his scientific studies ceased. The latter days of his life were spent in unsuccessfully combating what he considered an unjust tax, and he died in 1884, a very much discouraged man. Today Mendel is famous not for what he did in his profession but for the achievements of his leisure-time activities.

It is interesting to contrast the methods of study employed by Mendel and Galton, respectively. Galton's evidence (or data) was, in a sense, "hearsay evidence." Mendel gathered his evidence at first hand. Moreover, his experiments were controlled. Galton and Mendel had these two scientific tendencies in common: an impelling curiosity and a desire for exact measurement, an application of mathematics.

The modern study of heredity began with the rediscovery of Mendel's reports in 1900. Starting from his reports as a basis, new investigations have shown that Mendelian principles hold true for both animals and plants. Moreover, improved microscopic and genetic methods have apparently demonstrated that the determiners

FIG. 114. Gregor Johann Mendel (1822–1884). *Photograph furnished by the Central Scientific Company, Chicago.*

of hereditary characteristics, or the **genes** as they are called by the modern student of heredity, are located in the chromosomes of the nucleus of the cell. The study of the chromosomes and their behavior, then, is the study of the hereditary mechanism.

Meiosis. Under usual conditions, for each kind of animal or plant, we find a constant number of chromosomes in the somatic cells and in the primordial germ cells. The chromosome numbers of certain animals and plants are listed in the following table. Change in the number of chromosomes quite often results in a change in the individual organism. Suppose that the little fruit fly *Drosophila,* which has eight chromosomes in its body cells, produced gametes with eight chromosomes in each of their nuclei. If these gametes fused, the re-

CHROMOSOME NUMBERS ($2n$) OF SOME COMMON ANIMALS AND PLANTS

Animals	Chromosome Number $2n$	Plants	Chromosome Number $2n$
Man (*Homo*)	48	Pea (*Pisum sativum*)	14
Horse (*Equus caballus*)	60	Corn (*Zea mays*)	20
Ameba (*Entamoeba histolytica*)	6	Fern (*Dryopteris pseudo-mas*)	144
Housefly (*Musca domestica*)	12	Onion (*Allium cepa*)	16
Crayfish (*Cambarus virilis*)	200	Primrose (*Primula sinensis*)	18
Monkey (*Cebus*)	44	Cabbage (*Brassica oleiacea*)	18
Cow (*Bos taurus*)	38	Radish (*Raphanus sativus*)	18

sulting zygote would have sixteen chromosomes, or twice the number in the cells of the parents. But usually there takes place in the gametes a distinctive nuclear process called **meiosis** (*meiosis*—reduction) in which the number of chromosomes is reduced to one-half the number found in the parent. In other words, an animal with eight chromosomes, which is the $2n$ or **diploid** (*diploos*—double) number would produce gametes having one-half the diploid number, or four —the n or **haploid** (*haploos*—simple) number of chromosomes. As far as chromosomal behavior is concerned, meiosis in animals is practically the same for both the male, where it is known as **spermatogenesis** (*sperma*—seed; *genesis*—birth) and the female, where it is called **oögenesis** (*oön*—egg; *genesis*) (Fig. 115). The body cells and the primordial germ cells have the diploid or $2n$ number of chromosomes. The primordial germ cells continue to multiply for a period by mitotic cell division.

However, there comes a time when the individual chromosomes pair off side by side, a process called **synapsis** (*synapsis*—union). This pairing is not by chance, for as we study cells more closely we find that apparently each diploid cell really has two sets of chromosomes, one paternal set contributed by the spermatozoon and one maternal set contributed by the egg. The chromosomes of each pair differ from those of the other pairs. In other words, there are in each

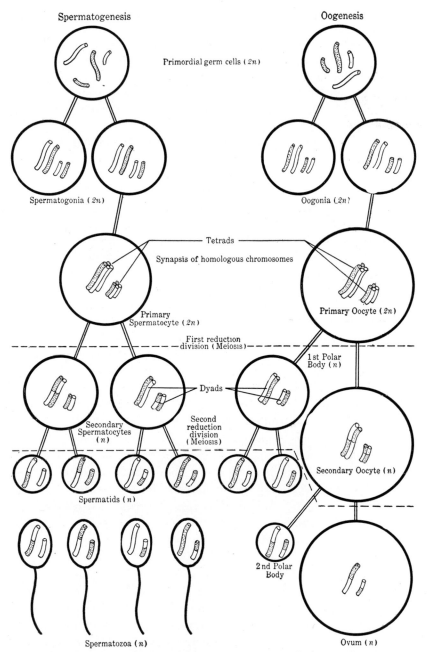

FIG. 115. Meiosis. Diagram showing the meiosis of germ cells of animals (gametogenesis). Stippled chromosomes represent the paternal contribution; clear chromosomes, the maternal contribution; and chromosomes that are half-stippled and half-clear show crossing over.

zygote, and in every diploid cell, pairs of homologous chromosomes. If a diploid cell has four chromosomes, it will have two pairs of homologous chromosomes. The homologous chromosmes resemble each other not only in appearance, but also, as revealed by the discoveries of modern heredity, in potentialities for the same structures, the same physiological processes, and the same influence in development.

Each member of the pair of homologous chromosomes is divided longitudinally to form two half-chromosomes or **chromatids.** Thus each pair of homologous chromosomes would be made up of four chromatids (a **tetrad**). The germ cells are now known as the **primary spermatocytes** in the male, and **primary oöcytes** in the female. (Study Fig. 115.) Suppose that there are two pairs of homologous chromosomes (four chromosomes) in the primary spermatocytes and the primary oöcytes. They arrange themselves in homologous pairs on the spindle. Each member of the pair is divided longitudinally to form four chromatids. Two chromatids (equivalent of one chromosome) go to one end of the spindle, and two chromatids go to the other end of the spindle. Recall that theoretically each cell had four chromosomes (two tetrads). Thus when the cell divides there are two cells, each of which has two chromosomes or one-half the number that was in the germ cell before reduction took place. This is the **first meiotic division.** This reduction division of the primary spermatocytes and the primary oöcytes gives rise to the **secondary spermatocytes** and the **secondary oöcytes.** They are similar in that they have n chromosomes, made up of two chromatids each. The cytoplasmic division of the primary oöcyte is unequal, so that one of the secondary oöcytes is much smaller; it is known as the **first polar body** (Fig. 115). The secondary spermatocytes and the secondary oöcytes now undergo a **second meiotic division** in which each resulting cell receives two chromatids which later will form two chromosomes. One of the daughter cells of the secondary oöcyte forms a **second polar body,** and the other forms an ovum (Fig. 115). All the polar bodies disintegrate, leaving but one mature ovum with n chromosomes and most of the cytoplasm with a rich supply of stored food for the coming offspring. All the sperm cells, having now n chromosomes, develop into mature spermatozoa with an equal amount of cytoplasm, though much less than that found in the surviving ovum. The spermatozoon has sacrificed food supply for motility. Thus we see how mature n haploid gametes, the bearers of heredity and the sources of the new individual, are formed.

MENDELIAN CROSSES AND CHROMOSOME BEHAVIOR

The more intensive study of the cell and heredity since 1900 has indicated that the **genes,** the carriers of heredity, are located not merely in the nucleus of the gamete but actually at particular places or **loci** (*locus*–place) in particular chromosomes. Consequently the modern explanation of the hereditary mechanism is very definitely linked with chromosomal behavior and distribution.

Monohybrid cross. Keeping in mind then the process of meiosis and the facts just mentioned, suppose that we experiment with the heredity of guinea pigs. For the sake of clarity we shall *assume* that in the diploid condition there are six chromosomes present in the cells of the guinea pig. (Actually there are thirty-eight.) Suppose that we cross a **homozygous** black male (*BB*) with a homozygous white female (*bb*). When two genes in two homologous chromosomes are alike, the animal or plant is said to be **homozygous** with respect to the character in question. Suppose the genes for black (*B*) and the genes for white (*b*) to be located in corresponding loci of certain homologous chromosomes. Thus the black homozygous guinea pig would have a gene for black (*B*) in each of a pair of homologous chromosomes. This homozygous genic condition we would designate as *BB*. Similarly the guinea pig homozygous for white has a pair of homologous chromosomes in each of which there is a gene for white (*b*) and which pair we would designate *bb*. (Study Fig. 116.) At the completion of meiosis in the male, each homologous chromosome with the gene *B* will have gone to a different male gamete. Thus each male gamete will carry *B*. A similar process will have taken place in the female except that each gamete or ovum will have a chromosome with the gene *b* (Fig. 116).

Fertilization takes place, and, when the zygotes have developed into adult guinea pigs, we find that all the animals are black. This generation of animals, called the **first filial generation** (*filius*–son), is designated as F_1. The parents of these animals represent the **first parental generation** or P_1. Since these F_1 individuals are mixed or **hybrids** (*Bb*), one might expect that they would be neither black nor white but some intermediate color such as gray. The fact that all F_1 individuals are black, even though we know that white (*b*) is present in the zygote, is explained by assuming that in the presence of black (*B*) the character white is not expressed. Thus we call black a **dominant character** and white a **recessive character.** In the shorthand of genetics, dominant characters are represented by capital letters and recessive characters by small letters. These characters which act as alternates in inheritance are called **alleles** (*allelon—another*).

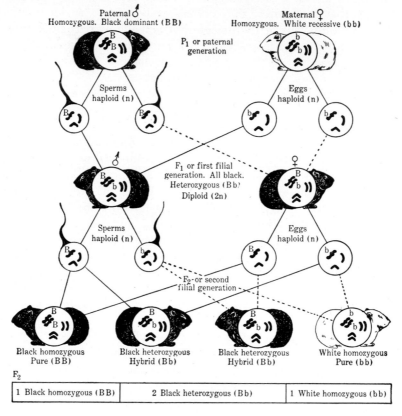

Fig. 116. Diagram of a monohybrid cross of homozygous black and homozygous white guinea pigs.

If we study the zygotes formed, it is seen that, in the pairs of homologous chromosomes we have been tracing, one paternal chromosome bears the gene *B*, and in the corresponding locus its homologous maternal chromosome bears the gene *b*. All animals in the

F_1 generation will have the genic make-up Bb. When the two genes in the two homologous chromosomes are unlike (Bb), the animal or plant is **heterozygous** for the character in question. Thus all the animals in the F_1 generation having the genic make-up Bb are heterozygous. Since black is dominant over white, all the animals in the F_1 generation will be black hybrids. (Study Fig. 116.)

Now suppose that the males and females of the F_1 generation are inbred. You will recall that the primordial germ cells are heterozygous, one chromosome having the gene B, and its homologous mate, in the corresponding locus, having the gene b. The germ cells undergo meiosis. The chromosomes normally separate after synapsis and go to different gametes, so that there are now B and b spermatozoa and B and b eggs (Fig. 116).

By chance each kind of sperm can fertilize either kind of egg. The possible combinations of male and female gametes bringing about the association of homologous chromosomes is shown as follows:

Sperm B may fertilize egg B to give a zygote BB (Black, homozygous).
Sperm B may fertilize egg b to give a zygote Bb (Black, heterozygous).
Sperm b may fertilize egg B to give a zygote Bb (Black, heterozygous).
Sperm b may fertilize egg b to give a zygote bb (White, homozygous).

Thus in this **second filial generation** (F_2) we find a ratio of three black guinea pigs to one white. However, an analysis of this ratio shows one homozygous black (BB), two hybrid heterozygous black (Bb), and one homozygous white recessive (bb). This ratio is the one usually obtained from a **monohybrid cross** in which there is only one pair of contrasting genes.

This random pairing or fusion of unlike gametes has been well illustrated by the following experiment. Suppose that we mix thoroughly 100 black marbles and 100 white marbles and then place them in two separate vessels with 100 marbles in each vessel. The mixed black and white marbles in each vessel represent the gametes, and the containing vessels represent the male and female parents. If a blindfolded person removes these marbles in pairs, each time taking one marble from each of the containers, the different pairs will be grouped approximately as follows: one-fourth of them will be black-black, two-fourths will be black-white, and one-fourth will be white-white. This is the same ratio as the one observed in the monohybrid cross of a black guinea pig with a white guinea pig. A similar test of the result of random pairing can be made by tossing coins, taking two successive tosses as a pair.

The different kinds of genic combinations found in the zygote as a result of various matings are much more easily seen by means of the checkerboard diagram. In this diagram the male gametes are usually placed horizontally across the top of the checkerboard, and the female

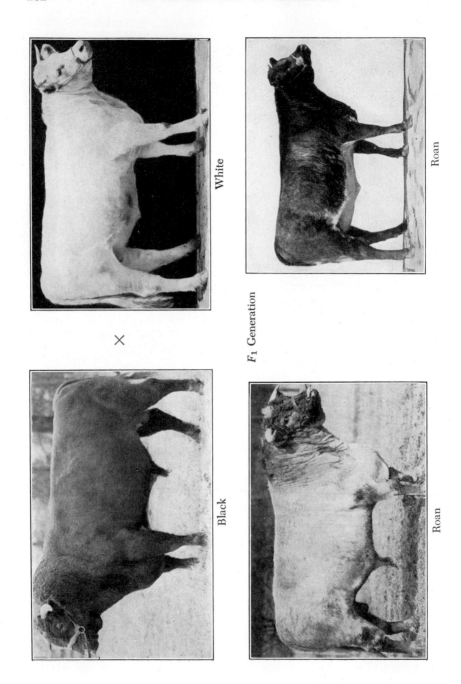

White

Roan

×

F_1 Generation

Black

Roan

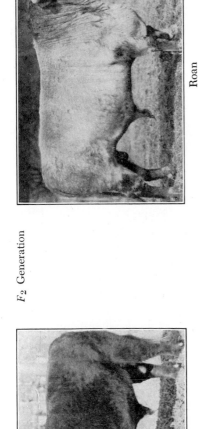

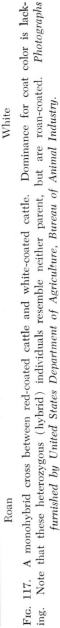

Roan

White

F_2 Generation

Black

Roan

Fig. 117. A monohybrid cross between red-coated cattle and white-coated cattle. Dominance for coat color is lacking. Note that these heterozygous (hybrid) individuals resemble neither parent, but are roan-coated. *Photographs furnished by United States Department of Agriculture, Bureau of Animal Industry.*

in a vertical column to the left. The female gametes are arranged in the same descending order as the male gametes are arranged in horizontal order from left to right. The use of the checkerboard can be almost easily understood by its application in the F_1 cross of the experiment just described.

MALE GAMETES

	B	b
B	BB	Bb
b	Bb	bb

FEMALE GAMETES

The modern geneticist recognizes two general types of individuals. Those individuals which are alike *externally* with respect to the characters in question, such as *all* the *white* guinea pigs, belong to one **phenotype.** All the black guinea pigs would belong to another phenotype. However, we have seen that the black animals are not all alike genetically, that is, in their chromosomes. Some are pure or *BB*, and some are hybrid or *Bb*. In other words there are two kinds of animals, *BB* and *Bb*, as judged from the *internal* make-up. These are known as **genotypes.** Thus, if we analyze the ratio of 3:1 we find that in the "3" there are: one phenotype (external) and two genotypes, i.e., *BB* and *Bb* (internal). The "1" has one phenotype and only one genotype, for all are white and *bb*.

In not all cases is one pair of alleles completely dominant over the other as in the cross just described. If red-coated shorthorn cattle are crossed with white-coated, the offspring in the F_1 generation are all roan-coated, a blend of both colors (Fig. 117). In the F_2 generation one-fourth of the cattle will be red, one-fourth white, and two-fourths roan. Thus it is clear that the roan-coated cattle are heterozygous, a result that would be expected if it is assumed that neither red nor white is dominant over the other (Fig. 117).

In the cross involving the red-coated and white-coated shorthorns, three phenotypes are readily distinguished—red-coated, white, and roan. There are also three genotypes—red-coated, white, and roan.

Dihybrid cross. The cross just described with the guinea pigs is the simplest that can be made. Suppose that, instead of a cross involving but one pair of contrasting characters (monohybrid), a cross is made between two animals having two pairs of contrasting characters, or, in other words, a **dihybrid cross.** This would involve two pairs of contrasting genes, which may be located in the same pair

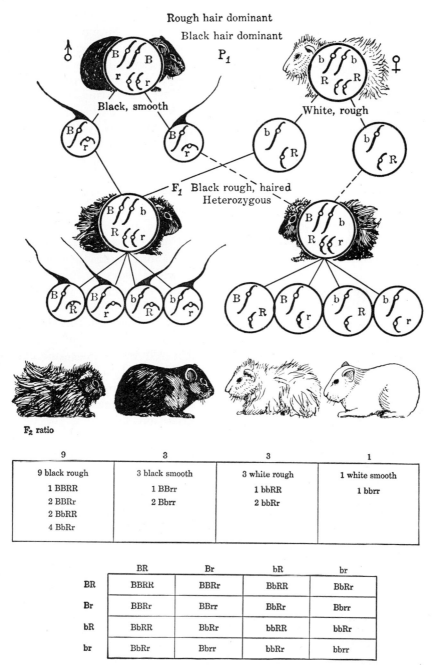

Rough hair dominant

Black hair dominant

P_1

Black, smooth

White, rough

F_1 Black rough, haired
Heterozygous

F₂ ratio

9	3	3	1
9 black rough	3 black smooth	3 white rough	1 white smooth
1 BBRR	1 BBrr	1 bbRR	1 bbrr
2 BBRr	2 Bbrr	2 bbRr	
2 BbRR			
4 BbRr			

	BR	Br	bR	br
BR	BBRR	BBRr	BbRR	BbRr
Br	BBRr	BBrr	BbRr	Bbrr
bR	BbRR	BbRr	bbRR	bbRr
br	BbRr	Bbrr	bbRr	bbrr

Fɪɢ. 118. Diagram of a dihybrid cross of homozygous black, smooth-haired male and homozygous white, rough-haired female guinea pigs. Genes are represented by small circles in the chromosomes. In the F₂ generation there are four phenotypes and nine genotypes.

235

of homologous chromosomes or in different pairs. Suppose that male guinea pigs, homozygous for black smooth hair, are crossed with female guinea pigs homozygous for white rough hair. Black and rough are dominant. If the genes are located in different paired homologous chromosomes, the genes of the male would be represented as *BBrr* and those of the female *bbRR*. These genes are shown in different chromosomes in the diagram in Fig. 118. In the process of meiosis, homologous chromosomes separate and go to different gametes. Hence the spermatozoa would be represented as *Br* and the ova as *bR*. These gametes in fertilization would form zygotes *BbRr* from which would develop the F_1 generation. All the F_1 guinea pigs would have rough black hair, the dominant characteristics. If the genes segregate independently of each other and by chance, these F_1 animals, both male and female, would have the following possible combinations of gametes: *BR, Br, bR, br.* (Study Fig. 118.) If these hybrid F_1 animals are inbred and the various types of spermatozoa fertilize, by chance, various types of ova, the resultant phenotypic ratio in the F_2 generation will be 9 Black Rough, 3 Black smooth, 3 white Rough, 1 white smooth. This cross is shown by the checkerboard in Fig. 118.

The basic principles of heredity discovered by Mendel and illustrated by the crosses just described remain valid today. However, as a result of more recent important discoveries made possible by improved instruments and techniques and by the concentrated study of many brilliant hard-working biologists, our knowledge of these principles has been modified and considerably increased.

Sex determination and sex linkage. From ancient times to the present, probably no phase of biology has been the subject of more speculation than sex determination. All sorts of wild suggestions have been advanced. Some held that the diet of the mother determined the sex of the offspring. Another explanation was that the offspring would be of the same sex as that of the older and stronger parent. Other speculations, equally fantastic, were held, such as the theory that one testis produced female-determining spermatozoa and the other male. Today biologists believe that sex is determined at the time of fertilization by the types of gametes, but that the ultimate development of the sexual characteristics of the individuals of certain groups may be changed by various environmental factors.

In 1902 McClung reported that in the testes of certain grasshoppers there was an odd-shaped, apparently unpaired chromosome which he thought was a sex determiner. This opened a new field of investigation. Later it was found that in the cells of *Drosophila* there were

(*Continued on page 238*)

Trihybrid cross. In trihybrid crosses, organisms having three pairs of contrasting characters are crossed, producing offspring in the F_1 generation which are hybrid or heterozygous for three pairs of characters. Such a cross can be worked out by the checkerboard, applying the same principles already stated, except that now there will be eight different types of genic combinations or gametes in the F_1 generation, which may produce sixty-four types of individuals in the F_2. Suppose that a cross is made between homozygous Tall Smooth Yellow, *TTSSYY*, and dwarf wrinkled green peas—*ttssyy*. If tall (*T*), smooth (*S*), and yellow (*Y*) are dominant, the F_1 generation would exhibit these characteristics. The gametic combinations possible in the F_1 hybrids would be *TSY*, *TSy*, *TsY*, *Tsy*, *tSY*, *tSy*, *tsY*, *tsy*. This is worked out in the accompanying checkerboard and gives the following phenotypic ratio for the F_2 generation.

27 TALL, SMOOTH, YELLOW
9 TALL, SMOOTH, green
9 TALL, wrinkled, YELLOW
9 short, SMOOTH, YELLOW
3 TALL, wrinkled, green
3 short, SMOOTH, green
3 short, wrinkled, YELLOW
1 short, wrinkled, green

MALE GAMETES

	TSY	TSy	TsY	Tsy	tSY	tSy	tsY	tsy
TSY	TSY / TSY	TSy / TSY	TsY / TSY	Tsy / TSY	tSY / TSY	tSy / TSY	tsY / TSY	tsy / TSY
TSy	TSY / TSy	TSy / TSy	TsY / TSy	Tsy / TSy	tSY / TSy	tSy / TSy	tsY / TSy	tsy / TSy
TsY	TSY / TsY	TSy / TsY	TsY / TsY	Tsy / TsY	tSY / TsY	tSy / TsY	tsY / TsY	tsy / TsY
Tsy	TSY / Tsy	TSy / Tsy	TsY / Tsy	Tsy / Tsy	tSY / Tsy	tSy / Tsy	tsY / Tsy	tsy / Tsy
tSY	TSY / tSY	TSy / tSY	TsY / tSY	Tsy / tSY	tSY / tSY	tSy / tSY	tsY / tSY	tsy / tSY
tSy	TSY / tSy	TSy / tSy	TsY / tSy	Tsy / tSy	tSY / tSy	tSy / tSy	tsY / tSy	tsy / tSy
tsY	TSY / tsY	TSy / tsY	TsY / tsY	Tsy / tsY	tSY / tsY	tSy / tsY	tsY / tsY	tsy / tsY
tsy	TSY / tsy	TSy / tsy	TsY / tsy	Tsy / tsy	tSY / tsy	tSy / tsy	tsY / tsy	tsy / tsy

FEMALE GAMETES (row labels at left)

eight chromosomes. The members of three pairs of these were visibly similar, and the members of the remaining pair were dissimilar in the male and similar in the female. In the male, one chromosome of this peculiar pair is a straight rod-shaped chromosome designated the X-chromosome, and the homologous chromosome, which is hooked at one end, is called the Y-chromosome (Fig. 119). Thus, in the males there are three pairs of chromosomes called **autosomes,** plus this *XY* pair called **sex chromosomes.** In the female there are also three pairs of autosomes and two X-chromosomes or sex chromosomes.

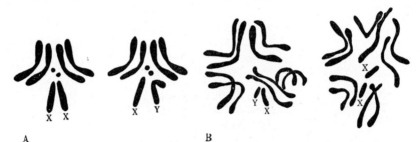

A   B

Fig. 119. The sex chromosomes of *Drosophila* (A) and the fly, *Caliphora* (B). *A, after Morgan and others. B, redrawn from Wilson, "The Cell in Development and Heredity." By permission of the publisher, the Macmillan Co.*

Experimentation has shown that these sex chromosomes play a part in determining sex.

If we study large random groups of populations of various animals, we find that females and males are produced in approximately equal numbers, as would be expected in the light of the following experimental evidence. All the female gametes should be alike in regard to sex chromosomes, each containing one X-chromosome. On the other hand, there would be two types of male gametes, one containing an X-chromosome and one a Y-chromosome. In fertilization, half the *X* female gametes might be fertilized by *X* spermatozoa to produce *XX* zygotes which should grow into females. Discoveries indicate that the Y-chromosome is not necessary for the differentiation of male characters, but that the real difference between the two sexes is caused by the number of X-chromosomes present in relation to the number of autosomes, i.e., *XX* in the female and a single *X* in the male. However, when the Y-chromosome is missing in *Drosophila,* the fly will be a sterile male.

Morgan, a famous biologist, had studied many generations of fruit flies (*Drosophila*) which had red eyes. One day he found a white-eyed male fly among all the other newly emerged red-eyed brothers and sisters. With the true scientist's bent for experimentation, he crossed this white-eyed male fly with a red-eyed female. However, he found nothing peculiar in the expected ratios obtained from the cross until he discovered in the F_2 generation that all the white-eyed flies

Fig. 120. Thomas Hunt Morgan (1866–1945). *Photograph furnished by William Huse, California Institute of Technology.*

were males! Normally there should have been approximately as many white-eyed females as white-eyed males.

It was plain that here was a problem in which sex is involved. As previously pointed out, other investigators had advanced the suggestion that sex was determined by the peculiar pair of sex chromosomes which had been seen in the cell. After considering all these lines of evidence, the hypothesis was advanced that this peculiar hereditary problem could be explained by assuming that the genes for eye color were in the sex chromosomes, in fact, only in the X-chromosomes. The Y-chromosome was assumed to carry no factors.

However, the method of science demands that assumptions or hypotheses must be subjected to much experimentation and proved by more evidence than can be gathered from just one experiment. Accordingly, Morgan continued his search for more evidence. He crossed a white-eyed male with heterozygous females of the F_2 generation, and from this cross white-eyed female flies appeared.

Now he was in a position to make the final, crucial experiment—crossing the white-eyed females with red-eyed males. If his assumptions were correct, there should be both white-eyed and red-eyed flies in the F_1 generation, and there should be both male and female white-eyed flies in the F_2 generation. There were.

Here we see the method of science, which gathers evidence from all sources, makes assumptions or hypotheses, but, and more important, seeks to substantiate or prove these hypotheses by further experimental objective evidence or data.

Suppose that we analyze Morgan's experiment. Let us assume, as Morgan did, that the genes for red eyes and white eyes are located in the X or sex chromosomes. Red is dominant. Suppose a red-eyed female is crossed with a white-eyed male. The F_1 generation will all be red-eyed, and one half of the flies will be males and the other half females (Fig. 121). If the males and females of the F_1 generation are mated, the F_2 generation will show the expected Mendelian ratio of 3 red-eyed flies to 1 white-eyed fly. However, all the white-eyed flies will be males (Fig. 121).

If a homozygous, white-eyed female is mated with a homozygous, red-eyed male, instead of a typical Mendelian F_1 generation in which all the flies have red eyes, we find that half the flies have red eyes and half have white eyes. Further, this ratio is divided along sex lines, for the red-eyed flies are females, and the white-eyed flies are males. Apparently the white-eyed male is the result of receiving from the mother an X-chromosome having a gene for white, and, since the Y-chromosome apparently has no gene for eye color, the males have white eyes. The female flies receive the gene for red eyes in an X-chromosome from the father, which is dominant over the recessive gene for white eyes found in the other X-chromosomes received from the mother. When these F_1 flies are inbred, instead of the $3:1$ ratio expected in the F_2 generation, half the flies have red eyes and half have white eyes. Further analyses by breeding of the F_2 generation show that only one-fourth instead of one-half of the flies are heterozygous for eye color. This change in inheritance can be explained on the

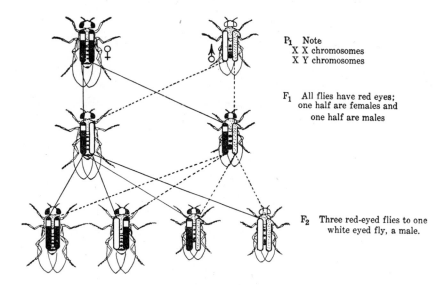

P₁ Note
  X X chromosomes
  X Y chromosomes

F₁ All flies have red eyes;
  one half are females and
  one half are males

F₂ Three red-eyed flies to one
  white eyed fly, a male.

A. Results of crossing a red - eyed female fly (*Drosophila*) with a white - eyed male.

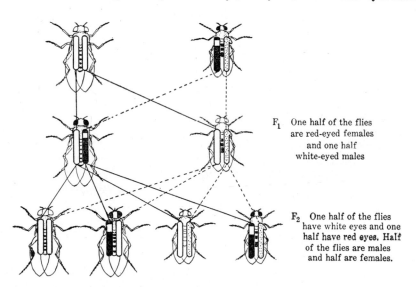

F₁ One half of the flies
  are red-eyed females
  and one half
  white-eyed males

F₂ One half of the flies
  have white eyes and one
  half have red eyes. Half
  of the flies are males
  and half are females.

B. Results of crossing a white - eyed female fly (*Drosophila*) with a red - eyed male.

Fig. 121. Diagram showing sex linkage in *Drosophila*. Note that eye color follows the sex chromosomes and therefore is sex-linked. *Adapted from various sources.*

basis of **sex linkage** and a study of the distribution of the sex chromosomes (Fig. 121).

Certain genes, if located in the sex chromosome, will bring out
characteristics necessarily associated with sex, and they are known as
sex-linked characters. Such characters are not confined to modifications of sexual structure, such as the type of gonad, but may include
eye color, color blindness in man, and others, depending on the animal.
Other factors often associated with sex such as the difference in plum-

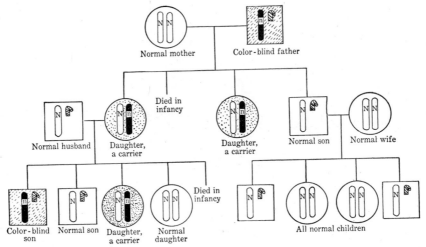

FIG. 122. Diagram illustrating the inheritance of color blindness, a sex-linked
character. A carrier is a heterozygous individual whose normal gene is dominant
over the defective gene.

age between male and female chickens, the usual absence of a beard
in woman, as well as certain differences in nervous temperament, are
known as **sex-limited** characters. Sex-limited characters depend for
their expression on the presence or absence of the sex hormones. These
phenomena have been discussed previously in connection with hormones (page 132).

Color blindness, or the inability to distinguish different colors, is an
example of sex-linked inheritance in man. Since the defective gene
is in an X-chromosome, the females, if they are color blind, must be
homozygous for the defective gene—the one affecting color vision.
Thus there are usually many more color-blind males than females.
A mother apparently may have normal color vision, but if one of her
X-chromosomes has a defective gene she may be heterozygous in this
respect. She will produce some gametes having an X-chromosome
with the gene for normal color vision, and some having an X-chromo-

some with a gene for color blindness. If the father is normal, he will produce normal X-gametes and Y-gametes, but any son receiving the defective X-chromosome from the mother and the Y-chromosome from the father will be color blind (Fig. 122). On the other hand, if a color-blind male is mated to a homozygous normal-visioned female, all the offspring will have normal vision, but the daughters will carry the defective genes.

Simple linkage and crossing over. The phenomenon of sex linkage just discussed not only is interesting in itself but also definitely in-

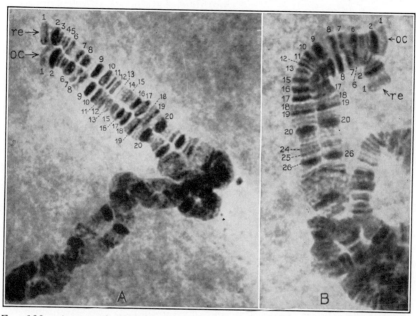

Fig. 123. A pair of chromosomes from the salivary glands of a hybrid insect. Note the apparently similar bands in the paired chromosomes which have been appropriately numbered. *Photograph furnished by C. W. Metz.*

dicates that the genes follow the chromosomes. As has been pointed out, the genes are not like many ultramicroscopic marbles confined in the nucleus of the cell by the nuclear wall but are apparently located on the chromosomes. Moreover, in the light of modern investigation, they seem to be arranged in a linear order along the length of the chromosome, resembling submicroscopic beads strung on a loose string (Fig. 123). If they are on the chromosomes, do they segregate independently at random, or do they always follow the chromosome? Apparently there is some independent segregation, but not quite so free as Mendel stated. It is believed that the segregation of the genes takes place after synapsis when the homologous chromosomes are separating from each other. It may be recalled that each chromosome is made up of two chromatids. Two chromatids, one from each chromosome of the pair, may form what is known as a **chiasma** (from the Greek letter χ). When the chromosomes separate, the chromatids may break at the region of contact. In this way parts of each chromatid, and therefore of each chromosome, may be interchanged, and thus, in a sense, "new" chromosomes are eventually formed (Fig. 124). This exchange of parts of the chromatids of homologous chromosomes with their contained genes is known as **crossing over.** The genes that formerly occupied definite loci in the original chromosomes now occupy corresponding loci in the new chromosomes.

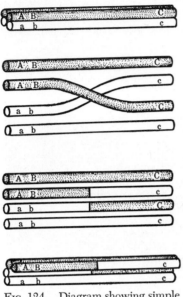

FIG. 124. Diagram showing simple linkage and crossing over between two chromatids. In pairing (synapsis), two chromatids of homologous chromosomes may be twisted together. When they separate (meiosis), the segments containing A and B, since they are close together in the chromatid, do not separate and so do not exchange places with a and b. Note that the segments containing C and c have interchanged.

Now, if the genes are arranged in linear order as the chromosome map of *Drosophila* seems to indicate, genes located farther apart in the chromosomes are more likely to move to the homologous chromosomes when they separate than are those which are closer together. The frequency of these genic exchanges may be used as a measure of the actual distance between genes. Characters then may be associated in inheritance in what is called **linkage,** the degree of linkage depending on the distance of the respective genes from each other.

Since the genes are carried on the chromosomes, there will be as many linkage groups as there are chromosomes. The foregoing discussion is of interest principally because it affords an explanation of the mechanism of genic segregation. The frequency of crossing over reveals the relative location of the genes, as may be shown in chromosome maps. It explains some of the divergences in expected Mendelian ratios.

We have already seen that sex linkage and simple linkage will change the original Mendelian concept of absolute freedom of the genes in segregation and, therefore, the ratios usually expected on the basis of the former Mendelian interpretation. Accumulated data from various experiments indicate that other conditions exist to modify and extend Mendel's original concept.

Other complications of Mendelism. We have seen that sex linkage, nondominance, crossing over, and simple linkage may change the ratios expected in both the F_1 and F_2 generations. In addition to these variations in Mendelian

Fig. 125. Inheritance in a mulatto family. *Photograph furnished by C. B. Davenport.*

heredity, other complications have been discovered which modify the usual expected results. Some of these conditions or examples will be briefly described.

Cumulative Genes. Briefly and simply the case of cumulative genes is this. Certain characteristics vary in the intensity of expression in accordance with the number of dominant genes present for that character. Nilsson-Ehle of Sweden found that two varieties of wheat, one of which had white grains and the other reddish brown, differed by three independent pairs of genes. When the two varieties were crossed, the F_2 generation produced wheat which exhibited six different shades of color ranging from white to red, the intensity of color depending on the number of dominant color genes present. Some such hereditary arrangement as this may account for color gradations as a result of crossing negroes and whites (Fig. 125).

Lethal Genes. Breeding experiments show that there are certain genes that begin to function early in the life of the animal or plant. It sometimes happens that some of these genes, which we may designate as n, are defective or lack something necessary for the development of certain structures. Such genes are called **lethals** (*letum*—death). If a normal gene designated as N is present in one chromosome of the pair, the combination will be Nn, and a normal plant or animal will develop. If, however, the organism is homozygous for lethals, or *nn*, it will fail to develop. Naturally the absence of certain phenotypic classes of plants or animals in either the F_1 or F_2 will result in a different ratio from the one expected. Lethal genes have been found in certain lines of plants and animals such as snapdragons, primroses, *Drosophila*, mice, guinea pigs, and man.

Various other modifications of Mendelian heredity have been found through modern experimentation, in the light of which we must change our views of the simplicity of the process. The three great principles established by Mendel which apparently still hold today are the principle of distinct units (genes), the principle of segregation, and the independent assortment of the genes.

Genes

It has been said that genes are known more by what they do than by what they are. However, today as a result of many brilliant investigations it is pretty well established that a gene is a single complex molecule of nucleoprotein—a molecule which can reproduce itself. Incidentally, it is believed that both viruses and genes are nucleoproteins. Since in the opinion of many biologists, self-reproduction is a characteristic which distinguishes living from non-living matter, genes "represent life at the most fundamental level; they are the basic units of life." Moreover, these chemical substances are relatively stable, for they can be handed down from generation to generation in a practically unchanged condition.

There is good evidence that genes influence development through control of the biochemical processes in the body. A clear connection between the genes and some of these physicochemical processes has been demonstrated by Beadle and his associates in experiments carried out on the bread mold *Neurospora*. By means of X-rays and other agents, Beadle produced varieties of *Neurospora* that could not utilize the food substances on which the untreated mold normally thrived. However, if some specific vitamin or other substance was added, the X-rayed mold was able to grow. Evidently the action of the X-rays caused a mutation by which the mold lost its power to produce this necessary vitamin since it was no longer able to manufacture the specific enzyme responsible for the production of the vitamin and other nutrients in its cells. These experiments with *Neurospora* seem to have demonstrated the genic control of the biochemical processes in numerous instances.

How do genes produce enzymes? Some have suggested that genes synthesize enzymes as by-products during the process of self-reproduction; others, that enzymes are actually genes freed from the chromosomes. Another suggestion is that the genes serve as master pat-

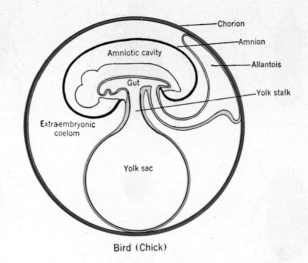

Bird (Chick)

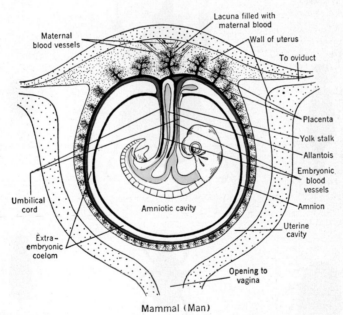

Mammal (Man)

PLATE XI. Embryonic membranes of bird (chick) and mammal (man).

Long - horned Beetle
(*Desmocerus*)

Caterpillar
Hunter
(*Calosoma*)

Scarab Beetle
(*Phanaeus*)

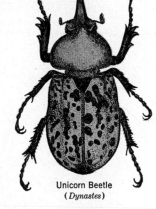

Lady - bird Beetle
(*Coccinella*)

June - bug
(*Pelidnota*)

Tiger Beetle
(*Cicindela*)

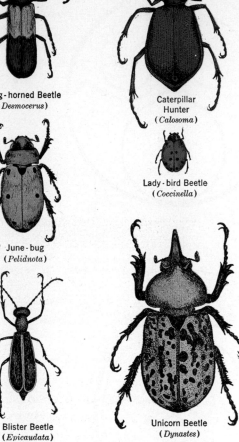

Blister Beetle
(*Epicaudata*)

Unicorn Beetle
(*Dynastes*)

Mexican
Bean Beetle
(*Epilachna*)

Colorado
Potato Beetle
(*Leptinotarsa*)

Japanese Beetle
(*Popillia*)

Milkweed Beetle
(*Tetraopes*)

PLATE XII. Coleoptera.

terns, "templates," for transforming other molecules into enzymes. According to Beadle there are several thousand genes distributed among the forty-eight chromosomes found in the human body cell— a sufficient number to provide patterns for thousands of big molecules.

Mutations and chromosomal aberrations.   In a plant or animal, genes may sometimes undergo a change, thus giving rise to new characters, which will breed true through successive generations.   Such changes are known as **mutations** (*mutare*—to change) or **sports.**

Fig. 126.   Mutation in sheep.   Sheep with normal legs at the right and short-legged Ancon sheep (mutant) at the left.   *Photograph furnished by Dr. W. Landauer, University of Conn.*

The white-eyed fly was a mutation.   About 1800 a New England farmer found a male lamb with short bowed legs in his flock of long-legged sheep, from which he developed a race of short-legged sheep, which, as Walter suggests, proved a real labor-saving device since the sheepraiser now built lower fences than formerly (Fig. 126).   Some other new varieties of animals resulting from mutations are hornless Hereford cattle, which arose from a mutant in a herd of Herefords at Atchison, Kansas, in 1891; tailless dogs and cats; and chickens with bare necks.

In addition to the changes that may be brought about in an animal by mutation, other new characteristics may appear as the result of changes in the chromosomes, known as **chromosomal aberrations.** Sometimes these changes also are called mutations.   Chromosomal aberrations usually involve a shift of parts of the chromosomes.   Thus a portion of a chromosome may break off and be lost (**deficiency**); or it may attach itself to another chromosome (**translocation**); or it may even reverse its position within the chromosome (**inversion**). Such changes may take place in nature or may be the result of the action of X-rays or other agents which bring about genic change. When it is understood that, in addition to the changes just described, mutations may occur in the genes in these added chromosomes and chromosome pieces, some idea can be gained of the complexity of the mechanism of variability in nature.

The discovery of the giant chromosomes of the salivary glands of some insects has made possible the detection of many of the changes just listed. By means of the bands of varying width which run across the chromosomes, geneticists have been able to identify specific regions in certain chromosomes (Fig. 123). Thus, by using these bands as landmarks, they can readily detect such changes as translocations, deficiencies, and inversions.

At the present time there is no conclusive evidence as to the cause of genic and chromosomal changes in nature. Experiments apparently have shown that genic changes may be induced by X-rays. Something like this may take place in nature from natural radiations. Other evidence indicates that extremes of temperature may bring about mutations, but the problem is far from solved.

How the gene works is an interesting question and one that can be answered only hypothetically at present. However, it seems very certain that the influence of a particular gene is not necessarily restricted to a definite part of the body but may affect the entire organism. On the other hand, not every character is the result of the action of a single gene, as we may have thought, but probably most characters are the result of the interaction of many genes. For example, Jennings points out that in *Drosophila* at least "fifty pairs of genes cooperate to produce the usual red color of the eye." Some genes may lay the foundation for the eye itself, after which others lay a basis for color, to which others add the proper materials for pigment. Any defect or change in one of these fifty genes will mean a change in the expected or "normal" structure of the eye. The pattern of an organism, then, is not the result of an accumulation of thousands of separate discrete particles into a "genetic mosaic or a piece of animated tiling," as East put it, but comes about rather as the result of the interaction of groups or "packets" of these chemical particles which we call genes. As a consequence, heredity is not such a simple phenomenon as a monohybrid cross might lead us to believe, but an unfolding process in which "a gene has manifold duties and numerous genes contribute their quotas toward the fulfillment of a seemingly simple task." Further, what any gene or group of genes may produce depends not only on their own constitution but also on the environmental conditions.

GENIC ACTION AND ENVIRONMENT

We have just pointed out that there are many influences which affect various genic combinations and, therefore, the heredity of animals. It would seem, however, that even in spite of the diverse behavior and arrangement of genes, they are responsible for what the young organism *may* become. But, on the other hand, what influences, if any, do the surrounding external conditions or environment have on the development of the individual plant or animal? With respect to this question there have grown up two schools of thought. One group holds that heredity is everything and environment is comparatively negligible, and that whatever the organism is to be and will be has been predetermined by its genes. Another group maintains that environment is everything and heredity is of little importance. As usual, the truth lies somewhere between the extremes. Dobzhansky, a prominent geneticist, states that "the outcome of development at any stage is a function of both the heredity of the developing individual and the environment in which the process takes place."

Acquired characters. We have been discussing heritable characters which, theoretically, owe their origin to genes located in the germplasm. How these characters express themselves, in many cases, depends on the surrounding environment. We have pointed out that heritable changes in characteristics, i.e., mutations, chromosomal reconstruction, and chromosomal duplications, may be brought about by changes in the gene or genes caused by certain environmental factors such as X-rays, or they may be variations arising from unknown causes within the organism. For the man of the street, one of the vexing questions of heredity today is: can variations or changes in structure which affect the somatoplasm, such as loss of limbs, body scars, blindness, and other acquired characters, be handed on to the succeeding generations? Can special training in various arts, in religion, in social attitudes, be made a part of the heritage of the next generation? "Can nurture as well as nature be transmitted?" The answer to this question is of real importance to plant and animal breeders and to physicians, sociologists, religious workers, and educators who are interested in man's physical and spiritual growth.

From the earliest time until about 1875, it was generally believed that acquired characters could be inherited. Lamarck (1744–1829) used this idea to explain evolution, and Darwin also incorporated it in his explanation of evolution. However, some doubt gradually arose as to the validity of the belief, and finally Weismann, about 1875, presented convincing arguments against the inheritance of acquired characters. It has been commonly observed that one-armed and one-legged individuals can become the parents of normal children; that the beautifully scarred and tattooed barbarians beget unmarred off-spring; that dehorned cattle produce calves which later develop horns. Weismann, a brilliant student of heredity and embryology, attempted to solve this problem by a carefully planned controlled experiment.

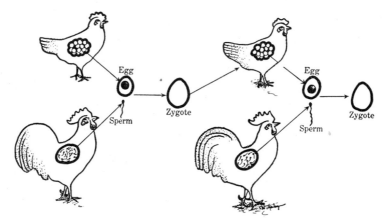

Fig. 127.   Diagram illustrating continuity of the germplasm.   Somatoplasm indicated by light outline and germplasm by heavy outline.

He cut off the tails of mice for twenty-two generations and found that the tails of the mice in the last generation were as long as those of the first. Based partly on the results of these experiments, Weismann formulated what is known as **germplasm theory of heredity,** which is sometimes called the **theory of the continuity of the germplasm.** According to Weismann, the organism is made up of two kinds of living substance or plasm, **somatoplasm** and **germplasm.** All the cells making up the body structures, such as brain, eye, stomach, liver, muscles, bone, and connective tissues, are somatic cells. The supporting tissue of the sex organs themselves is somatic. The primordial germ cells and the gametes developed in the gonads constitute the **germplasm.**

The somatoplasm which makes up the bulk of the individual lives its life cycle and dies. It is mortal. On the other hand, the germplasm is able to produce more germplasm in the form of gametes. These fuse, and the zygote thus produced may form a new individual containing germplasm from which will be formed new somatoplasm.

The somatoplasm is merely the temporary home for the potentially immortal germplasm, which, like a continuous stream, flows eternally on, receiving tributary streams of germplasm from generation to generation. (See Fig. 127.) Theoretically, germplasm not only is potentially immortal but also, as will be pointed out later, is free from any influence or contamination by the somatoplasm. Each germ cell is an independent unit in the body. According to Castle, "germ cells are guests in the body, not members of the household."

The Lysenko controversy. In recent years the Russian geneticist Lysenko, and his fellow Russian biologists have rejected the conclusion drawn from the countless experiments performed by numerous geneticists all over the world that acquired characteristics cannot be inherited. The Lysenkoists maintain that heredity cannot be based on substance such as the genes and the germplasm. They assert that relatively mild environmental influences not affecting the chromosomes can produce hereditary changes in plants and animals. Some of the evidence for these conclusions is derived from experiments in which, according to their interpretation, they claim to have transformed winter wheat, which ordinarily must be planted in the fall to mature the next year, to spring wheat, which, when planted in the spring of the year, will mature in the same year. However, when these experiments are repeated by geneticists outside Russia these results cannot be obtained. Examination of the Russian procedures reveals no control plants and no care to sow in any given plot the grains of only one kind of wheat, or to sow only grains genetically pure, i.e., homozygous for the character in question. Sonneborn very aptly points out, "In Lysenko's first claim for success, a single seed from the entire plot (of winter wheat) gave rise to all the later generations of spring wheat!"

As further proof of his theory, Lysenko reports that a shoot from a young tomato plant bearing, say yellow, fruit, can be grafted onto an older tomato plant bearing fruit of a different color. The graft grows and subsequently bears fruit, and the seeds from this graft combination when planted, give rise to plants having the mixed characteristics of both components of the graft. According to Lysenko, "All parts of the plants and all parts of each cell—even the sap—are believed to be the materials of heredity which form an intimately interacting genetic system." In other words, the Soviet geneticist maintains that the sap carries the physiological potentialities for the heredity of the plant.

There are valid reasons for questioning the conclusions of the Lysenko school. The experiments lacked adequate controls, and the data were not subjected to statistical analysis. Furthermore, geneticists in

England, Germany, Canada, and the United States when repeating these experiments have been unable to obtain the same results. Finally, the results obtained can be explained by the chromosome theory of heredity.

From what has been said it is clear that certain principles of the scientific method have been violated by the Russian geneticists. However, the most serious aspect of this situation is the interference of the Soviet government in the scientist's search for truth. The Soviet government has placed its stamp of approval on Lysenko's theories and has dismissed opponents of the theory from its various scientific institutions. It has tried to establish what is true and what is false by decree, whereas truths can be established only by logical procedure, by carefully planned and equally carefully executed scientific investigation carried out by scholars who are free to record and interpret the data objectively, without bias or the influence of authority of any kind. It has been well said that "facts do not fall this way or that because of political decrees." Unfortunately, government interference in scientific research in Soviet Russia has spread from genetics to the fields of physiology and medicine as well. Huxley sums up the situation in these words, "Do we want science to continue as the free pursuit of knowledge of and control over nature, or do we want it to become subordinate to political theory and the slave of national governments?" True science can flourish only in an atmosphere of freedom.

Response to environmental changes. The following selected examples show that animals can be changed and modified by environment. In *Drosophila* extra legs or branched legs are found in a mutant variety of fly if the flies develop in low temperatures. Goldschmidt, by artificially controlling the temperature, has been able to produce a whole series of different patterns of the butterfly *Vanessa io*. Other investigators have been able to change the color and pattern of moths by feeding some of the young on oak leaves and others on walnut leaves. If certain green parrots of South America are fed on the fat of catfish, their plumage becomes a variegated mixture of red and yellow. The axolotl is a salamander, one of the Amphibia, and for a long time it was considered a distinct species. It has prominent red external gills, a rather thick body, and a flattened tail adapted for swimming (Fig. 128). In this condition it may become sexually mature, rear its young, in fact live out its entire life span. Now if this axolotl is deprived of water, a tremendous change takes place. The gills disappear and the form of its body changes in practically every detail. Indeed, this animal is so different from the axolotl phase that for many years it had been considered an entirely unrelated animal called *Ambystoma*—an amphibian version of Dr. Jekyll and Mr. Hyde.

Stockard found that, if the developing eggs of the common sea minnow (*Fundulus*) were placed in solutions of various magnesium salts, as many as sixty out of a hundred of these minnows developed only one eye instead of the usual two. By other methods he has been able

FIG. 128. Effect of change from an aquatic habitat to a land habitat on *Ambystoma*, an amphibian. *Above*, the aquatic form. Note the gills and flattened paddlelike tail. *Below*, the land form. Note the disappearance of the gills and change in the general shape of the animal.

to produce three-eyed fish, double-headed fish, and various other strange forms (Fig. 112). Child has shown that, if the environment of planarians is changed by the addition of certain chemicals to the water in which they live, animals can be produced having three eyes, or two heads, or no eyes, or even no heads. Other general environmental effects might be described, such as the change in the color of the pelage of the Arctic hare from its white of winter to its brown of summer.

An example of sex differentiation induced by environment is found in the marine worm *Bonellia*. The female worm is much larger than the male and has a rounded body from which extends a relatively long proboscis divided at the end (Fig. 129). The male is a very small animal. Young embryos of *Bonellia* are neither male nor female. If in the course of their wanderings some of these small embryos happen to become attached to the proboscis of the female, they become males. Those not so attached usually develop into females.

Other instances of environmental effects have already been described, among which are the abnormal animals resulting from a disturbance of normal hormone action. One of the classic examples is reported by Crew. A Buff Orpington chicken started life as a hen, laid eggs, and was the mother of chicks. Later she began to develop the plumage, combs, and spurs of the male. She crowed and exhibited other male behavior. Later this chicken was mated with some virgin hens and became the father of two normal chicks. An autopsy following the death of this animal showed that the ovary of her hen days had been destroyed by a tumor caused by tuberculosis and that a testis-like organ had developed. Examples of these already mentioned are the freemartin; cretins resulting from abnormal functioning of the thyroid due to lack of iodine; giants and dwarfs caused by abnormal pituitaries. Such influences as vitamin deficiencies make themselves felt, as in rickets.

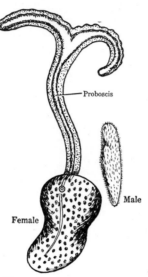

Fig. 129. A marine worm, *Bonellia*. *From Parker and Haswell, "Textbook of Zoology," Vol. I. By permission of the publisher, the Macmillan Co.*

From what has just been said, we may gather that, in many cases at least, certain characters of animals are the result of the influence of both the genes and the environment. However, it must be emphasized that the potentiality for every character must be present in the genes. The genes determine what an organism *may* become, i.e., represent its potentialities or possibilities, but what it *does* become depends also on its environment. Further discussion of the significance of these facts is reserved until we consider human heredity and eugenics.

IMPROVEMENT OF ANIMALS THROUGH BREEDING

The art and practice of plant and animal breeding are very old, dating back to the earliest times. As primitive peoples advanced in learning and civilization, man began to train animals to do his work.

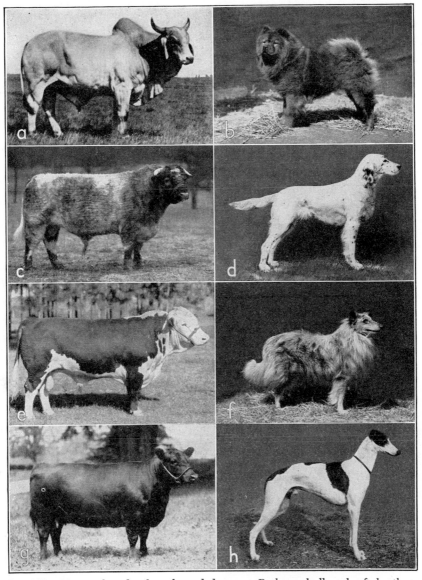

Fig. 130.   Various breeds of cattle and dogs.   *a*, Brahman bull; *c*, beef shorthorn bull; *e*, polled Hereford bull; *g*, Aberdeen Angus cow; *b*, chow; *d*, English setter; *f*, collie; *h*, greyhound.   *Photographs furnished by the Bureau of Animal Industry, U. S. Department of Agriculture.*

His growing communities demanded more and better beef and pork, which in turn required more and more fodder, grain, and grasses in all seasons. Communication and warfare demanded beasts of burden and swift couriers. So man began to tame the wild animals, cultivate the grasses and herbs, and in his own primitive way—yet the best he knew—tried to improve what he had. He selected the best of his stock and made crosses. New varieties gradually emerged, but at tremendous cost in time and labor, since, up to 1900, the method used for the most part was a combination of hit or miss, or "trial and error." Today the professional breeder studies his carefully recorded pedigrees and, in the light of his knowledge of genic behavior, works out his matings before he makes them.

Our modern dogs are believed to have descended from wolves. By the occurrence and preservation of mutations, cross-breeding, and careful selection, man has developed the different varieties of today. The different types of hogs have been derived from the wild boar, which in the wild state is a savage beast with tough meat and little lard. Domestication and breeding have resulted in the production of "well-bred" hogs weighing as much as a thousand pounds. The wild type "razor-back" of the southern mountains is the domestic variety gone "wild." Goodale, by careful breeding experiments with Rhode Island Red chickens, was able to develop a strain in which the young hens began to lay 55 days earlier than the parents, and in this way he increased winter egg production from 36 to 67 eggs per hen. These and other scientifically controlled breeding experiments have resulted in different types of horses, cattle, pigeons, as well as many other varieties of animals (Fig. 130).

16

Human Heredity and Eugenics

We have seen how in various animals some physical and physiological characters are transmitted from parents to offspring. We have pointed out that certain mental characteristics and behavior reactions seem to be associated with the anatomical sexual characteristics of an animal, which are the result of the reactions of certain genes. This would indicate that mental as well as physical traits are inherited. It must be said here, however, that man in the past and even in the present has paid more attention to the breeding of wheat, pigs, and chickens than he has to the breeding of his own kind. As Carruth puts it, "The only extensive positive impulses to breeding given under civilization have been the breeding of negroes and hybrids for slaves, and the breeding of women for concubines in the Oriental countries, and the subsidizing and breeding of men for cannon fodder in various great imperial countries."

The earlier conceptions of human heredity rested on several lines of fallacious reasoning. For example, it was believed that the blood of our ancestors flowed in our veins. In other words, "blood will tell." Now blood is but one type of somatoplasm, which Weismann showed was not inherited. Accordingly, each individual is "blue-blooded" in his own right, since he made his own blood.

In the next place, in tracing family trees the attention and appraisal given men have not been accorded to women. This may be because woman's place in society is not quite so conspicuous. But from the standpoint of heredity we know that women contribute as many chromosomes to the next generation as men. Further, in reviewing our ancestry it is only human to stress the best and to forget the undesirable.

Now, as we are to make a scientific study of heredity, we must approach the problem with open minds. In the next place, we must consider all the data, that is, all we can find, bearing upon the problem. The true scientist cannot seize upon and exploit only that evi-

257

dence which supports his own preconceived notions and ignore evidence which seems to point in another direction. The scientist must be on guard not to stress extremes, whether good or bad, and thus to ignore the average. Moreover, all factors which might have bearing on the problem must be considered. Last but not least, accurate measuring devices which are objective should be used whenever possible.

A number of studies have been made of human genetics and its relation to man's biological and social problems. This science, now known as **eugenics** (*eu*—well; *genos*—birth), received much attention from the Greeks; after a lapse of interest through the centuries it was reestablished by Sir Francis Galton, who said that eugenics was the "study of all the agencies under social control which may improve or impair the inborn qualities of future generations of man, either physically or mentally." In other words, it was "the science of being well born."

It is extremely difficult, if not impossible, to carry out actual controlled experimental studies of human heredity. Man is a highly unsatisfactory laboratory animal because of both his high intelligence and his violent likes and dislikes, which prevent his being controlled by the experimenter. For the most part random matings of men and women have supplied the accumulated data upon which are based the conclusions regarding the inheritance of various human traits. Further, there is such a long time between generations and usually so few offspring that it is almost impossible to follow through controlled matings and secure adequate data. In *Drosophila* various lines have been studied through hundreds of generations, for a new generation can appear in a 10- or 12-day period. Weismann, in a comparatively short time, was able to study 22 generations of mice.

The available data of human heredity have come from studies of scattered family histories, from records of public institutions, and from the studies by privately endowed agencies such as the Carnegie Institution of Washington and its Eugenics Record Office at Cold Spring Harbor, Long Island, New York. Careful study of various human genealogies indicates that many traits are inherited according to the same principles as the traits and characters found in other animals. These characteristics may be grouped under physical or visible traits; physiological or functional traits; and mental traits. We shall consider some of these traits and, finally, their relation to the social adjustment of the individual.

SOME PHYSICAL OR VISIBLE HERITABLE TRAITS

Stature is a trait which seems to be determined by the number of genes for tallness or shortness present in the individual.   In crosses between tall and short individuals, shortness seems to be dominant.

Abnormalities of fingers and toes are apparently heritable.   Some of these are **polydactyly** (*poly*—many; *daktylos*—finger), where more

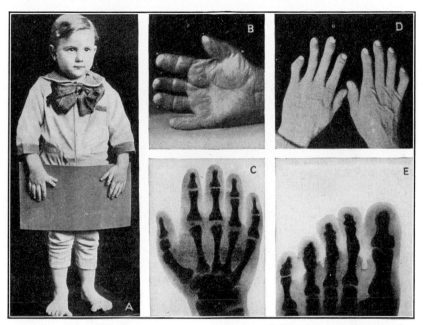

Fig. 131.   Heritable abnormalities in man.   *A*, polydactyly; *B*, brachydactylous hand; *C*, X-ray of brachydactylous hand shows a joint missing in each finger; *D*, symphalangy; *E*, zygodactyly.   *Photographs furnished by Nathan Fasten.   A, D, and E, by permission of the* Journal of Heredity; *B and C, by permission of the* Journal of Genetics.

than five fingers or five toes are present; **brachydactyly** (*brachys*— short), where the fingers and toes are very much shortened owing to the absence of one of the bones in the finger or toe; **syndactyly** (*syn*— with), a condition of webbed fingers or toes, or a condition in which the thumb and little finger, or the great toe and little toe, are over-developed and the other digits are underdeveloped (Fig. 131).   This is commonly known as "lobster-claw."

Eye color has been much studied with reference to its inheritance. There are but one or two basic pigments in the iris of the eye.   Eye color is determined by the amount and distribution of these color granules in the iris. If these pigments are missing the eye appears red or pink, since the blood flowing through the blood vessels is no longer masked by the pigment but becomes visible. In individuals with this defect the hair is white, owing to the lack of pigment. Man and other animals in which these conditions are found are known as **albinos** (*alba*—white) (Fig. 132).

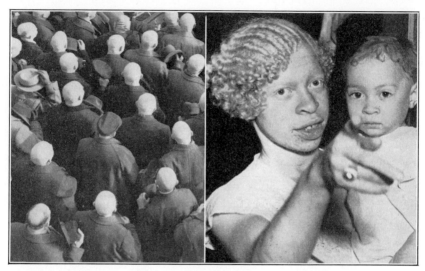

FIG. 132. Baldness and albinism, heritable traits of man. *Photographs furnished by the Acme News Pictures, Inc.*

Texture and color of the skin are hereditary traits. Sometimes the skin becomes dry, thick, and scaly in appearance. This condition, known as **ichthyosis** (*ichthys*—fish), seems to be dominant over normal skin. "Rubber skin," or **cutis laxa,** is a skin defect in which the skin becomes loose and may be pulled out from the body for a distance. Attention has already been called to the fact that in crosses between negroes and whites the skin colors appear to be due to cumulative factors. There are more than one hundred abnormal skin conditions that are known to be inherited.

Hair characteristics have been a favorite study not only in man but also in guinea pigs and mice. Studies of hair are concerned with whether it is straight or curly, its color or lack of color, and baldness. Hairs that are round in cross section are usually straight, and wavy hairs are somewhat flattened. Some consider the wavy character to be dominant over straight; others contend that hair type is due to the interaction of a number of genes. **Baldness,** of which there are various degrees and patterns, seems usually to be inherited, but it may be caused also by disease. The reason this character is more prevalent in men than in women is that it is dominant in males and recessive in females. It is a sex-limited character. The **color of the hair** is the result of the combinations of two primary pigments, brown and red. Brown pigment is usually dominant over light or yellow. Light blond hair is caused mainly by recessive genes. The various shades of hair may be the result of cumulative factors or of incomplete dominance. We have already called attention to the influence of the lack of pigment in albinos. Premature grayness may be inherited, or it may be attributed to other causes.

Certain characters of the mouth, ears, and nose are apparently hereditary. Some families are afflicted by the loss of certain teeth or even all of them. Cleft palate and hare lip, the result of the failure of certain embryonic jaw processes to fuse, are hereditary. In some families the tongue is held down by the membrane underneath. Odd as it may seem, this abnormality apparently occurs only in the males.

HEREDITARY PHYSIOLOGICAL OR FUNCTIONAL DEFECTS

Not only are many human structural characters apparently hereditary, but some functional defects are passed along as well. Among the defects of the eyes is **cataract,** which is responsible for more than one-eighth of all the cases of blindness. This defect, which centers in the lens of the eye, causing it to become opaque, has various forms. Sometimes it appears to be induced by other causes, such as diabetes, malnutrition, and poisons. We have previously called attention to the hereditary transmission of **color blindness,** which seems to be a sex-linked character. Other eye defects which appear to be hereditary are a certain type of **night blindness** or inability to see in weak light; **myopia** or short-sightedness, which behaves as a recessive; **hyperopia** or far-sightedness, which seems to be inherited as a dominant. Keenness of vision seems to be inherited also.

About 30 per cent of all cases of deafness seem to be hereditary. Deafness associated with mutism is determined by homozygous recessive genes. Middle-ear deafness (**otosclerosis**) appears at about thirty years of age and becomes worse. This type of deafness is accompanied by "noises in the head." Still another type of deafness which seems to be hereditary is inner ear (labyrinthine) deafness, in which the auditory nerve degenerates.

In the blood and blood vessels one of the best-known hereditary weaknesses is **hemophilia,** or the tendency of the blood to clot too slowly. Naturally any severe wound is likely to result in death. This defect is sex-linked and is lethal in the homozygous condition.

Previously, attention has been called to the four different blood groups, A, B, AB, and O, which may be present in various individuals. Their antigen-antibody reaction has also been described. Investigation has shown that these groups are hereditary. It has been found that in addition to the A, B, and O agglutinogens about 87 per cent of the population possess an **Rh factor** in their red cells. In other words they are Rh positive. If the Rh factor is lacking they are Rh negative. The term Rh is derived from "rhesus," the name of a type of monkey whose blood plasma was an important factor in making this discovery. The Rh factor exists in eight different alleles. No harm will be done in the transfusion of Rh-positive blood into Rh-positive blood. However, continued transfusions of Rh-positive blood into Rh-negative recipients brings about the formation in their plasma of anti-Rh substances. These cause agglutination with resultant serious consequences, and often death.

Sometimes an Rh-positive man may father a child to an Rh-negative woman. The developing fetus inherits an Rh-positive factor from the father, and this Rh-positive blood of the fetus brings about the formation of anti-Rh bodies in the blood of the mother. These antibodies apparently cross the membranes into the fetal blood stream. Here they bring about agglutination and destruction of the red blood cells resulting in anemia, which may prove fatal to the fetus. The mother is unharmed. If such a child survives it may be feebleminded.

Heredity and disease. In the mind of the average person the belief persists that various diseases can be inherited. Indeed, to the casual observer, this often seems to be true. However, careful study has shown that diseases in themselves, with the possible exception of **cancer,** are not inherited, but that certain structural and physiological defects or tendencies are handed down which make the individual peculiarly liable to contract the disease. The almost universal belief among authorities is that, in **tuberculosis,** genes are transmitted for weak lungs, bones, joints with non-resistant protoplasm, making an individual more susceptible to tuberculosis bacilli. The question of the inheritance of cancer is still unsettled. Some individuals and families seem to show a higher percentage of cases than others. Moreover, identical twins often have the same type of cancer in the same organ. Various members of a family may be affected by the same type of growth even in the same organ. However, there is as yet no conclusive evidence of human inheritance of cancer.

Many people are afflicted with maladies such as hay fever, asthmas, and eczema. These are known to the medical profession as **allergic diseases,** which in the opinion of many are hereditary. Here again the disease itself is not inherited but, rather, a sensitiveness to specific substances. For example, the pollen from a certain species of ragweed will send some sensitive individual into a sneezing fit from which he emerges with inflamed eyes, running nose, and a feeling of genuine discomfort. Other substances, more than 200 of them, ranging from pollen of flowers to feathers and horsehair, may cause similar symptoms. The presence of the gene responsible for the sensitiveness can be detected only when the irritating agent is present in the environment.

Thus far in our discussion of human heredity, attention has been centered on the inheritance of undesirable traits. Either justly or unjustly, man overlooks the normal or average and is interested in the bizarre and unusual. However, these traits are more easily studied than the usual and commonplace and, attracting attention more readily, have been observed and reported in greater numbers and with more accuracy.

HEREDITY AND MENTALITY

We have already studied briefly the inheritance of certain physical or visible traits peculiar to such anatomical structures as the appendages, the eye, and the skin. Other hereditary physiological or functional traits have been briefly surveyed. These studies have involved traits that are clear cut and quite apparent when exhibited by the individual. Accordingly it has been possible to reach rather plausible definite conclusions concerning the type of inheritance involved and the possible environmental effects. However, certain mental and moral traits which make up man's individual personality are not so evident and present real difficulties of analysis. These traits are not clear cut and tend to blend into each other. Perhaps the most important area for exploration is intelligence. A second personality area is that of criminal tendencies, but whether these are inherited is a question about which there is much controversy.

Mental disorders. Insanity is a definite disease or defect of the nervous system and not a condition of general retarded nervous development. Insanity may appear as a direct result of accident, alcoholism, disease, or some radical environmental change resulting in undue nervous strain. Some one or all of the conditions just mentioned may uncover some hidden hereditary mental sickness. There are no definite conclusions as yet as to the part heredity may play in many mental diseases, although some evidence exists for the inheritance of certain types. The most positive statement that can be made at present is that heredity may contribute a "predisposing tendency or weakness" in the nervous system. Only when a mental defect shows itself in the same way for a number of generations under the same or different conditions and in definite genic ratios can a trait be said positively to be inherited.

Schizophrenia, sometimes inexactly called **dementia praecox,** results in various types of behavior such as delusions of persecution or grandeur, apathy, carelessness, and lack of interest in the other sex. This mental disorder accounts for about 20 per cent of the patients in mental hospitals. **Manic-depressive** insanity so affects the individual that he is subject to maniacal phases in which he may commit criminal or violent acts, or to depressive phases during which he may commit suicide. These two types of mental disease appear to be the result of inherited weaknesses and are responsible for about 57 per cent of the inmates of our state mental hospitals. **Huntington's chorea** (*choreia* —dance) comes on about middle life and shows itself in defective speech and general tremors of the body, followed by dementia. This trait behaves as a Mendelian dominant. Traced back in heredity, it is supposed to have come from six persons who came from England to the United States in the seventeenth century. Another form of nervous disease which appears to be hereditary to some extent is **epilepsy,** although it may also be caused by some kind of injury. In a fit of epilepsy the individual loses consciousness, has spasms and convulsions, and often froths at the mouth. The chance of an epileptic parent having an epileptic child is about 1 in 10. Another common nervous disorder, **paresis,** or softening of the brain, is almost always caused by a venereal disease, syphilis. It is not hereditary. A type of imbecility called **phenylketonuria** is caused by a single recessive gene which apparently so interferes with a certain chemical action that phenylpyruvic acid accumulates in the blood and is eliminated in the urine. Under normal conditions phenylpyruvic acid is oxidized to CO_2 and H_2O. The exact relation between this chemical reaction and imbecility has not been established.

SOME HEREDITARY TRAITS IN MAN AND THEIR PROBABLE TYPE OF INHERITANCE

Dominant	Recessive
Skin, Hair, Nails	
Black skin (two genes, incomplete dominance)	"White" skin
Dark hair (several genes)	Light hair
Non-red hair	Red hair
Freckles	No freckles
Curly hair (hybrid, wavy)	Straight hair
Woolly hair (negroid type; several genes)	Straight hair
Normal	Hairless (hypotrichosis)
Early baldness (dominant in male)	Normal
Scaly skin (ichthyosis)	Normal
Thickened skin (tylosis)	Normal
Free ear lobes	Adherent ear lobes
Eyes	
Brown	Blue or gray
Hazel or green	Blue or gray
Normal eye	Nearsightedness (myopia)
Farsightedness (hyperopia) (short eyeball)	Normal
Glaucoma (excessive pressure in eyeball)	Normal
Skeleton and Muscles	
Short stature (several genes)	Tall stature
Dwarfism (achondroplasia)	Normal
Extra digits (polydactyly)	Normal
Split hand ("lobster-claw")	Normal
Hare lip and cleft palate (also a recessive?)	Normal
Rupture, susceptibility to	Normal
Circulatory and Respiratory Systems	
Nose bleed and blood cysts (telangiectasis)	Normal
High blood pressure (hypertension)	Normal
Allergy	Normal
Resistance to tuberculosis	Susceptibility to tuberculosis
Cancer	
Cancer of the stomach(?)	Normal
Nervous System	
Normal	Congenital deafness
Auditory nerve atrophy	Normal
Huntington's chorea	Normal
Normal	Amaurotic idiocy
Normal	(?)Schizophrenia
Manic-depressive psychoses(?)	Normal

Special talents (dominance uncertain):
  Musical ability.
  Ability in drawing, painting, sculpture.
  Mathematical ability.

INTELLIGENCE

What is intelligence? Stern states that "Intelligent behavior is regarded as behavior which, on the basis of an inborn capacity, makes *good* use of the social inheritance such as language and numbers, or scientific and moral concepts."

Measuring intelligence. I.Q. Attempts have been made to measure intelligence by various intelligence tests the results of which are expressed by an intelligence quotient, known as the I.Q. A score of 90 to 110 is average and denotes, theoretically, an individual who can make an average normal adjustment to life situations. A score of 140 is indicative of genius; 120, of a very superior intellect; scores from 70 to 0 are indicative of feeblemindedness. The validity of the I.Q. as an accurate measure of intelligence will be discussed later.

The following statement from Stern * presents a new point of view on intelligence testing.

In recent years, psychologists have made important progress in subdividing the mental abilities of man into distinct so-called primary abilities, such as ability to visualize objects in space, to memorize, or to reason inductively. It was found that two individuals with the same I.Q. may be very different regarding their endowment of primary abilities. In the future, studies on the nature-nurture problem, in respect to intelligence will have to be concerned rather with primary abilities than with over-all scores. Unfortunately, to date, the best objective data on intelligence are available only in terms of I.Q. scores.

Feeblemindedness. Feeblemindedness is not insanity but a condition of deficient or dwarfed mental development. For example, a man of forty may have the mind of a child of ten. There are three general classes of these feebleminded individuals: **idiots,** with the mind of a child of two and incapable of caring for themselves; **imbeciles,** with the mental age of a child of six; and **morons,** with the mental age of a normal child of twelve. According to a recent survey, approximately 15 per cent of the population of the United States has an intelligence level of about twelve years of age or under. In a sense, of all these classes, morons are the most dangerous to society for they attain physical and sexual maturity and may even appear normal. Quite often these people are self-supporting and are found in various manual occupations. It is from this group of individuals of low mental, moral, and spiritual stature that the majority of prostitutes, criminals, and paupers come.

* Curt Stern, *Principles of Human Genetics,* W. H. Freeman and Company, San Francisco, p. 492.

Studies seem to indicate that "Mongolian" idiocy is hereditary. Among other peculiar characteristics the "Mongoloid" child is of short stature and has Mongoloid facial features, especially around the eyes. Mongoloid children are born more often to mothers who are past the age of thirty-five. Apparently the process of aging on the part of the mother makes possible the expression of certain genes.

FIG. 133.   A group of imbeciles known as Mongols because of their fancied resemblance to members of the Mongolian race. *Photograph furnished by Kate Brousseau, Institute of Family Relations, Los Angeles, California.*

There is good evidence that not all feebleminded individuals are the result of their heredity.   External causes such as prenatal injuries or injuries at birth to the brain as well as certain glandular deficiencies, such as that of the thyroid, may be the causative factors.

Environment and I.Q.   Several investigators have carried out studies on twins to determine the normal differences in intelligence. It may be recalled that identical twins are supposed to have their origin in one zygote.   It is evident that they would thus have similar genetic patterns.   Fraternal twins originate in different zygotes, and thus the gene pattern would be different for each of the respective twins.

The most extensive of these studies of twins are those of Newman, Freeman, and Holzinger.   They found that the average difference in

I.Q. of 50 identical twins reared together was 5.9 points, whereas that of 52 non-identical twins reared together was 9.9 points. Thus we note a difference in intelligence between the two kinds of twins reared in the same environment. Apparently heredity plays an important role in the determination of the I.Q. differences between two non-identical twins, but it is evident that environmental differences effect the I.Q. scores of identical twins reared together. However, the influence of environment is more strikingly shown when members of the pairs of identical twins are reared apart. In 19 cases the difference in I.Q. scores is 8.2, from which the conclusion may be drawn that the environmental differences provided by separate homes were able to double the differences in I.Q. scores of identical twins. In the study by Newman of identical twins reared apart, there was good evidence that better schooling and other educational advantages resulted in the favored twin having a higher score. After a survey of the various studies made on twins, Stern concludes that "only considerable difference in environment can bring out a great difference in I.Q. scores of identical twins."

Intelligence and socio-economic status. It is customary to consider individuals in the business and professional groups as the intellectual and social leaders in society, and to expect that the majority of future leaders will come from these groups. However, at the present time there is not sufficient evidence to warrant the certain conclusion that there are genetic differences between various socio-economic groups. It is difficult to set up criteria to evaluate the amount of social prestige, education (which cannot be measured by college degrees), and other items which determine the standing of the individual in the community. There is no doubt that environment is an important influence in bringing about differences of the "expressivity" of mental traits, but mental tests have not yet been devised which measure innate mental capacity irrespective of environment. However, the results of intelligence tests given to children of different socio-economic levels both in the United States and in Russia apparently indicate that the mean I.Q. scores decline from the highest professional group to that of the unskilled workers, but it is difficult to determine how much of this difference is determined by environmental condition and how much by heredity.

Of course, it will be readily recognized that in each group there are some individuals with definitely subnormal intelligence and also individuals making high scores. The picture is further blurred by the fact that many children from the lower groups score higher than their parents and some children in the upper groups score lower than their parents and children from the lower socio-economic groups. It is quite evident that no socio-economic group is the sole possessor of the genes that are in control of intelligence. There are no sharp boundaries between groups for there is a rise and fall between them. Any differences between the various socio-economic groups is not absolute in the sense that any layer of a population is exclusive possessor of the genes that effectively control intelligence. In other words some individuals in the next generation may fall into a higher group and vice versa. Moreover, there is a possibility of inter-group mixture through marriage. There is no doubt that the environment plays a part in these results but, as a well known geneticist writes, "it is hard to avoid the conclusion that environment is not the sole agent." When the observed mean I.Q. scores are studied in connection with the observed birth rates in the different socio-economic levels, various investigators are of the opinion that there is a decrease from one to five points in I.Q. for the population as a whole, but these cannot be checked with actual observations since no actual tests have been made of successive generations.

EUGENICS

Fasten states that the aim of eugenics is to "develop a social consciousness, which will result in the humane treatment and eventual elimination of the hopelessly crippled, diseased, and mentally incompetent, and at the same time increase the number of children produced by normal individuals constituting our present civilization."

It has been pointed out previously that in order to survive an animal must be able to make adjustments to its environment. In fact, inability to adjust frequently results in death not only to the individual but also to the race. Thus unfit organisms are continually weeded out from among the fit. In other words, only the most adaptable, or the fittest, survive. The selected fit under natural conditions are considered to be the strong and the most desirable. If such natural selectivity is true of other animals, why is it not applicable to man? But many think that civilization with improved living conditions, better medical care, and other devices is causing a reversal of this situation by apparently making it possible for the unfit to survive. Yet, on the other hand, why could not man by proper use of his knowledge of genetics, purposefully improve future generations by the perpetuation of what man considers "desirable germplasm"? Why not put eugenic measures into practice?

When we study human heredity, we must realize that pure-bred stock is achieved only by close inbreeding, such as the mating of brother and sister, mother and son. Records of such matings must be kept over a number of generations, which for man would amount to several hundred years. But there has been little inbreeding of man, and few accurate records of such matings have been kept. We do not know what is in the germplasm of any particular family or group. The situation has been well summed up by Johannsen in the statement that "from the point of view of a pure-bred dog, we are all curs."

Early eugenic studies. The early classic studies of human heredity such as those of the Jukes and the Kallikaks are of interest from an historical standpoint and also because they serve to illustrate a doubtful scientific approach. For years these studies have been cited to prove the hereditary basis of various types of criminality, mental deficiency, and moral degeneracy. It is now clear that there was no very careful screening of the data collected in connection with these family histories. The validity of the Jukes study particularly has been much in question in recent years. It does not seem to hold up under a scientific mode of attack. It is doubtful that pauperism, prostitution, criminality, morality, and social habits have a hereditary basis. At least thus far, this has not been proved by scientific studies. Moreover, at the time these studies were made, there were no standards to evaluate feeblemindedness. In the next place, not all the descendants of the families were studied. It seems also that no allowance was made for environmental influence. Hogben, a well-known student of heredity, says, "if social biology ever becomes an exact science, the dreary history of the Jukes will be regarded as we now regard alchemy."

A study of the Edwards family is often cited as an example of the manifestation of good heredity. Richard Edwards, the father of Jonathan Edwards, first married a brilliant but erratic woman named Elizabeth Tuttle. Growing weary of erratic genius, he divorced Elizabeth and later married Mary Talbot. Of the 1,394 descendants studied in 1900, all were eminent citizens. Among them were found doctors, lawyers, clergymen, statesmen, and teachers. It should be noted in passing that the most brilliant members of the Edwards family were descendants of the first union.

Eugenicists have proposed two programs for human betterment. One is aimed to reduce the "unfit." Such a program is called **negative eugenics.** Various measures are proposed to increase the birth rate of the genetically "fit" or in other words "increase the frequencies of favorable alleles." These proposals constitute **positive eugenics.**

Negative Eugenics. The two methods most frequently proposed for the elimination of the undesirable portion of the population are

segregation and **sterilization.** These are the only ways to get rid of defective genes on a large scale. Marriage too often only covers them up. In the segregation of defectives, the two sexes are separated and placed for life in different institutions where they must be carefully supervised and cared for. Naturally this method requires an annual expenditure of millions of dollars, which we all pay. Moreover, in actual practice, inmates of these institutions often wander off and become the origin of new generations with poor germplasm.

The process of sterilization deprives the individual of his powers of reproduction but leaves his other functions unimpaired. This operation consists of closing, cauterizing, or removing a portion of the sperm duct of the male or of the oviduct of the female. The result of these operations is to prevent the escape of ova or spermatozoa and thus forestall fertilization. The normal sexual behavior and responses are unimpaired. After any of these operations, the defectives could be released and allowed to marry. In **castration** and **ovariotomy** the entire gonads are removed and the individual sex behavior is much changed. This operation should be performed only in extreme cases.

Some people object to sterilization, claiming that it interferes with the rights and privileges of the individual, is inhumane, and tends to promote sexual promiscuity. The answer to these arguments is that there actually is no interference with the life of the individuals concerned except that they cannot become parents. Furthermore, we must remember that laws in modern society tend to disregard the individual and are based on the principle of the greatest good to the greatest number. In the next place, there is nothing severe, excessively painful, or dangerous about the operation. Moreover, in those states and nations where sterilization laws are in effect and enforced, there has been no noticeable increase in sexual promiscuity. Others contend that there are insufficient data on which to decide the fate of an individual and that society may lose some geniuses by this method. Then there are some who fear the abuse of legalized sterilization by unscrupulous persons.

At the present time more than thirty states and several foreign countries have eugenic sterilization laws. California, Virginia, and Michigan have applied the law with apparently satisfactory results to more individuals than the other states, but it is clear that to be effective the law must be more universally adopted and enforced. The answering argument to those who oppose sterilization is furnished by Justice Holmes' pithy comment that "three generations of imbeciles are enough."

One of the most effective ways to get rid of defective traits is to **inbreed**—that is, to mate father with daughter, brother with sister, and the like. The professional plant and animal breeder does this constantly, selecting his desirables and discarding the undesirables until a supervariety of corn, wheat, sheep, or horses is produced. Theoretically this procedure could be carried on with man, but obviously the practical obstacles are insurmountable. In passing, it may be said that inherently there is no objection to marriages between cousins or even between brothers and sisters if there are no hidden recessive defective traits that may appear in a homozygous condition. Perhaps the best examples of human inbreeding studied thus far are found in various European royal families, in some of which there has been a high percentage of desirable traits and in others many undesirable ones.

Positive Eugenics. According to Davenport, marriage may be viewed from different angles. In a novel it is the climax of courtship; in law it is regarded as two lines of property descent; in society it means the fixing of a certain status; but in eugenics "it is an experiment in breeding." In the light of the last statement and in accordance with the general principles of genetics, only the fit should mate. To encourage desirable mating it has been proposed that all those contemplating marriage must pass a rigid physical and mental test to determine what, if any, undesirable traits they may have which would be transmitted. Such a requirement would involve a careful weighing and balancing because some of our greatest scientific and literary men have been weak physically. Moreover, to determine the mental and physical traits there should be available also a careful compilation of individual genealogies. In the event of failure to pass the examinations, permission to marry would be given only after certain operations had been performed which would eliminate all possibility of offspring, or certain information had been given concerning the control of reproduction. The advice of William Penn to "marry only for love, but be sure that thou lovest what is lovely" seems to summarize the situation. But the problem is to determine who is to decide "what is lovely."

The fit should not merely be *allowed* to marry but should be *encouraged* to marry and to reproduce as rapidly as possible. Some of the encouragements offered in various countries of the world today are: bonuses for children, which will enable the parent to support a large family in comfort; assured incomes for a family based on family size; tax reductions favoring the heads of large families (today most tax reductions are in favor of the defective); the encouragement of bachelors and spinsters to marry by levying heavier taxes on this group, together with employment and housing discrimination favoring the man with a family.

It is interesting to note the steps which Sweden is taking to meet her population problem and declining birth rate. Sweden appointed a population commission made up of representatives from different political parties among whom were expert economists, statisticians, physicians, and biologists. Among other things, this commission recommended that the sale of contraceptives be controlled by the board of health and that more liberal provisions be made in the income tax for parents. It established health centers for mothers and children, set up a scale of payments to cover most of the expenses incident to childbirth, arranged for free school meals, and fostered low-cost housing projects for families.

Improvement of the environment. It cannot be overemphasized that, in any program of race improvement, it must be recognized that environment does play a part and that the finished product is the result of both heredity and environment. We have already seen that certain genes will produce one kind of an individual under one set of environmental conditions and another type under other conditions. It has been pointed out that environment plays a real part in the development of animals as seen in such examples as *Bonellia* and the axolotl. Apparently the expression of the hereditary potentialities of the germplasm depends on its surroundings. Evidence has been presented which indicates that man's heredity and development follow the same general principles as those we have seen operating in other animals.

One of the glaring weaknesses of the early studies of human heredity was the emphasis placed on heredity to the practical exclusion of environment. But no one can dispute the conclusion that such environmental factors as food, climate, family life, education, and economic status help to prevent exact similarity in all people. However, it is quite obvious that men are not alike in genic make-up, for they come from parents who differ with respect to families and even races. The first group of factors Galton called **nurture** and the second group, **nature.** So the problem may be stated another way, which is the more important, nature or nurture? The same environment may have different effects on people with different genic make-up. Thus a child allergic to cow's milk may get a severe reaction from drinking it, whereas a non-allergic child may thrive on such a diet. Two students of different intellectual capacities may have the same degree of achievement if the demands of the teacher are such that both can meet them. Under a different teacher with higher standards, one may do satisfactory work and the other fail. Desirable genes will express themselves in a good environment but may fail to show their presence in a bad environment. Consequently, our school curricula should be rich and varied in order to offer a wide variety of choices to match the genic combinations as far as possible. Moreover, physical as well as mental development requires proper housing conditions with plenty of space for fresh air and sunlight with its vitamin-producing ultraviolet. In many progressive communities and states, free medical and psychiatric clinics are being established. Some are opposed to these programs, claiming that they tend to increase the number of unfit, which, if nature were allowed to take her course, would vanish from the picture simply by dying. Gradually we are coming to realize that mental sickness may be the result of either environment or heredity.

Difficulties of the eugenics program. The measures already suggested for human betterment, such as sterilization, segregation, and marriage restrictions, being kept in mind, what are the possibilities of the elimination of undesirable traits and their genes? If the trait were conditioned by a single dominant gene F, there would be in the population individuals who were FF or Ff. Let us suppose this gene manifests itself completely early in life. If the reproduction of *all* these FF and Ff individuals were prevented, then this undesirable (F) trait would be eliminated from the next generation unless there were mutations. On the other hand, suppose the trait were conditioned by recessive genes which might be represented by a. Albinism is such a trait. Then an albino will be aa and an individual apparently normal but carrying hidden genes (heterozygous) for albinism would be Aa. Now if all albinos were aa individuals, they would be easily recognized even in childhood, since these genes are completely penetrant. But even if all aa albinos were denied parenthood, this trait would not be eliminated in the first generation. Moreover, not all of them will be denied parenthood. The eugenist faces a real task when he attempts to eliminate traits carried by recessive genes, for this type of inheritance is very hard to discover except when the individual becomes homozygous for the two recessive genes. Apparently normal individuals may become the parents of albino (aa) children. Children afflicted by certain diseases and abnormalities are born mostly to parents who are heterozygous for defective genes. In England about one in 20,000 persons is an albino. When this situation is analyzed statistically, it appears that the carriers of albinism (Aa) are 280 times as numerous as the albinos (aa). It is estimated that by strict enforcement of the eugenics program it "would take two hundred generations (5,000 years) to reduce the proportion of albinos in the population to one-half the present frequency." It is quite apparent that any laxity in the enforcement of the eugenics program would result in much less reduction. Some undesirable genes, like those responsible for Huntington's chorea, often manifest themselves late in life after people have married and borne children.

However, some geneticists point out that means may be devised sometime in the future whereby it will be possible to distinguish the carriers of the defective genes. Further, one should realize that most of the serious hereditary defects are comparatively rare and that there "are so many different defects that relatively little can be blamed on each one taken separately."

Dunn and Dobzhansky * make the rather pessimistic statement about the efficiency of the negative eugenics program.

> Where defects due to recessive genes are concerned the efficiency of steriliza-
> tion is in general low. Only if a recessive defect is very common in the popula-
> tion can sterilization of all the afflicted persons produce a substantial decrease of
> their numbers in the next generation. For defects which are rare, or caused by
> recessive genes which show only in certain environments, or dependent on two
> or more recessive genes present in the same individual, very little is accomplished
> by sterilizing even all the defectives in a single generation. To be sure, if a
> sterilization program is continued for many generations, the defect will become
> eventually less common than it was to begin with. The process may, however,
> take centuries or even millenia.
>
> Our opinion regarding the worthwhileness of such a program will depend on
> how dear to us is the comfort of remote posterity compared to the discomfort of
> contemporaries. It is, perhaps, not too selfish to say that posterity should be
> allowed to tackle its own problems and to hope that it may have better means
> for doing so than we have.

The value of the eugenics program. We have seen that the selective process of eugenics is extremely slow in action. This may be advantageous in that recessive single and multiple factors may not suffer by unwise or hasty selection. If we had been selecting on the basis of physical perfection, the world would not have had Robert Louis Stevenson, Steinmetz, Chopin, or Poe, nor would it have been possible for this germplasm to be handed down.

From what has been said it can be seen that a perfect society of supermen and superwomen through the employment of eugenic meas-ures is not "just around the corner"! The following observations of Stern † sum up the situation: "If the hopes and fears of the eugenics movement seem greatly exaggerated in the light of a numerical treat-ment of the problems, it should not be forgotten that the idealism which concerns itself with the genetic fate of future generations has a

---

* L. C. Dunn and T. H. Dobzhansky, *Heredity, Race and Society*, New Ameri-can Library of World Literature, 245 Fifth Ave., New York 16, N. Y., p. 75.

† Curt Stern, *Human Genetics*, W. H. Freeman and Co., pp. 537–538.

sound core. To say that the loss of supposedly desirable genotypes in one, or even many, generations of differential fertility is small does not remove the fact that it is a loss which may be regrettable and, possibly, even have serious consequences. To state that reproductive selection against severe physical and mental abnormalities will reduce the number of the affected from one generation to the next by only a few per cent does not alter the fact that these few per cent may mean tens of thousands of unfortunate individuals who, if never born, will be saved untold sorrow. Conversely, even a slight increase of desirable genotypes, through positive eugenic measures, would be a social gain."

17

The Scientific Naming
of Animals
Taxonomy

Whenever we wish to talk about things, people, or incidents, we must have names by which we may designate them. It is difficult to carry on a conversation about anything for which we have no name, and so we proceed to select or coin a name for the thing in question. In the earliest development of speech there is evidence that names of some kind were applied to all the things that man observed in his surroundings. Thus the plants and animals received names, as did also the streams, the seasons, and the varying climatic conditions that exert such a profound influence on man's comfort. Of course, different tribes and clans in the same and different sections of the country often gave different names to the same plant. Intercommunication among these various groups was lacking or very poorly developed, and consequently there could be no uniform terminology.

Beginnings. Scientists take note of the beginning of science when known facts are first arranged in logical sequence; when knowledge becomes organized, and when such organization makes accurate prediction possible. The first approach to a scientific study of plants and animals was made by Greek scholars, Aristotle and Theophrastus. Not content with the mere naming of organisms, these philosophers attempted to group them according to some scheme of classification. We know from experience that, in dealing with large numbers of different things, some sort of grouping or classification becomes imperative. So these early Greek naturalists, recognizing an ever-increasing number of plants and animals, found it necessary to devise a system of classification. To illustrate the artificiality and looseness of these early schemes of classification, it is only necessary to mention the primary grouping of plants into herbs, shrubs, and trees, and that of animals into air dwellers, water dwellers, and land forms. These beginnings were crude and often based on purely philosophical speculations, but they provided later workers with ideas and a foundation.

The efforts of the early Greeks were followed by eighteen centuries of darkness and stagnation. The first spark of awakening scientific activity appeared in the first half of the sixteenth century. Then came a long line of investigators who devoted themselves assiduously to the task of improving their knowledge of plants and animals, and especially to the development of a system of classification. Strange as it may seem in this age of specialization, the majority of these early workers were men who had been trained either as doctors or as preachers.

Beginnings of modern classification. In the early years of the eighteenth century a Swedish botanist, Carl von Linné, known throughout the scientific world as Linnaeus, developed a new scheme of classification and established a new method of naming plants and animals.

Since Linnaeus has such an important place in biology, a brief story of his life may prove interesting. He was born in Sweden in 1707, the son of a poor country clergyman. He was sent to Wexio to prepare for the ministry but apparently was uninterested in this profession. Later, under the guidance of a Dr. Rothman, Linnaeus took up the study of medicine. At the age of twenty Linnaeus entered the University of Lund and thence on to Upsala, where he became intensely interested in the study of plants and came under the guidance of Celsius, the Dean of the University. Here Linnaeus began to give private lectures in botany, which were quite popular with the students. While at Upsala, Linnaeus received a grant which enabled him to make an exploratory journey into Lapland. On this journey he made a large collection of plants.

Linnaeus next went to Holland to complete his studies for the degree of Doctor of Medicine. Meantime, Linnaeus continued his study of the plant kingdom, and in 1735 he published his *Systema Naturae* (Natural System), in which he proposed a classification based on what he considered natural relationships. Some of the older artificial schemes of classification divided plants into woody and herbaceous plants, and then made subdivisions of these groups based on their medicinal uses. Gerard, an English physician, proposed such classes as trees, shrubs, fruit-bearing plants, rosins, gums, roses, heaths, mosses, mushrooms, and sea plants. The classification devised by Linnaeus was based on the number and position of the stamens and pistils. It was decidedly artificial, but the notable contribution of his work was the new idea and spirit which it introduced and the excellent organization it presented. His publication made Linnaeus famous and marks the dividing line between the old philosophical school that had its origin in ancient Greece and the scientific school of modern times.

Linnaeus now became an authority in the field of botany. In 1741 he was made Professor of Botany at Upsala, where he soon became the foremost member of the University. He soon became recognized throughout the world as an authority on questions of natural science,

Fig. 134. Linnaeus (Carl von Linné) 1707–1778, the founder of modern taxonomy. *From Holman and Robbins, "Textbook of General Botany." By permission of W. W. Robbins and of the publisher, John Wiley and Sons.*

and was consulted by both governments and private individuals. He died in 1778.

Present-day systems of classification. Following the general method developed by Linnaeus, plants and animals are now grouped into certain defined categories. All individuals that have essentially the same structure and life history are included in a grouping or category known as a **species.** For example, all common house cats belong to the same species. If a number of different species are found to possess certain fundamental characters in common, they are grouped into a larger category called a **genus.** Thus there is a large number of animals such as lions, tigers, and leopards that have general characteristics like those of the house cat, yet in other specific respects these animals are very different. Because of this general similarity, domestic cats, lions, and tigers, representing three distinct species, all belong to the same genus.

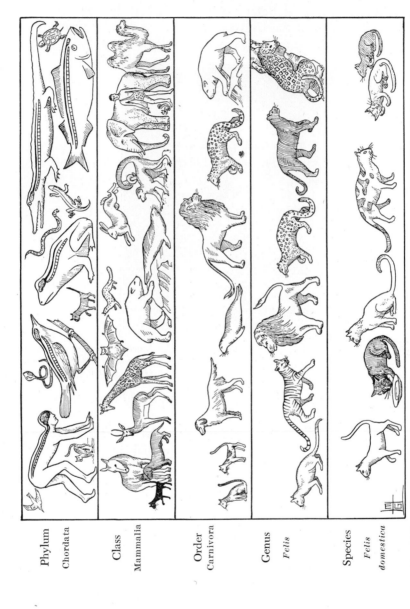

Phylum
Chordata

Class
Mammalia

Order
Carnivora

Genus
Felis

Species
Felis domestica

Fig. 135. Diagram showing resemblances and differences in the categories used in the Linnean system of classification. Note that there is an increasing dissimilarity among the animals in passing from species to phylum.

In a similar manner, on the basis of resemblances, like genera are grouped into **families,** families into **orders,** and orders into **classes.** There are but few characteristics that are common to all the members of a certain class. The class to which the cat belongs includes all animals having hair and mammary glands. Therefore, this class (Mammalia) is made up of a heterogeneous assemblage including man, cats, lions, cows, horses, rabbits, and many other animals that have in common hairy skins and mammary glands, as well as a few other less obvious characteristics that determine this particular category (Fig. 135).

Classes are grouped into divisions or **phyla** (*phylon*—race or tribe). Each phylum represents one of the largest divisions of the plant or animal kingdom, for its members need have fewer characteristics in common than those of any of the other categories already mentioned. The presence of a notochord, a dorsal nerve cord, a backbone in most forms, and a few other features characterize the **phylum** (Chordata) to which the cat belongs, and this category includes a large number of very dissimilar animals such as man, fish, frogs, snakes, birds, and elephants, because all of them possess the few characters necessary for membership in this phylum.

Any or all of these categories may be subdivided into smaller groupings designated by such terms as **subkingdom, subphylum, suborder, subfamily,** and **subgenus.** Linnaeus thought that a species was a fixed, immutable category, but today we know that intergrades occur and that some species are extremely variable. Consequently, categories, called **varieties,** may be formed as subdivisions of the species. This method of grouping may be illustrated by the classification of the common cat:

Kingdom—Animalia
Subkingdom—Metazoa
Phylum—Chordata
Subphylum—Vertebrata
Class—Mammalia
Order—Carnivora
Family—Felidae
Genus—*Felis*
Species—*domestica*

SCIENTIFIC NAMES

The concepts of genera and species existed before the time of Linnaeus, but no one had consistently used generic and specific names to designate organisms. Linnaeus adopted this usage and emphasized it by constant application in all his work. Its convenience was recognized at once, and it became the universally accepted method of naming plants and animals. The name of the genus plus the name of the species forms the scientific name of the organism, and the system is therefore known as the **binomial system** (*bi*—two; *nomen*—name). The person who first publishes the name of a genus or species is considered the author of that group, and his name or its abbreviation is placed after the name of the group. Thus we see that the scientific name of the common house cat is *Felis domestica* Schreber.

The necessity for some such system of nomenclature becomes quite obvious when one recalls that common names are almost as variable as the people who use them. An organism that is tagged by a certain common name in one locality is given an entirely different name in another locality. Thus the common bird *Colaptes auratus,* known quite generally as the flicker, may be called high hole, yellow hammer, golden-winged woodpecker, clape, wakeup, or 120 other names in as many different localities. From this illustration and numerous others that could be cited, we may conclude that common names applied to plants and animals are merely nicknames, and like nicknames they have only a very restricted local value. The only genuine, widely recognized name is the scientific name established in the system of binomial nomenclature. It can readily be understood how such a system eliminates much of the confusion resulting from the use of common names by providing world-wide uniformity in the naming of organisms.

In the time of Linnaeus, Latin was the accepted scholarly language throughout Europe, and all important documents and scientific articles appeared in this language. Thus the first scientific names were Latin names. These early names have been preserved, and the use of Latin in naming plants and animals has been universally accepted —quite fortunately, because the Latin language, being no longer spoken, is not subject to variation. It is a fixed (dead) language, and the Latin scientific names are thus destined to remain unmodified throughout the years. Likewise, in the time of Linnaeus, Latin was also the universal language of scholars, and consequently scientists everywhere were more likely to use the same name for any given organism. Thus still greater uniformity was given to binomial nomenclature.

Returning to our previous illustrations, we see that the scientific name of the cat, *Felis domestica* Schreb., is the name known to scientists everywhere. Thus we see that the system of binomial nomenclature and the use of the Latin language as a medium of expressing the names have been extremely important in the development of our knowledge of plants and animals. Aristotle is supposed to have known about 520 species of animals. Consequently, the naming and classification of these organisms presented a much simpler problem than that which confronts the taxonomic biologists of today, who have recorded approximately 1,000,000 species of animals.

The scheme of classification developed by Linnaeus has been replaced by others, but the general method he introduced is now used by all systematists throughout the world. As our knowledge of animal relationships has increased, the work of classification has been improved and a closer approach has been made to the ultimate goal —a natural system of classification. As contrasted with an artificial system of classification based on superficial resemblances, a natural system is one based on relationships determined by inheritance or, in other words, "blood relationship." International congresses of zoologists convene from time to time to formulate rules of taxonomic procedure, and thus the greatest possible uniformity in scientific nomenclature is sought.

WHAT IS A SPECIES?

Just as the classification proposed by Linnaeus has been changed, so also has the concept of species been modified. Linnaeus considered each species "a thought of God," an immutable group created by the Almighty and remaining constant through all time. According to this interpretation, a lion was created as such, could never be modified in any way, and therefore would always remain a lion. This, of course, would be equally true of man, dog, horse, or sponge, and every other organism. A species once created might become extinct, but it would never change, and therefore it could give rise to no new species. This concept was known as "Special Creation." We now know that such rigid categories do not exist. Today a species is generally interpreted as a mere taxonomic concept (**Linnaean concept**) for a group of individuals of the same kind. The individuals comprising a species are thought to be very closely related by descent (ancestry), as indicated by their resemblances. This modern Linnaean concept of species, as we have seen, does not coincide precisely with his original definition of a species. Some workers have proposed establishing the species on the basis of specific reactions of the protoplasm, and this is known as the physiological concept of species. However, all the schemes of classification now in general use employ the modified Linnaean species-concept.

Geneticists generally consider a species as a natural group whose characteristic features are determined by the genes and genic combinations. Usually, animals of one species cannot be crossed with those of another, and, where such crosses can be made successfully, the resultant hybrids are almost or completely sterile. Interspecific and hybrid sterility are regarded as agencies that help to keep species clearly delimited as natural groups.

18

Protozoa, Sponges,
and Coelenterates

We have already learned that all living organisms are made up of protoplasm and products of protoplasm which differ somewhat in different organisms. The protoplasm of each species of animal differs in some way from that of all other species. Though these differences may be slight, they are sufficient to cause the development of thousands of varied forms. However, no matter what form protoplasm may assume, it possesses those fundamental characteristics such as organization, metabolism, sensitivity, growth, and reproduction, all of which we have already studied. When we attempt a survey of the animal kingdom, we find creatures of all sizes and shapes, presenting strange variations and devices responsible for carrying out the fundamental life processes. These living things which are grouped into the animal kingdom, as we have already seen, are further subdivided into smaller groups based on fundamental resemblances. We are now going to present a "bird's-eye" view of various animals and show something of their modes of life, relationships, and the role they play in the general economic and social interests of man.

PHYLUM PROTOZOA
(*protos*—first; *zoon*—animal)

Protozoa are generally microscopic animals which for the most part live in either fresh or salt water although some live in the soil and others, as "uninvited guests," in the blood, body cavity, and intestines of other animals, including man. Protozoa exist either as single cells or as groups of cells called colonies. In colonies, for the most part, each cell is like every other cell, although some colonial groups have a certain amount of differentiation or specialization of cells that perform specific functions. No tissues or organs are present in Protozoa. The animals belonging to this phylum are separated into various groups according to certain fundamental resemblances.

Class Sarcodina (*sarx*—flesh), or the amebalike Protozoa. Protozoa of this group have peculiar organs of locomotion called **pseudopodia** (*pseudo*—false; *podos*—foot). By studying the ameba, a member of this group, we shall acquire some understanding of the nature of sarcodinians in general. Amebas may be found on the surface of the mud in ponds and ditches and on water plants. If we examine some scrapings of mud or plants under the microscope, we may see irregular-shaped masses of protoplasm—amebas—flowing over them. Here and there projections of protoplasm push out from the animal, and the animal moves. These projections are pseudopodia. If we examine the ameba more closely (Fig. 136), we find that the extreme outer zone of the body, the **ectoplasm,** is fairly transparent and free from the granules found in the inner zone, which is darker in color and very granular. The inner zone is the **endoplasm.** If we stain the ameba, it is possible to see the nucleus lying in the endoplasm. Scattered through the endoplasm are vesicles containing fluid and particles of food. These are **food vacuoles.** If in its wanderings the ameba encounters a bit of food, it "swallows" it by the simple process of flowing around and over it, and later completely surrounding it with protoplasm. The food is digested and absorbed into the surrounding protoplasm. The solid waste is eliminated at any place by the animal's flowing away from it. As Causey puts it, "There never was a principle of hygienic science or of table manners it [ameba] hasn't violated successfully."

Metabolism of course goes on in this bit of protoplasm. Oxygen diffuses into, and carbon dioxide diffuses out of, the protoplasm throughout its entire surface. As we look more closely at the endoplasm, we may see a small, transparent vesicle appear and then disappear by apparently squeezing together. Later it may reappear. This is the **contractile vacuole,** which helps regulate the amount of water in the ameba.

The ameba has **sensitivity.** It moves toward some substances and engulfs them; it avoids other substances by flowing away from them. When shocked by electricity or subjected to vibrations, it pulls in the pseudopodia and contracts into a sphere.

Reproduction takes place by fission. Under unfavorable conditions, such as the drying up or freezing of the surrounding water, it may form a **cyst** by secreting a resistant enveloping membrane and in this quiescent state await the return of better living conditions.

All the Sarcodina are unicellular and have pseudopodia, but some are not so simple as amebas. The pseudopodia of certain forms are blunt; others are fine, radiating, and raylike. Certain of these ani-

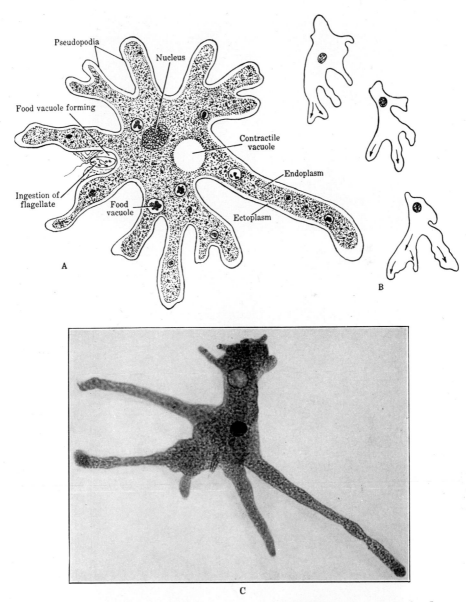

FIG. 136. *Amoeba.* *A*, structural details. *B*, manner of locomotion. The flow of protoplasm is indicated by arrows. *C*, Photomicrograph of living *Amoeba proteus. Photograph furnished by the Carolina Biological Supply Company.*

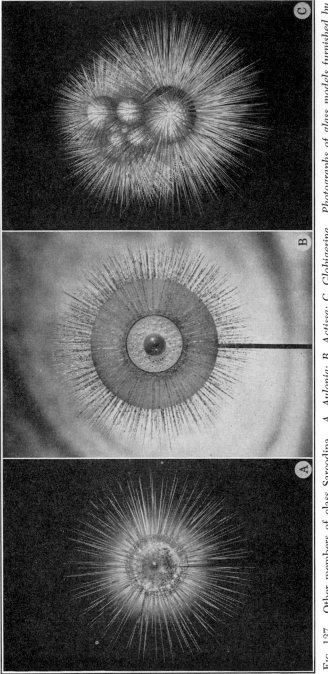

Fig. 137. Other members of class Sarcodina. A, Aulonia; B, Actissa; C, Globigerina. Photographs of glass models furnished by the American Museum of Natural History.

mals cover their naked protoplasm by secreting shells of silica or calcium carbonate (Fig. 137). In fact, many of the layers of limestone and chalk rock are made up of countless billions of these little shells of sarcodinians that lived millions of years ago. The pyramids of Egypt are built of limestone made from these shells.

Aside from rock formation, we have little good to say of these animals. *Endamoeba gingivalis* has been erroneously blamed with assisting in pyorrhea. This ameba is spread by kissing. A relative, *Endamoeba histolytica,* enters the digestive tract from filth on poorly washed lettuce, celery, and the like, or in polluted water. It reaches the large intestine and there feeds on the intestinal wall and red blood cells, causing ulcers and causing bleeding and amebic dysentery. Some may get into the liver and cause liver abscesses.

Class Flagellata (*flagellum*—little whip). These little animals are called flagellates because they usually move by pulling themselves along by the lashings of one or more long whiplike strands of protoplasm called **flagella.** Their bodies, though pliable, are rather definite in shape with a well-defined anterior end.

Like amebas, these animals are single-celled, have food vacuoles, and many have pseudopodia (Fig. 138). In some flagellates the food is engulfed in ameba fashion. In some, the food is absorbed through the entire body surface; in others, the food enters through a definite spot to which it is drawn by currents set up in the water by the lashing flagella. Many of these forms resemble green plants in that they have chloroplasts and manufacture their own food. In fact, many botanists lay claim to these organisms because, in addition to having chloroplasts, many of them form spores after the fashion of plants. Some biologists believe that the Flagellata are more primitive than amebas because of their plant characteristics and because some flagellates have a somewhat ameboid body to which is attached a flagellum.

Some flagellates form colonies with certain of the cells specialized for reproduction and others for feeding and locomotion. However, differentiation has not proceeded far enough to form tissues or many-celled animals, **Metazoa.**

The Flagellata contribute their share of plagues to man. Some live in reservoirs and give man's drinking water a most surprising taste and "audible odor." There are also a number of parasitic forms. One of them, *Giardia,* seen under the microscope looks like the face of an owl. *Giardia* lives in the upper bowel and may cause nervousness on the part of the host.

Two groups of flagellates are especially important, the *Leishmania* type and the trypanosome type (Fig. 138). They live in the blood and other tissues and are the cause of a number of serious diseases. The *Leishmania* parasites may become localized in either the viscera or the skin.

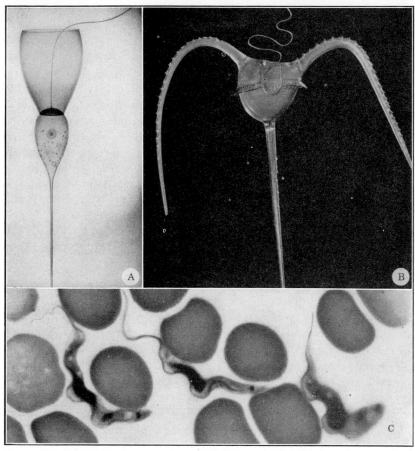

Fig. 138. Other members of class Flagellata. *A, Monosiga; B, Ceratium; C, Trypanosoma. A and B photographs of glass models furnished by the American Museum of Natural History. C, photomicrograph furnished by General Biological Supply House.*

Leishmania diseases.   Kala-azar or "black sickness" is found in India, North China, around the Mediterranean, and in Sudan and has been known to depopulate entire villages. Apparently the disease is transmitted by the bite of the sandfly. The parasites occur in the blood and are especially abundant in the spleen, liver, bone marrow, and lymphatic system. The white corpuscles of the body become gorged with these apparently indigestible flagellates. Destruction and avoidance of sandflies may be one way to prevent the disease.

Oriental sore occurs quite frequently in the eastern Mediterranean region and southwestern Asia. Sandflies may be the transmitting agents, and it is certain that the disease can be transmitted by contact with an infected individual. Oriental sore is a shallow ulcer which may persist for several months to a year or more. One attack gives immunity.

Espundia occurs from Mexico and Central America to northern Argentina. Extensive sores appear on the ears, face, forearms, and legs which become eroded and secondarily infected. Often the disease attacks the nasal cavities, the mouth, and pharynx. It is quite possible that the disease is transmitted by sandflies.

Trypanosome diseases. Sleeping sickness is a trypanosome disease of equatorial Africa (Fig. 139). These parasitic flagellates are

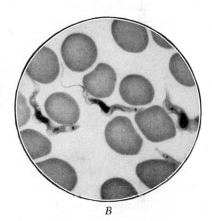

A B

Fig. 139. A, African sleeping sickness: advanced stage. B, trypanosomes, causing sleeping sickness. A, *reproduced from Culbertson "Medical Parasitology" by permission of Columbia University Press.* B, *photomicrograph furnished by the General Biological Supply House.*

carried by a tsetse fly which has probably become infected from sucking the blood of some other intermediate host. When the fly bites a person it loses some of the protozoans in the saliva. The trypanosomes get into the blood stream, where they multiply. After several weeks or months, the person bitten becomes feverish, loses flesh, and lacks "pep." Eventually the parasites infect the cerebrospinal fluid, and then the victim passes into a slumber from which he usually never awakes. Thus far no certain cure has been discovered for sleeping sickness.

Chagas' disease is caused by a trypanosome parasite apparently carried by a large, blood-sucking bug (*Triatoma megista*) which lives in the mud of thatched native houses. The disease is contracted when the feces of the infected bug are rubbed into the tissues of man. The disease, found in Brazil, Argentina, Venezuela, and Uruguay, is more common among infants and young children. Severe infections may result in death.

Besides trypanosomes found in man, others have been found in horses, camels, cattle, pigs, dogs, monkeys, and armadillos.

Class Sporozoa (*sporos*—spore; *zoon*—animal). All the species of this group are parasitic not only on animals of other phyla but even on other Protozoa. They have no means of locomotion, and they lack contractile vacuoles. As the name of the class indicates, one of the characteristics of these animals is the tendency to form spores at some time during the life cycle. In the formation of spores the nucleus of a "parent" animal may divide a number of times. Each nucleus appropriates some cytoplasm, and the parent breaks up into a number of small sporozoa each with a nucleus and some cytoplasm.

Perhaps we can get a better picture of a typical animal of this group if we study a malarial parasite, *Plasmodium*. When a female mosquito (*Anopheles*) bites a person, there may be injected into the blood stream some saliva containing *Plasmodium* in the form of **sporozoites** (Fig. 140). The sporozoites enter the red blood corpuscles, grow, and break up into young spores (**trophozoites**). After a certain period the corpuscle bursts, releasing many new parasites and much waste material into the blood stream, causing a chill. The young spores enter new corpuscles and multiply. So the cycle continues unless quinine, plasmochin, or atabrine is administered to kill the parasites when they escape from the corpuscles. Sometimes the chills come every third day and sometimes only every fourth day, depending on the life cycle of the particular species of *Plasmodium*.

Quite often these malarial parasites form sex cells, or **gametocytes.** When the gametocytes reach the stomach of a female mosquito, the female gametocytes are fertilized by spermatozoa (from male gametocytes), and the resulting zygotes then develop into wormlike forms (**oökinetes**). These burrow through the stomach walls and encyst themselves. Asexual reproduction follows within the cyst, forming many slender sporozoites, the stage infective to man. The sporozoites later migrate to the salivary glands of the mosquito where they remain until she—for it is the female mosquito—bites another victim and the vicious circle is started again. Study carefully the diagrammatic sketch of the life history in Fig. 140. It is estimated that malaria is responsible directly or indirectly for one-half of the annual deaths of human beings of the world exclusive of war and accident. There are more than a million cases of malaria per year in the United States.

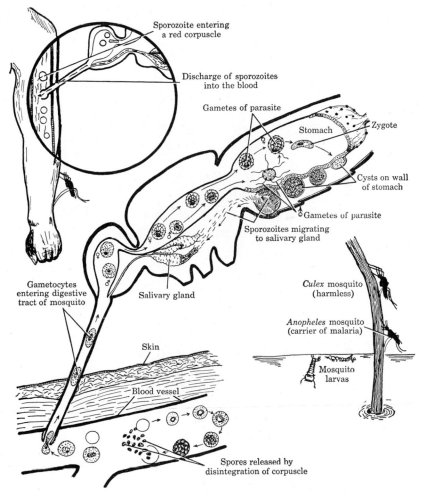

FIG. 140. Life history of the malarial parasite, *Plasmodium*.

Parasitic Sporozoa are found in other animals and in man; however, many of them are comparatively harmless. Some forms may cause the death of rabbits and chickens. Others cause Texas cattle fever and diarrhea in cattle. Still others are responsible for a chronic disease in silkworms known as **pebrine**. Birds may have bird malaria but often show no ill effects. Many Protozoa have an even more complicated life history than the malarial parasite.

Class Ciliata (*cilium*—eyelash). The body is covered with an outer, rather tough transparent **pellicle** through which protrude small **cilia,**

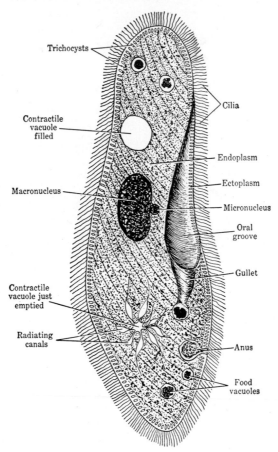

Fig. 141. Structure of *Paramecium.* *After various authors.*

used in locomotion. In many of these Ciliata the number of cilia may be very restricted and other structures called **cirri** may be present to assist in movement. Another characteristic is the presence of two kinds of nuclei in the cell. There is usually a large nucleus which controls the vegetative processes of the cell and one or more smaller nuclei which are responsible for the hereditary characters. Although no tissues or organs are present, many animals of this group are very complex. The protoplasm in various regions of the cell is highly modified, and structures known as **organelles** (little organs) may be present (Fig. 141). Ciliata are widely distributed in fresh and salt water, and a few live as parasites in man and other animals. A better idea of this group can be obtained by studying the structure and behavior of *Paramecium*.

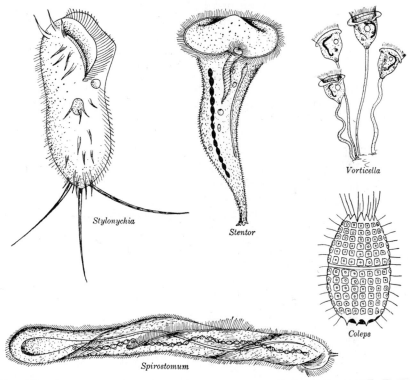

Stylonychia

Stentor

Vorticella

Coleps

Spirostomum

Fig. 142. Various members of the class Ciliata. *Modified from various sources.*

Paramecium is found in most stagnant pools. It is shaped somewhat like the sole of a slipper and is covered with numerous cilia which propel the animal through the water. Leading from the anterior end of the animal is a furrow known as the **oral groove** which leads down into the animal as the **gullet.** The cilia along this groove are somewhat longer and create a current of water flowing down into the gullet and bringing in such food as bacteria and protozoans. As in amebas, these ingested food particles lie within food vacuoles. As they circulate through the protoplasm the food is digested and assimilated. Oxygen and carbon dioxide are exchanged through the general body surface, and two **contractile vacuoles** eliminate excess water (Fig. 141).

Under the pellicle is a region containing protective structures called **trichocysts** (*thrix*—hair). When the animal is attacked by other protozoans, as it often is, the trichocysts shoot out and form around the body a jellylike network which may keep the enemy at bay. One of the enemies, another protozoan called *Didinium nasutum,* can eat animals ten times its own size and one or two hours after such a meal it is ready for another.

Paramecium reproduces asexually by transverse fission. Sometimes two individuals may unite and exchange nuclear material, a process called **conjugation.** A somewhat similar process of nuclear reorganization called **endomixis** may take place in a single individual. Conjugation and endomixis seem to impart new health and vigor to the animals.

Several of the Ciliata are reported to be parasitic in man, but the most troublesome one is *Balantidium coli,* a rather large form visible to the naked eye. It is normally parasitic in the digestive tract of hogs, from which in an encysted condition it escapes with the feces. Man introduces it into his digestive tract by eating improperly washed food. Normally this parasite seems perfectly content to swim around in the large intestine devouring fecal matter, but sometimes it attacks the intestinal wall, causing ulcers. Dysentery follows, and frequently death results. Proper sanitation for both hogs and man is the best way to prevent the disease.

PHYLUM PORIFERA

(*poros*—channel; *ferre*—to bear)

The Porifera or sponges live mostly in salt water, although a few forms are found in fresh water. The phylum is well named, for the animals are literally full of channels or **canals** which open to the outside through **pores.** Portions of the canals are lined with cells which resemble the flagellates. Each of these cells has a flagellum surrounded by a **collar.** These cells make up the **gastric epithelium.** The beating of the flagella brings the food and oxygen-laden water into the sponge through certain pores and canals and expels it through others which are larger and more centrally located. The larger central canals or cavities (**spongocoeles**) open to the outside by a large opening called the **osculum** (little mouth) (Fig. 143). The food, consisting of microscopic animals and plants, is engulfed by the cells of the gastric epithelium and digested as in the Protozoa. Sponges have no circulatory system and food is transferred by ameboid wandering cells as well as by diffusion since every cell has one exposed surface. Excretion and the exchange of oxygen and carbon dioxide take place

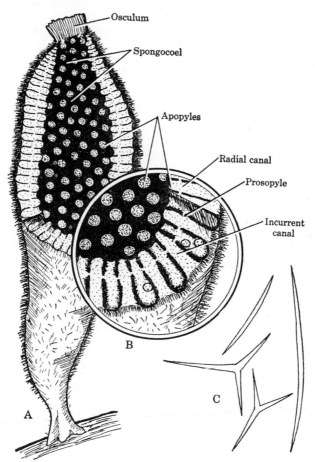

Fig. 143. Anatomy of the sponge, *Scypha* (*Grantia*).

through the surface of the cell in the same way as in Protozoa. Solid wastes may be eliminated by wandering ameboid cells which carry them to the outside.

Sponges reproduce asexually by budding and also in some species by the formation of **gemmules** (little buds). A gemmule is a group of cells enclosed within a resistant coat which enables it to live through unfavorable conditions. Sponges may reproduce sexually also. The zygote develops into a free-swimming larva which, after swimming for a time, settles down and develops into an adult animal. We have already noted the remarkable powers of regeneration possessed by sponges.

The mention of flagellated and ameboid cells brings to mind at once the Protozoa, and, indeed, sponges are not far removed from this phylum. However, in sponges we find specializations not present

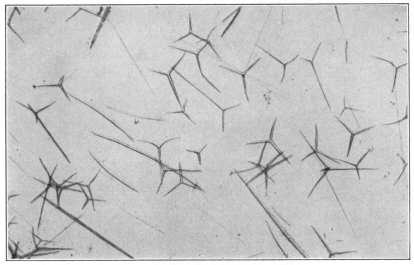

Fig. 144.   Spicules of sponge.   *Photomicrograph furnished by General Biological Supply House.*

in the Protozoa. The gastral and dermal epithelia are **tissues.** Between the two layers is a rather indefinite jellylike layer in which are found cells that furnish the skeletal structure of the sponge. In most sponges the supporting skeleton is made up of finely branched needle-like structures called **spicules** (Fig. 144). In some sponges they are made of calcium carbonate; in others they may be finely spun needles and threads of glassy silica. The spicules not only support but also protect the sponge, for they offer no encouragement to the buccal cavities of would-be diners. Some sponges are supported by a skeleton of a more flexible, tough substance called **spongin.**

Although sponges do have tissues, no organs are present. In addition to the dermal and gastral epithelia already mentioned, we may mention the skeletal-producing cells found in the jellylike layer. Contractile fibrils have developed in the cells which surround the pores, but there is no nervous tissue. The pore cells are both motor and

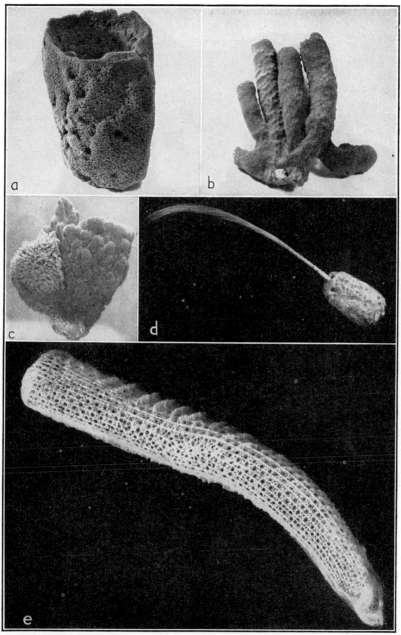

Fig. 145. Types of sponges (Phylum Porifera): *a*, bath sponge, *b*, finger sponge; *c* (*left*) grass sponge, (*right*) sheep's wool sponge; *d*, glass rope sponge; *e*, Venus' flower basket. Sponges *d* and *e* have skeletons of "spun glass." *Photographs a, b, d, and e furnished by Erwin S. Koval; c, by Fish and Wildlife Service, U. S. Department of the Interior.*

sensory in function and therefore constitute a neuromuscular mechanism.

As indicated above, the Porifera are doubtless related to the Protozoa. Although they are too complex to be classified with that phylum, they show no fundamental similarities with animals higher in the evolutionary scale. Someone has pointed out that sponges

FIG. 146.   A sponge market in the Bahama Islands.   *Photograph by Ewing Galloway, New York.*

apparently went up an evolutionary blind alley in the animal kingdom and remained merely sponges. They are considered members of that great group of many-celled animals, the Metazoa.

The value of the total yield of the sponge fisheries of the world amounts to more than $3,000,000 each year. The bath sponge of commerce has a skeleton of spongin, and it is this skeleton that we use.

In preparing bath sponges, the animals are torn from their moorings usually by divers who bring them to the surface and place them on the deck of a vessel where they are allowed to die and rot. Then the decayed and softened flesh is washed and squeezed from the skeletons, which are carefully sorted and prepared for the market. Sponges are propagated commercially by "planting slips" attached to stakes fastened to a frame which is lowered to the ocean bottom. This frame is raised after a year or so and the sponge crop is harvested.

Classes of Sponges

Based on their skeletogenous structures, three classes of sponges are recognized.
Class Calcarea (*calcarius*—limy). These are the simplest sponges with spicules
of calcium carbonate. To this class belongs the sponge Scypha which has just
been described.

Class Hexactinellida (*hex*—six; *aktis*—ray). To this class belong the so-called
glass sponges whose skeletons are made up of six-rayed silicious spicules which
may exist free or may be fused to form a latticelike support.

Class Demospongiae (*demos*—people; *spongia*—sponge). This large class includes all those sponges possessing non-six-rayed silicious spicules. In addition to

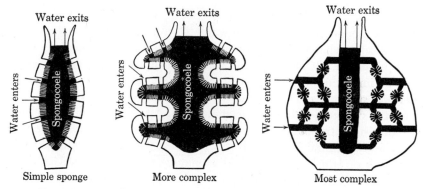

Fig. 147. Canal system of sponges. *Modified from various sources.*

spicules there may be present the horny flexible spongin. Some of the skeletons
of the Demospongiae are composed entirely of spongin. These are the familiar
commercial sponges previously mentioned.

Canal systems. Sponges exhibit three main types of canal systems. In the
simple sponges the water enters the spongocoele directly through a pore (**ascon**
type) (Fig. 147). In the more advanced type water courses through pores and
two canals before reaching the spongocoele (**sycon** type). In the third and most
complex system the rather thick dense body of this type of sponge is penetrated
by a complex branched canal system in which there are small spherical chambers
lined with choanocytes. Water eventually reaches the spongocoele (**leucon** type)
(Fig. 147).

PHYLUM COELENTERATA OR CNIDARIA
(*koilos*—hollow; *enteron*—intestine; *cnidos*—thread)

The Coelenterata are aquatic animals, most of which are found in
salt water. In this phylum are jellyfishes, sea anemones, corals, and
the fresh-water hydra. The Coelenterata are sometimes spoken of
as "modified gastrulas" since the bodies of the animals are made up
of only two well-defined cell layers, an outer **epidermis** and an inner
gastrodermis. Between the layers is a jellylike layer or **mesoglea**

which has no definite cellular structure. The gastrodermis lines the digestive cavity, called the **gastrovascular cavity.** These animals are **radially symmetrical;** i.e., they can be divided into three or more fairly similar parts or segments. Animals such as the earthworm, grasshopper, and chicken, which can be divided into two equal similar parts only by one plane passing through the long axis of the body, are said to be **bilaterally symmetrical.** Tentacles are usually present, and the animals are equipped with stinging cells called **nematocysts** (*nema*—thread; *cyst*). Many of the coelenterates have an **alternation of generations (metagenesis)** in their life history, a phenomenon that will presently be explained.

Class Hydrozoa (*hydra*—water serpent; *zoon*). One of the simplest of the Coelenterata is the fresh-water *Hydra* (Fig. 148). *Hydra* is a sessile, somewhat tubular animal about one-fourth to one-half of an inch in length. It has a double wall made up of an outer **epidermis** and an inner **endoderm** between which is the **mesoglea.** The gastrodermis surrounds the digestive or **gastrovascular cavity.** The **mouth,** surrounded by an elevated liplike structure, the **hypostome,** is both the entrance and exit of the gastrovascular cavity. Surrounding the hypostome and mouth is a circlet of **tentacles** equipped with batteries of stinging cells called nematocysts. The animal thus described is often called a **polyp.**

A hydra extends its tentacles into the surrounding water as long flexible lines. When some animal, such as a tiny aquatic worm or the water flea *Daphnia,* happens to swim by, it comes in contact with one or more of these fishing lines and also with the "trigger hairs" of the nematocysts, causing them to explode. In this reaction, they shoot out small strands, some of which may wrap around parts of the prey while others, tipped with poison, penetrate the victim and paralyze it. Then the tentacles contract, and the struggling prey is drawn to the mouth and moved on into the digestive cavity. Here it is partly digested into smaller food particles which are moved about and distributed by the lashings of the flagella found on some gastrodermal cells. The particles are then engulfed by pseudopodial processes of these cells, in which digestion is completed. Indigestible portions, such as the hard shells of some animals, are later ejected through the mouth, for there is no anal opening in *Hydra* or other coelenterates. Food is distributed by diffusion to other body cells. The oxygen-carbon dioxide problem is solved in the same way as in Porifera and Protozoa, by direct interchange between cells and environment.

The adjustment mechanism is better developed in *Hydra* and the Coelenterata than in Protozoa and Porifera. Contractile fibrils are located in the basal regions of the epidermal and gastrodermal cells, but no true muscle tissue is present. Since certain epidermal cells are both sensory and motor they are called **epitheliomuscular cells.**

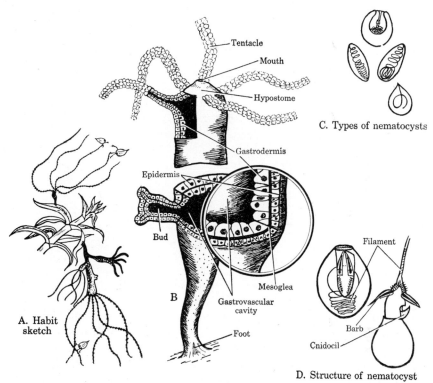

Fig. 148. Anatomy of hydra. *C, after Hyman in* Trans. Amer. Microscopical Soc., Vol. L. *D, redrawn from Borradaile and Potts, "Invertebrata," by permission of the publisher, the Macmillan Co.*

Nerve cells are arranged in the form of a **nerve net,** as has been pointed out elsewhere. In a sense, this may be considered a very primitive nervous tissue.

Hydra can move from place to place by turning cartwheels—that is, by attaching its tentacles and releasing its foot or base, which then bends over and becomes attached in a new place. It may move by the creeping of its foot. Sometimes cells located in the foot form a bubble of gas, and, attached to this "balloon," the animal rises and floats around on the surface, suspended mouth downward in the water. *Hydra* is very sensitive; when stimulated by touch, jarring, chemicals, and other stimuli, it will contract both tentacles and body (Fig. 149).

Hydra reproduces asexually by budding and sexually by eggs and sperms produced in ovaries and testes, respectively. *Hydra* also possesses powers of regeneration almost equal to those of sponges.

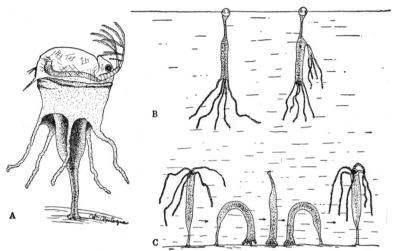

FIG. 149. *A,* hydra disgorging a daphnid too large to be ingested (swallowed); *B,* hydra floating attached to a gas bubble; *C,* the "walking" of a hydra by alternate attachments of base and apical regions.

Obelia and alternation of generations.

Obelia is a colonial salt-water hydroid. It resembles a tiny bushy plant and grows attached to wharves, piling, or seaweed (Fig. 150). The bushy animal bears a number of little polyps called **hydranths,** which resemble little hydras except that they are all connected by a common **gastrovascular cavity** whose walls make up the **coenosarc.** Thus, when some members of the colony eat, all eat—a really communistic set-up. In *Obelia* the hydranths and stalk are protected by a chitinous or horny sheath.

In addition to the nutritive polyps or hydranths, reproductive polyps, called **gonangia,** are present. The differentiation of members of a colony for special functions is an example of **polymorphism,** for the individuals making up the colonial animal *Obelia* appear in more than one form. A gonangium consists of a central stalk called the **blastostyle** on which produced by budding are small, rounded **medusa buds.** All these structures are enveloped by a globular transparent covering, the **gonotheca.** The asexually produced medusa buds escape through an opening in the end of the gonotheca and swim away to live their own free, independent life. A study of Figs. 151 and 152 will show that the medusas, superficially, do not resemble very closely the hydranths of the parent colony but that they actually have many points in common.

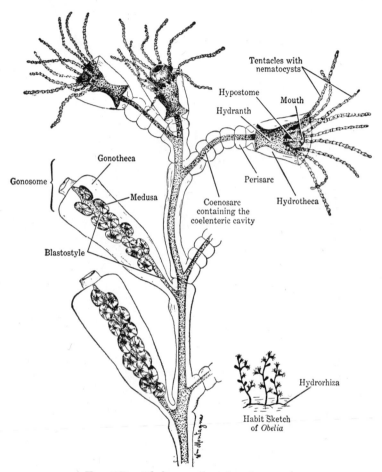

FIG. 150. *Obelia,* a colonial coelenterate.

The medusas are either male or female. In reproduction, the zygote does not develop into another medusa but into an *Obelia* colony (Fig. 152). In other words, the children resemble their grandparents. We have seen that the fixed *Obelia* colony reproduces asexually by budding, giving rise to a new generation in the form of the medusas which in turn reproduce sexually a new generation which is the colonial *Obelia.* This phenomenon, known as **alternation of**

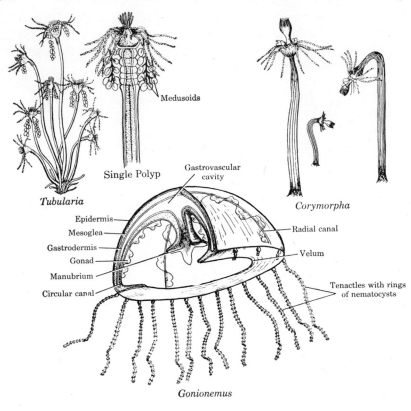

Medusoids

Single Polyp

Tubularia

Corymorpha

Gastrovascular
cavity

Epidermis

Mesoglea

Gastrodermis

Gonad

Manubrium

Circular canal

Radial canal

Velum

Tenactles with rings
of nematocysts

Gonionemus

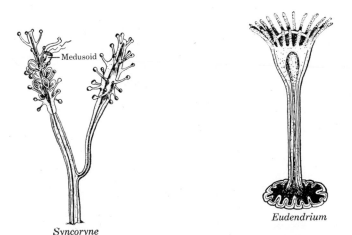

Medusoid

Syncoryne

Eudendrium

FIG. 151. *Gonionemus*, and other Hydrozoa. *Modified from various sources.*

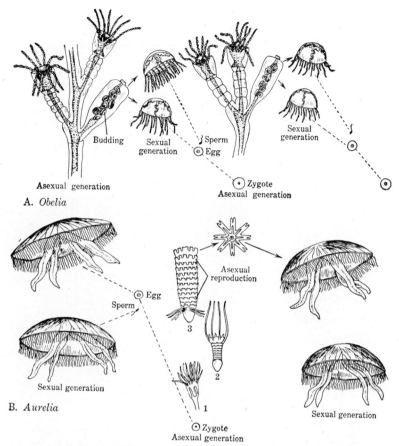

FIG. 152. Alternation of generations in a hydroid, *Obelia* (*A*), and in a jellyfish, *Aurelia* (*B*).

generations, is found more or less well developed in most of the Coelenterata except the sea anemones and corals (*Anthozoa*).

Class Scyphozoa (*skyphos*—cup; *zoon*). The jellyfishes become much larger than the medusas of the Hydrozoa. Ordinarily they measure 3 or 4 inches in diameter, but some may be as much as 6 feet across (Fig. 153). Some of the real giants may measure 12 feet in diameter and have trailing tentacles more than 100 feet long. They swim slowly about by undulations of the body and the waving of **oral arms** or "lips" which extend outward from the corners of the mouth. In some forms the lips become several feet in length. The long arms as well as a fringe of tentacles around the margin of the animal are equipped with nematocysts, which solve the food and protection problems (Fig. 153). The jellyfish are of little importance to man, but they serve as food for whales and numerous fishes. However, the nutritive value must be exceedingly small, for many jellyfishes are almost 99 per cent water.

As in the Hydrozoa, there is an alteration of generations in the Scyphozoa, but here the medusa stage is conspicuous whereas the polyp is small and relatively inconspicuous. The sexually produced zygote of the medusa grows into a polyp.

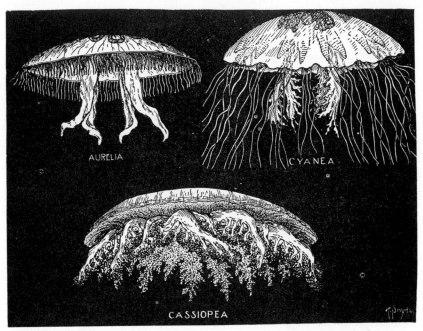

Fig. 153. Various jellyfish (Class Scyphozoa). Note the arms which assist in locomotion and the tentacles equipped with nematocysts. *By permission of the General Biological Supply House.*

As the polyp develops, a succession of grooves encircle the body and, by constriction and consequent transverse fission, eventually convert the polyp into a series of segments that resemble a pile of saucers. This is the asexual phase of reproduction. Finally, beginning with the top saucer, each segment frees itself and swims away to complete its transformation into an adult medusa or jellyfish (Fig. 152).

Class Anthozoa (*anthos*—flower; *zoon*). The Anthozoa are the sea anemones and corals (Fig. 154). There is no alternation of generations in this class, and the medusa stage is missing. The animals occur as polyps only. Some of the polyps may reach a diameter of 1½ feet, and many of them are brilliantly colored. Several circles of **tentacles** surround the **mouth,** which opens into a **gullet** (Fig. 154). The gullet leads to the **gastrovascular cavity,** which may extend up around it. The gastrovascular cavity is divided peripherally into small compartments by **mesenteries (septa),** some of which help to

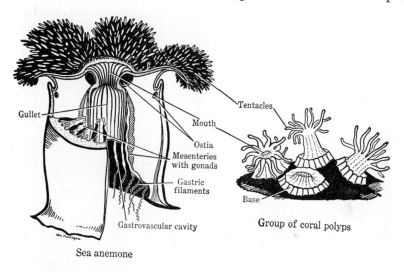

Gullet

Tentacles

Mouth

Ostia
Mesenteries
with gonads

Gastric
filaments

Base

Gastrovascular cavity

Sea anemone

Group of coral polyps

Coral atoll

FIG. 154.   Sea anemone and corals; class Anthozoa. *Upper right redrawn, modified from Buchsbaum's "Animals Without Backbones," University of Chicago Press.*

hold the gullet in place and increase the digestive surface of the gastrovascular cavity. Along the free edges of the mesenteries are found the **gonads** and the **gastric filaments** equipped with a type of **nematocyst.** The young animals pass through the early stages of development in the gastrovascular cavity, from which they escape through the mouth to find new habitations. Anemones may reproduce asexually by a type of fragmentation such as pulling apart into two halves or tearing off pieces of the body as they move about.

Fig. 155.   Corals from the Great Barrier Reef of Australia.   *Courtesy of Nature Magazine, Washington, D. C.*

The corals resemble the anemones very closely in structure, but they secrete a skeleton of lime that protects and supports the body. Usually they are colonial and live in the more shallow ocean waters. Coral islands, atolls, and coral reefs (Figs. 154 and 155) have been formed from the broken coral "skeletons." The Great Barrier Reef extends for hundreds of miles along the coast of Australia. Other species, the so-called precious corals, are red or pink and are highly prized for necklaces, charms, and other ornaments. Some coral brings as much as $400 to $600 an ounce.

19

Flatworms, Roundworms, and Segmented Worms

PHYLUM PLATYHELMINTHES

(*platus*—broad; *helmins*—worm)

The members of the phylum Platyhelminthes live in both fresh and salt water, and many of them are parasitic on man and other animals. They are, as the name implies, flattened worms which are bilaterally symmetrical. They have a digestive cavity the entrance and exit to which is through the mouth.

Class Turbellaria (*turbellae*—a stir). The little fresh-water worm *Dugesia* (*Planaria*) is often found on the under surfaces of aquatic plants, rocks, and debris. When discovered, it is usually contracted into a velvety mass and is often mistaken for a leech. When disturbed or dislodged from its hiding place in the water, it straightens out and is seen to be an animal generally less than an inch long with two simple **eye spots** on the broad or head end (Fig. 156). In the midventral surface of the body, about two-thirds of the distance from the head, is an opening, usually called the **mouth,** through which is often protruded the tubular pharynx (**proboscis**), at the end of which is the opening into the alimentary tract. The pharynx attaches to and pulls the food into the much-branched and pouched digestive tract. Here it is partially digested; the fine food particles are engulfed and digested by the cells in the digestive tract, and the food is distributed to other cells of the body by diffusion. There is no special respiratory apparatus. The excretory mechanism is made up of two lateral networks of fine tubes which open to the surface by minute pores. Lateral branches of this system end in tiny enlargements known as **flame cells,** each bearing a tuft of cilia. The beating of the cilia, resembling the flickering of a flame, causes a current of liquid to move through the tubules (Fig. 14).

There is a well-defined nervous system consisting of **cerebral ganglia** ("brain") and two **lateral nerve cords** which are connected by numerous cross branches. Probably the **eyes** can distinguish only the difference between light and darkness.

Dugesia is a true hermaphrodite, but its own eggs are never fertilized by its own spermatozoa, for the spermatozoa of two different animals are interchanged. The eggs, containing an abundance of yolk, are laid outside the body and hatch there. *Dugesia* reproduces asexually by transverse fission. It also has remarkable powers of regeneration.

The Turbellaria are of no special economic importance but most of them are interesting as the only free-living members of the phylum. These animals have muscle, connective, and nervous tissue which have combined to produce well-defined organs and systems. In addition to the ectoderm and endoderm of the preceding phyla, they have a well-defined **mesoderm**. In other words, these Metazoa are **triploblastic** (*triplex* —triple; *blastos*—bud), while the Porifera and some Coelenterata, although Metazoa, are only **diploblastic** (*diploos* —double; *blastos*).

Class Trematoda (*trematos*—hole; *eidos*—form). These are all parasitic animals known as flukes, many of which have an interesting and complicated life history. They resemble *Dugesia* in a general way but usually possess two **suckers**, one surrounding the mouth and another farther back on the body, a characteristic responsible for the name of the class (Fig. 157). The sheep liver fluke was first discovered by de Brie in 1379, who recognized it as the cause of a disease of sheep known today as "liver rot." Adult flukes have been found in other animals such as cats and dogs, and many forms are parasitic in man.

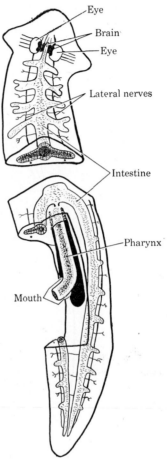

Fig. 156. *Dugesia* (*Planaria*), a free-living, fresh-water member of the phylum Platyhelminthes (flatworms). *Redrawn, modified from Buchsbaum's "Animals Without Backbones," University of Chicago Press.*

Human liver flukes are most important. *Opisthorchis sinensis* (*Clonorchis sinensis*) is found in the Far East, particularly in Korea,

Japan, China, and parts of India.   Man becomes infected when he eats that questionable delicacy—raw fish—in which these parasites are

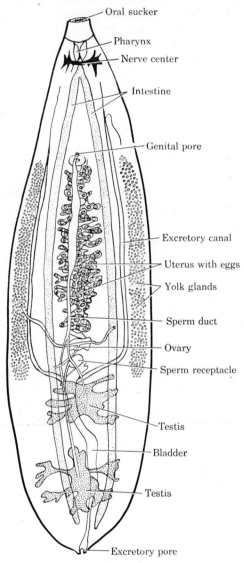

FIG. 157.   Anatomy of the human liver fluke, *Opisthorchis* (*Clonorchis*).

encysted.   The adults live in the bile ducts of the liver and the gall bladder.   These flukes are hermaphroditic.   The fertilized eggs pass out of the host with the feces.   In most flukes, eggs hatch to produce a free-swimming form called a **miracidium** (Fig. 158). The egg of *Opisthorchis,* however, does not hatch immediately into a miracidium stage but is eaten by snails. In the snail, the miracidium emerges from the egg and transforms into a **sporocyst,** which in turn produces asexually another form called a **redia.** The redias finally produce

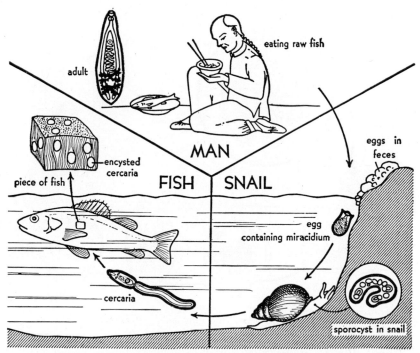

Fig. 158. Life cycle of the Chinese liver fluke, *Opisthorchis* (*Clonorchis*). *From Buchsbaum, "Animals Without Backbones." By permission of Ralph Buchsbaum and of the University of Chicago Press.*

cercarias which escape from the snail and bore into and encyst themselves in the flesh of the fresh-water fish. Man eats the raw fish, and in his stomach the young fluke emerges from the cyst and works its way up the bile duct into the liver. Here it attaches itself and feeds on man's blood. The parasite may live here for years causing anemia and various liver disturbances. Man can escape infection by not eating raw fish and by proper disposal of human feces.

Lung flukes (*Paragonimus*) normally form hollow, cystlike tubes in the lungs. The cysts contain eggs, several worms, and broken-down tissues. The eggs escape from the bronchial tubes and are

thrown off in the sputum.   The miracidia enter a snail, in which they
pass through the sporocyst stage and an additional stage known as the
redial stage.   The cercarias leave the snail and, if fortunate, encyst
themselves in a crayfish or a crab.   Man becomes infected by eating
raw crabs.   The infection is quite prevalent among the Japanese and
Chinese (Fig. 159).

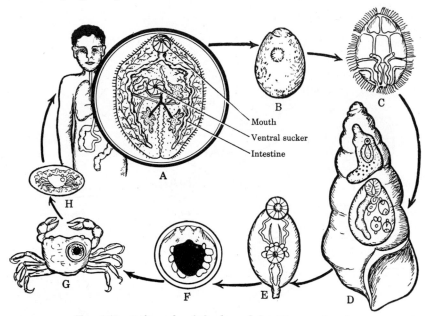

Mouth

Ventral sucker

Intestine

FIG. 159.   Life cycle of the lung fluke (*Paragonimus*).

Blood flukes (*Schistosoma*) in Egypt affect 65 to 85 per cent of
the population.   According to Christopherson, these flukes are "ac-
countable more than anything else for the indolence of spirit, want
of character, and backward condition of development of the Egyptian
peasant."   In some parts of Africa and tropical America, these parasites must be ranked among the most dangerous of human diseases.
The eggs are laid in the blood vessels of the walls of the intestine or
bladder, through which they bore and escape with the feces or urine,
although some may be accidentally carried to the liver or lungs, where
they set up inflammation.   The egg must be in a watery medium,
where it develops into a **miracidium** which immediately must find
the suitable species of snail.   In the snail the parasite passes through
a **sporocyst** stage, finally emerging as a **cercaria** which swims around
and penetrates the skin of the human individual who may be in the

water bathing. Millions of Japanese and Chinese become infected when they stand barelegged in the shallow water planting rice. The cercarias may also be ingested with drinking water. Eventually they find their way into various regions of the blood system (Figs. 160 and 161).

Intestinal flukes live in the intestinal tract of pigs and man, particularly the large intestine. Here they cause inflammation and diarrhea. The intermediate host is the snail, and the cercarias encyst on water plants. Man becomes infected with some species of flukes by eating the stems, leaves, and "fruity" nuts of the water plants that contain the encysted cercarias, and with other species of flukes by eating raw fish.

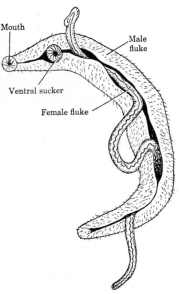

Class Cestoda (*cestos*–girdle). The cestoda are the tapeworms, all of which are parasitic. Like the flukes, these animals have lost their sense organs and all power of locomotion. There is even no digestive tract, for they live literally in a river of digested food which needs only to be absorbed. Most of the common tapeworms have the same general structure and life history (Fig. 162). The animal anchors itself in the wall of man's intestine by its knoblike "head" (**scolex**), on which are several **suckers** and often **hooks** as well. The scolex is connected by the neck to a chain of segments called **pro-**

Fig. 160. Blood fluke (*Schistosoma*). Note the male carrying the female in its ventral groove. *Redrawn from Chandler, "Introduction to Parasitology."* (*After Looss and Leuckart.*) *By permission of John Wiley & Sons.*

glottids. There may be hundreds or thousands of proglottids extending for ten or twenty feet or, in the case of the broad fish tapeworm, sixty feet! Each proglottid has a complete set of male and female reproductive organs. The nervous and excretory structures of each proglottid form integral parts of the nervous and excretory systems of the entire worm.

New proglottids are continually forming in the region nearest the scolex, hence the mature proglottids are at the other extremity of the worm. The mature proglottids, containing thousands of eggs, are continually breaking off and being discharged with the feces of the

host.   Some of the discharged eggs, depending on the species of
worms, cling to the contaminated food of a cow or a pig.   They hatch

FIG. 161.   Japanese children infested with *Schistosoma japonicum*, a blood fluke.
*Reproduced from Culbertson, "Medical Parasitology," by permission of Columbia
University Press.*

in the intestine, and the hooked embryos bore their way into the
blood vessels of the intestine and travel by way of the blood stream
to the muscles of this intermediate host, where they reorganize to

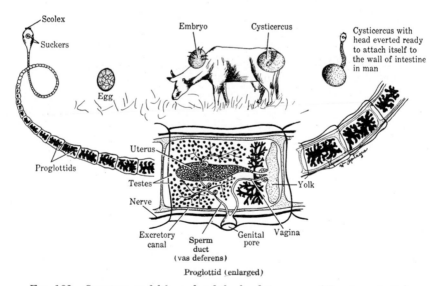

FIG. 162.   Structure and life cycle of the beef tapeworm (*Taenia saginata*).

form **cysticerci,** known as **bladder worms** (Fig. 162).   The cysti-
cercus is a little sac of liquid with the scolex of the future worm

turned into it. Eventually the intermediate host is killed and eaten by man. If the beef or pork is poorly cooked, the bladder worms are unharmed. Once they get into man's intestine, they simply evert, attach themselves, lose the bladder, and begin forming proglottids. The effect on the host is nervousness, anemia, and often loss of weight.

Some tapeworms, like certain of the flukes, have more than one intermediate host. The larva from the eggs of the "broad fish tapeworm" must be eaten by small crustaceans which in turn are eaten by the fish. Man then eats the raw fish. This tapeworm has been introduced into this country from Europe and is prevalent in the waters of Minnesota, northern Michigan, and Canada.

The method used for combating not only these parasites, but parasites in general, involves proper cleanliness in handling and preparation of food, proper disposal of wastes, and, whenever possible, the elimination of the intermediate host. The wide prevalence of parasites in the Orient is the result of the eating of uncooked food and the improper disposal of human excreta with consequent contamination of both the land and streams.

Often man is the intermediate instead of the final host for a cestode parasite. The larval stage of *Echinococcus granulosus* sometimes occurs in man and the adult in dogs. The larva develops into a "bladder" form on whose inner walls grow smaller bladders, each containing numerous "heads." This "hydatid cyst" may reach the size of an orange or even larger. Such cysts may be found in the liver, spleen, bones, or even the brain of man. They cause epilepsy and like disturbances. Constant seepage of fluid from the cyst may bring on attacks of allergy, nausea, and anaphylactic shock.

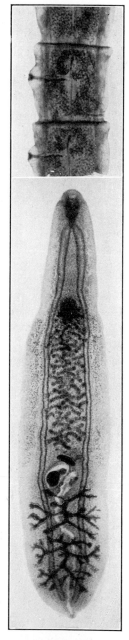

FIG. 163. *Upper,* proglottids of tapeworm; *lower,* human liver fluke. *Photographs copyrighted by Albert E. Galigher.*

PHYLUM NEMATHELMINTHES
(*nematos*—thread)

The nemathelminthes are round, slender, unsegmented worms usually pointed at both ends. They are found widely distributed in the soil, in salt and fresh water, and as parasites. The "horsehair" worm is probably the most familiar member of the phylum. It has been said that if we could wash away all the soil from a block of infected earth and leave the nematode worms in position, the outlines of the block would remain. Almost any collection of debris examined under the microscope contains these little worms, which can be seen whipping along by the contortions of the body. The unsegmented cylindrical bodies are covered with a thick tough cuticle. The worms possess longitudinal muscle layers but lack circular muscles. They move by simply "thrashing about."

A tubular digestive system is present with an entrance through the mouth and an exit through the anus. The sexes are usually separate. The phylum is of greatest interest because it numbers among its members some important parasites of man and other animals.

Ascaris. One of the most common parasites of this phylum is *Ascaris,* a roundworm found in the intestine of man. These worms may vary from a few inches to a foot in length. *Ascaris* is found most frequently in children, particularly those living in the tropics. Some of these youngsters may harbor anywhere from two to three hundred worms. The worm is fairly robust with a simple tubular intestinal tract. There are no vascular or respiratory systems, and the nervous system is poorly developed, with no sensory organs present. The worm is protected against digestion by a heavy outer horny cuticle. The bulk of the worm is occupied by the sex organs, for its main business in life seems to be to eat and reproduce.

The female *Ascaris* really lays eggs, as many as 200,000 a day, and she works almost every day! The eggs pass out with the feces, and in each egg a tiny worm develops. After a time the eggs get into man's body via fresh vitamin-rich vegetables—improperly washed—in bad drinking water, and on soiled hands. The eggs hatch. The young larvas tour the body via the blood stream. Eventually they bore from the blood vessels of the lungs into the bronchial tubes. They work their way up to the pharynx and are then swallowed and pass into the intestine, where they feed on digested food. Quite often they produce no ill effects, but sometimes the host is nervous, anemic, and subject to epilepsy and dyspeptic disorders. Real trouble arises when the wanderlust strikes these worms and starts them on a journey which may end in the liver or in the brain, where they form abscesses (Fig. 164). Sometimes they crawl up and escape through the mouth and nasal passages.

The **hookworm** (*Necator* in America) is another parasitic round-worm common in the southern part of the United States. About 1900, Stiles made the assertion that much of the laziness and shiftlessness of the "poor whites" of the South was due to an infection with hook-worm, dubbed by the newspapers in derision the "lazy germ."

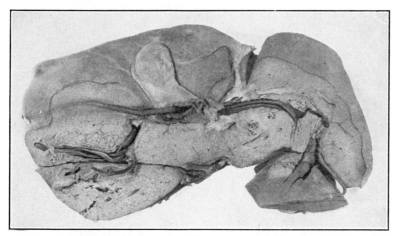

FIG. 164. *Ascaris* embedded in the bile passages of the human liver. *Photograph furnished by Army Medical Museum, Washington, D. C.*

The adult worm lives in the intestinal tract. It punctures the walls of the blood vessels of the intestine and drinks the blood of the host. Loss of blood continues even after the worm has had its meal, for it injects a secretion into the wound which prevents clotting of the blood (Fig. 165). The continual loss of blood results in anemia, lowered vitality, and increased susceptibility to disease, particularly tuberculosis. Infected children are stunted mentally and physically. Today proper sanitation and medical treatment have done much to eliminate hookworm infection and thus remedy social and economic conditions in the South (Fig. 165).

The female hookworm lays eggs at the rate of 8,000 to 10,000 per day. One stool may contain as many as 4,000,000 eggs. The eggs develop into tiny larvas which lodge in the soil. Now, if a barefooted person comes along and contact is made with the larvas, they may penetrate the skin to the blood vessels of the foot. Thence they will travel to the heart and pass out into the lungs (Fig. 165).

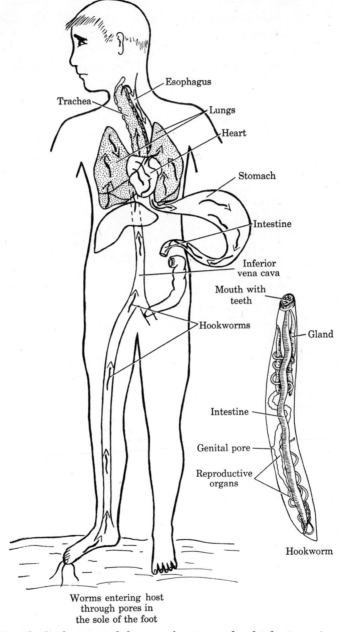

Worms entering host
through pores in
the sole of the foot

FIG. 165.   The hookworm and diagram showing mode of infection.   Arrows indicate the course followed by the hookworm from the time it penetrates the foot
until it reaches the small intestine where it attacks the intestinal wall.

Here they bore through the walls, go up through the trachea to the mouth, and travel down the alimentary tract to the intestines, where life begins for the hookworm.

Trichina is another roundworm which in the adult condition lives in the intestinal tract of man or hogs. In the adult condition it causes no harm. In the intestinal tract, the female gives birth to larvas,

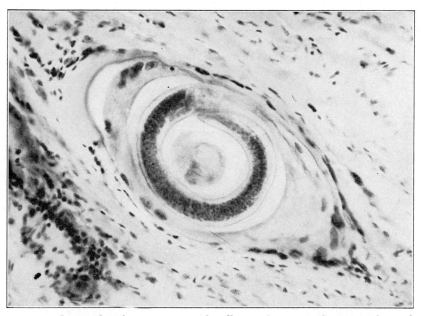

Fig. 166. Larva of trichina worm, *Trichinella spiralis*, encysted in striated muscle fibers in pork found in infected sausage. *Photomicrograph by permission of General Biological Supply House.*

which then migrate to the diaphragm and voluntary muscles of the body such as those of the ribs, tongue, and eyes, where they coil up into a loose spiral and encyst (Fig. 166). When they are present in as large numbers as a billion or more they frequently cause the death of the victim. Man acquires these unwelcome visitors by eating poorly cooked pork. The pig becomes infected by eating fragments of other pigs or rats and in time the larvas encyst in the muscles of the pig. Autopsies show that about 20 per cent of the population have been infected with trichina at some time or other. Contrary to popular belief the government does not inspect pork at the packing house. All pork should be thoroughly cooked. One ounce of fresh pork sausage may contain 100,000 encysted worms!

Wuchereria (*Filaria*) is a small worm that may be carried to the skin by a mosquito when it bites a person. The worms penetrate the skin and dam up the blood and lymph channels of certain parts

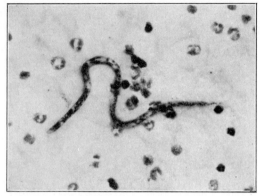

Fig. 167.   *Wuchereria* (*Filaria*).   *Photomicrograph furnished by General Biological Supply House.*

of the body, causing them to enlarge to many times normal size (Fig. 168). This disease is known as **elephantiasis.**

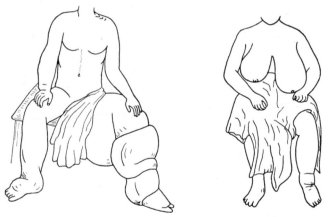

Fig. 168.   Elephantiasis.   Effects of infection with the round worm *Wuchereria* (*Filaria*).   *Modified from Chandler, "Introduction to Parasitology." (After Manson.) By permission of John Wiley & Sons.*

Pinworm (*Enterobius*) is a common infection particularly in children. The adult worms live in the cecum, appendix, and neighboring parts of the intestine. The eggs are laid and usually pass out with the feces. When members of a houschold are infected, eggs may be present not only on the hands of the members of the household but also on the clothing, bed linen, towels, floor, upholstery, and furniture. Infection takes place by entrance of the egg through the mouth.

African eye worm (*Loa loa*) is a human parasite found in western and central Africa. The adults live underneath the skin of man and creep from place to place, causing an itching and creeping sensation. Often they are found around the pupil of the eye (Fig. 169). The intermediate host of this worm is the mango fly. The young larvas invade the proboscis of the fly, and when the fly bites a person they are often deposited in the skin of the host. These parasites cause little damage to the host other than discomfort.

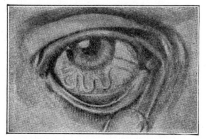

FIG. 169. *Loa loa* in the eye. (*After Fulleborn.*) *From Chandler, "Introduction to Parasitology." By permission of Asa C. Chandler and of John Wiley & Sons.*

Guinea worm (*Dracunculus*) is found parasitic in man from central Asia to Arabia and also in the East Indies, Egypt, and central Africa. In western India sometimes as much as 25 per cent of the population suffer from guinea-worm infections. The victims may suffer permanent deformities such as loss of limb or may even die from secondary infections. The female worm is the more important of the sexes. It reaches a length of 2.5 to 4 feet but is only $\frac{1}{25}$–$\frac{1}{13}$ of an inch in diameter. It crawls around under the skin. The native doctor, using a split stick, grasps the worm firmly, and then by carefully twisting the stick he winds the worm around it and thus extracts the worm from the host. Care must be taken that this treatment is carried out under antiseptic conditions. The intermediate host in the life cycle of this worm is a small water animal called *Cyclops*. Man becomes infected by drinking water containing *Cyclops*. In western India the infection is always more severe in those communities served by "step wells" where the people wade down into the water to fill the containers. It is during this time that the parent worm ejects her offspring through a hole in the skin of the host; also the drinking water may contain infected *Cyclops*.

Many other members of this phylum are parasitic on man, other animals, and plants. The fact should be emphasized that there are also many species of roundworms that are non-parasitic.

PHYLUM ANNELIDA

(*annulus*—ring; *eidos*—resemblance)

The worms of this group are very different from the ones already described.   The annelid worms are round and made up of a series of very similar joints or **segments.**   Moreover, this rather extended division or **segmentation (metamerism)** has a definite bearing on the internal organization as well.   This segmentation brings peculiar interest to the phylum for, as we shall see later, the two phyla ranking above the Annelida in structural complexity show some evidence of segmentation.   It is also of interest to note that the members of this phylum have red blood. Annelida include the common earthworm and many brilliantly colored and more complex aquatic forms, for annelids live not only on land but in fresh and salt water as well.   Very few are parasitic.

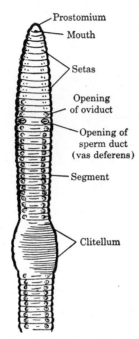

Prostomium

Mouth

Setas

Opening of oviduct

Opening of sperm duct (vas deferens)

Segment

Clitellum

Fig. 170.   Ventral view of the external anatomy of the earthworm.

Class Oligochaeta (*oligos*—few; *chaite*— hair).   The common fishing worm belongs to this class, as do all those round, segmented worms that have comparatively few stiff bristles or **setas** along the sides of the body. The anatomy and behavior of the earthworm should prove especially interesting because the animal is so much at home in practically all gardens and lawns.

The earthworm, called *Lumbricus*, lives in a subterranean burrow from which it emerges usually at night.   It attains a length of some 10 or 12 inches and has 120 to 160 **segments.   A mouth,** located at the anterior end, is overhung by a protruding upper lip called the **prostomium** (Fig. 170). The prostomium scrapes up particles of soil and vegetable matter and pushes them to the mouth, through which they are sucked by the muscular **pharynx** (Fig. 171).   There is some nourishment in the soil, but earthworms may obtain most of their food by devouring leaves or other parts of plants and even meat.   This food and the soil pass from the pharynx through a narrowed tubular **esophagus** to an enlarged **saccular crop** where they may be stored until they are ground to a pulp in the tough muscular **gizzard.**   From the gizzard

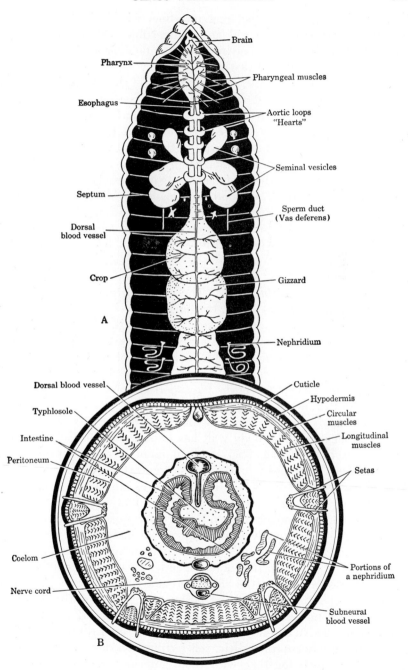

Fig. 171. Internal anatomy of the earthworm.

the material passes into the long intestine, where much of it is digested and absorbed, the soil and indigestible residue being eliminated through the **anus.** This residue may be deposited at the mouth of the burrow at night as **castings.**

The absorbed food is distributed by means of the blood, which flows through a **closed** circulatory system. This system consists mainly of a **dorsal** and a **ventral blood vessel** which are connected by branches in almost every somite. The blood is forced anteriorly by the contractions of the muscular wall of the dorsal vessel and is further propelled into the ventral vessel by five pairs of muscular **aortic arches** which encircle the esophagus. Other vessels are present besides those described. The blood contains hemoglobin. This suggests at once that the blood provides for the distribution of oxygen and carbon dioxide. The major portion of the oxygen-carbon dioxide exchange between the worm and its environment takes place through the moist skin. Membranous walls called **septa** divide the well-developed **coelom** into compartments corresponding to the "rings" seen on the outside of the worm. These compartments of the coelom are filled with coelomic fluid. In the fluid are ameboid wandering cells that may remove certain wastes. Most of the waste is removed from the coelomic fluid and transported to the exterior by the action of paired **nephridia** which are found in most of the segments (Fig. 171). Wastes may be removed from the blood by **chloragen cells** which line the coelom and cover the blood vessels. Some waste may be stored in the animal as pigment.

The seemingly simple movement of the earthworm is really somewhat complicated. The body wall has two sets of muscles, an outer layer of **circular muscle** fibers and an inner layer of **longitudinal muscle** fibers. Attached to the setas are certain muscle fibers by which they are moved. When the earthworm moves, the setas along the posterior end are protruded, anchoring that region in the burrow. The body is elongated when the circular muscles contract, exerting pressure on the relatively incompressible body fluids. Since the posterior end is anchored, when the circular muscles contract, the resulting elongation shoves the anterior end forward and lengthens the worm. Next, the setas of the anterior region are anchored, the longitudinal muscles contract, and the posterior region is drawn forward. This process repeated brings about locomotion (Fig. 172).

The reproductive activities of *Lumbricus* are interesting. Although the animals are **hermaphroditic,** self-fertilization does not take place. Two worms come together with their anterior regions overlapping (Fig. 173). Mucus is secreted, forming a broad slime band that encloses about 28 segments of each worm and assists in the transfer of spermatozoa. Spermatozoa from each worm are deposited in the

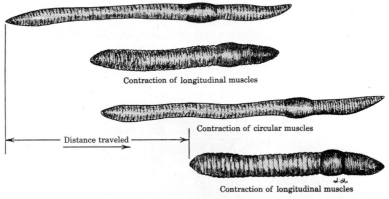

Contraction of longitudinal muscles

Contraction of circular muscles

Distance traveled

Contraction of longitudinal muscles

Locomotion

Fɪɢ. 172.   Diagram illustrating mode of locomotion of earthworm by alternate contraction of the longitudinal and circular muscles of the body wall.

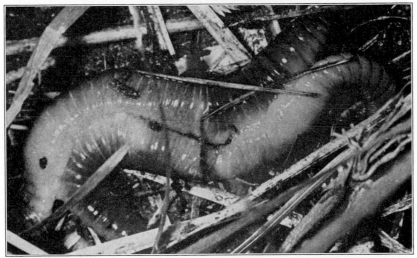

Fɪɢ. 173.   Copulation of two earthworms for the exchange of spermatozoa. The worms are held together by slime bands. *Photograph furnished by the General Biological Supply House.*

seminal receptacles of the other (Fig. 174). After this exchange of spermatozoa the worms separate. On each worm there is a swollen region (segments 32 to 37) called the **clitellum** (*clitellae*—saddle). This now gives off a secretion which forms a band or girdle of mucus. As the band is pushed forward by contraction of the body wall, it receives from the oviducts the eggs and, farther forward, the spermatozoa previously deposited by the other worm. The eggs are now fertilized. The slime band slips off the body as a cocoon, and in it the zygotes develop.

The earthworm has two dorsal anterior **cerebral ganglia** ("brain") connected to a ventral **nerve cord** that has an enlargement or **ganglion** in each segment. Earthworms are quite sensitive to light, especially at the anterior and posterior ends, and usually leave their bur-

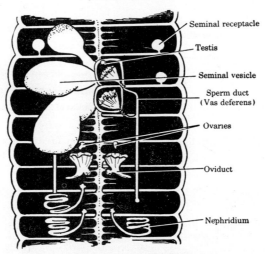

FIG. 174. Sex organs of earthworm.

rows only at night. They are positively hydrotropic, a reaction that drives them to deeper haunts during dry and cold weather. They are apparently able to taste or smell at any place on the outer surface of their bodies. Earthworms are very sensitive to vibrations.

Earthworms are of indirect value to man in that they help to keep the soil porous, permitting water to enter more readily and assisting in the aeration of roots. The leaves, dragged into the burrows and only partly eaten and digested, help to build rich humus so necessary for plant growth. Charles Darwin estimated that the castings of earthworms brought to the surface one-fifth of an inch of new soil each year—18 tons per acre—and that a rocky field might have all its rocks buried in one generation.

Class Polychaeta (*poly*—many; *chaite*—hair). The annelids of this class are common along seacoasts and more generalized than those of class Oligochaeta which includes the earthworm. They are called polychaetes because they have many bristles along the sides. · These bristles are usually arranged in bundles, a pair of bundles for each segment. Often there are present segmentally arranged pairs of fleshy lobed projecting appendages called **parapodia** (*para*—beside; *podos*) (Fig. 175). Many of the polychaetes have a rather well-defined head region. Polychaetes, unlike the hermaphroditic oligochaetes, have separate sexes.

Probably the best-known polychaete is the marine clam worm (*Neanthes virens* formerly called *Nereis*). This bluish-green poly-

Fig. 175. Clam worm *Neanthes* (*Nereis*) (Class Polychaeta). *Photograph furnished by* Nature Magazine.

chaete lives in burrows in the sand or mud, or under stones (Fig. 175). At night when it searches for food, it may leave the burrow entirely or merely protrude the anterior end of the body. It is capable of swimming through the water by graceful undulations of the body. With the exception of the head region and the last segment, the body of the clam worm is made up of 200 or more similar segments. The head region is made up of one segment differentiated into a **prostomium** which bears two short **prostomial tentacles,** a pair of short stubby **palps,** and two pairs of minute **eyes** (Fig. 176). Posterior to the prostomial region is the **peristomium** which has four pairs of dorsal **peristomial tentacles.** The tentacles, palps, and eyes are specialized sensory structures which assist the animal in finding food, avoiding enemies, and making other behavior adjustments necessary for life.

Beneath the prostomium will be found the **mouth** through which may be extruded the **pharynx** which is equipped with two horny-toothed jaws which grasp the food when the pharynx is extruded and drag it back into the animal; in other words, "swallow it," when the pharynx is withdrawn.   The pharynx leads into a narrowed tubular **esophagus** which receives the digestive fluids from two **digestive glands.**   The esophagus opens into the **intestine** which continues through the body segments to the anus at the posterior body segment.

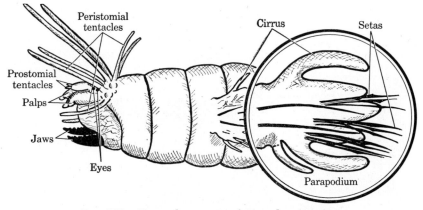

FIG. 176.   External anatomy of *Neanthes* (*Nereis*).

The polychaetes resemble the oligochaetes in many respects.   They possess a well-defined coelom which is divided up, as in the earthworm, by septa into a series of chambers which correspond to the external segments.   The coelom is filled with a fluid in which are dissolved various products of metabolism.   Ameboid cells will also be found in the coelomic fluid.   Apparently the coelom and its fluid have a function somewhat similar to the blood.   As in the earthworm there is a well-defined circulatory system of dorsal and ventral vessels with interconnecting capillaries.

Oxygen and carbon dioxide exchange takes place through the skin. However, in the clam worm, the oxygen-carbon dioxide exchange is facilitated by the flattened **parapods** each of which is equipped with an extensive network of capillaries (Fig. 176).   In almost all segments there is a pair of nephridia very similar to those present in the earthworm.

The nervous system also resembles that of the earthworm.

Other polychaetes.   Not all polychaetes are as free living as *Neanthes.*   Some live in tubes of hardened parchmentlike mucus which they rarely if ever leave.   The parapods of these forms have

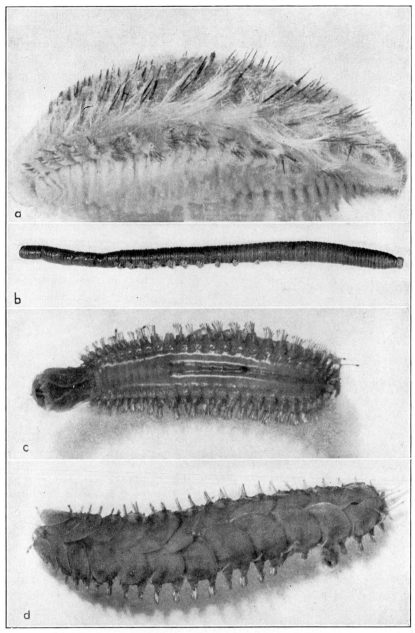

FIG. 177. Types of Annelida: *a*, sea mouse (*Aphrodite*); *b*, lugworm (*Arenicola*); *c*, ventral and *d*, dorsal view of *Lepidonotus*. Note the scales on the back. *Photographs by David Huntsberger.*

degenerated, and the head region is reduced. However, the heads are often equipped with long colored tentacles, and some worms have gill filaments. Jaws are missing and the pharynx cannot be everted. In the burrowing forms the heads and parapods are not well developed, but they have a pharynx which can be everted for feeding. (See Figs. 177 and 178.)

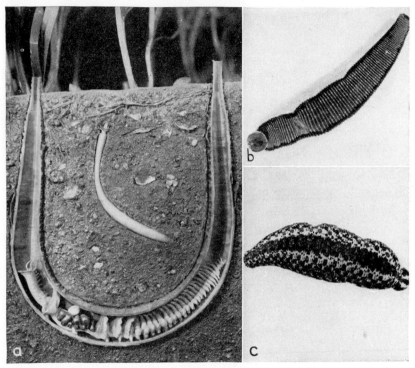

Fig. 178. Types of Annelida: *a*, tube-dwelling annelid (*Chaetopterus*); *b* and *c*, medicinal leeches (*Hirudo*). *Photograph a furnished by American Museum of Natural History; b and c, by Mrs. P. S. Tice.*

It has already been mentioned that the polychaetes are not hermaphroditic. The spawning habits of the palolo worm of the South Pacific have already been mentioned (page 198). In some forms there is a specialized phase called heteronereis in which the posterior part of the animal has enormous parapodial lobes and greatly developed bristles—modifications which make increased activity possible. Buchsbaum * gives an interesting account of the sexual activities of the "fire worms" of Bermuda.

* Ralph Buchsbaum, *Animals Without Backbones*, Chicago: The University of Chicago Press, 1948, p. 231.

. . . the meeting of the sexes involves the exchange of light signals. The worms come to the surface to spawn each month a few days after the full moon at about an hour after sunset. The female appears first and circles about, emitting at intervals a greenish phosphorescent glow which is readily visible to observers on the beach. The smaller male then darts rapidly toward the female, emitting flashes of light as it goes. When the two sexes come close together, they burst, shedding the sex cells into the sea water. Then the spent worms, reduced to shreds of tissue, perish. It has been suggested that the phosphorescent flashes of spawning polychaetes were the lights seen by Columbus on the night he approached the New World.

Class Hirudinea (*Hirudo*—leech). These annelids have no bristles, and there is no correspondence between the external and internal segmentation. Unlike other annelids leeches have a definite number of segments throughout life. Moreover, the leeches possess a sucker at each end of the body (Fig. 178).

Most leeches live on the blood of vertebrates. After attaching themselves by the suckers, they make a wound with the teeth which are down in the anterior sucker and pump themselves full of blood by the muscular action of the pharynx. The coagulation of the blood during mealtime is prevented by the injection into the wound of the host of a substance called **hirudin.** The much-pouched digestive tract holds enough blood to take care of the food problem of the leech for several months. Leeches have very little economic importance.

20

Arthropods

PHYLUM ARTHROPODA
(*arthros*—joint; *podos*—foot)

Like the Annelida, arthropods have a serially segmented body, though in some animals several segments may be fused together. Unlike that of the annelids, the cuticle covering of the body is usually in the form of a horny shell or **exoskeleton** which is thinner between the segments, a device insuring flexibility. This covering is composed mostly of **chitin,** a horny flexible substance which is waterproofed by a waxy surface layer. The cuticle in arthropods is differentiated into jaws, the hard parts of the pincers and walking legs, lenses for the eyes, wings, and other specialized structures. Further, there is a pair of somewhat long, **jointed chitinous appendages** on some segments, a characteristic that gives the name to this phylum. A better understanding of the anatomy and physiology peculiar to the members of this group will be obtained later from the description of the crayfish and grasshopper.

Arthropods are familiar to us as spiders, insects, crabs, scorpions, and the like. They are found in all habitats, and, as far as different kinds or species are concerned, they are the most numerous of all the animals. Their great number and wide distribution should indicate a great variation in structure and habits among the members of the phylum. Of all the invertebrates, they are the most highly developed, not only structurally but also socially, for here are found the ants, white ants or termites, bees, and wasps.

Class Crustacea (*crusta*—a shell). Most of the 20,000 species of this group live in the water. The class contains such animals as shrimps, crabs, lobsters, pill bugs, and the common crayfish. Almost all members of the class breathe by means of gills and have two pairs of antennas, which are the distinguishing characteristics of Crustacea. The common crayfish is a typical arthropod and crustacean. These animals, living in lakes, streams, ponds, and underground water, eat almost anything and, in turn, are eaten by most fishes. The crayfish is completely protected by its somewhat heavy chitinous **exoskeleton** which is hardened by the addition of certain calcium salts. The fused head and thorax, known as the **cephalothorax,** is covered by the rigid chitinous **carapace** (Fig. 179). The **abdomen** is covered by a jointed segmented exoskeleton. This light protective armor, however, does

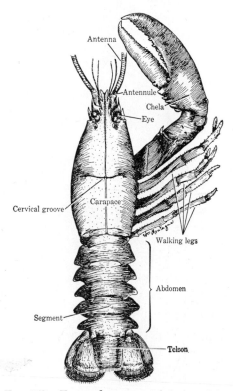

FIG. 179. External anatomy of the crayfish.

not grow, and so the growing crayfish is compelled to shed it periodically. The molting crayfish, just after the shell is lost, is called "a softshell." The animal swells up by the abnormal absorption of water, and, by the aid of stored lime, soon secretes a new shell.

As the crayfish walks slowly through the water on its four pairs of **legs,** it takes stock of its surroundings by feeling and "smelling" with its paired **antennas** and **antennules** located on the **head.** It looks around by moving its stalked **compound eyes** which bring to it mosaic images. Sometimes it goes into violent reverse by rapidly flapping its broad paddlelike **tail (telson)** (Fig. 179).

Two large modified walking legs (**chelipeds**), equipped with terminal pincers, catch prey or grasp the food and tear it up. Food is then transferred to the **mouth parts,** where it is further ground by the horny **mandibles.** It is then passed into the mouth and through

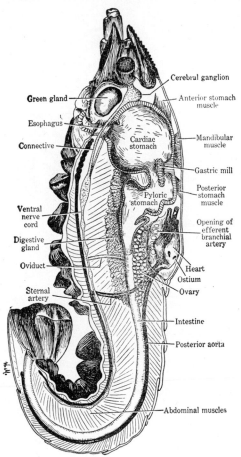

Fig. 180. Internal anatomy of the crayfish.

the **esophagus** to the **stomach** (Fig. 180). Here it is ground exceedingly fine by three serrated teeth and then strained through a sieve of bristles into the **intestine** and into **digestive glands** for digestion and absorption. The digested food is absorbed partly by the digestive gland and partly through the intestinal wall (Fig. 180).

The colorless **blood** circulates through the crayfish not only in vessels but also through **sinuses** or **hemocoels.** The blood is pumped through the body by a dorsal **heart** which fills with blood entering through little openings called **ostia.** When the heart contracts, the ostia are closed by valves. The blood distributes the oxygen which it receives as it passes through the feathery, plumed **gills** found under the edge of the carapace. Carbon dioxide is eliminated here also. Other wastes of general metabolism are eliminated by means of a pair of **green glands,** which function as kidneys. They are located in the head.

The nervous system is much like that of the earthworm. There is a dorsal **brain** in the head near the eyes. A pair of connectives

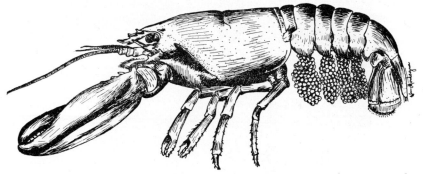

FIG. 181. "Berried" lobster. Note the eggs attached to the swimmerets on the ventral side of the abdomen.

links the brain to the ventral nerve cord, which is a double structure made up of fused paired ganglia and their connectives. In the abdominal region, where the metameric arrangement of the animal is most apparent, there is one fused ganglion for each segment. However, in the region of the cephalothorax some of the ganglia apparently have fused. For example, the subesophageal ganglion represents five or six pairs of ganglia which were separate in the embryo. From these ganglia nerves pass out to the mouth, appendages, and sensory organs (Fig. 188).

Crayfish are either male or female. The **testes** of the male are located under the heart. From them lead two twisting sperm ducts, which open at the base of the last pair of walking legs. In the breeding season, the male finds a female and transfers the spermatozoa to her. As the eggs are laid, the spermatozoa are released. The eggs are fertilized and fastened to the abdominal appendages where they develop into young crayfish. A female may carry between 300 and 600 eggs (Fig. 181).

Crustacea vary in size from microscopic forms to large lobsters and crabs. There is a wide range of variation in shape. One small fresh-water form called the fresh-water flea (*Daphnia*) is almost completely enclosed in a transparent chitinous shell. Fresh-water fleas use their antennas as swimming organs and move jerkily through the water.

a

b   *c*

Fig. 182. Types of Arthropoda (Class Crustacea): *a, Squilla; b*, edible crab (*Cancer*); *c*, sea hermit crab in an empty conch shell. *Photograph a, by Erwin S. Koval; b, by Fish and Wildlife Service, U. S. Department of the Interior; c, by John G. Shedd Aquarium, Chicago, Illinois.*

They have a dorsally placed brood pouch in which the young develop. Another rather common form is *Cyclops*, a small one-eyed crustacean whose anterior region is covered by a large shieldlike carapace. Other species closely related to *Cyclops* live on the surface of the sea in large numbers, giving it a red appearance by day and causing bio-luminescence at night. These small surface-living forms constitute a large part of the food of fresh- and salt-water fishes. Many crusta-ceans are parasitic, and some (*Sacculina*) are parasitic on other crus-taceans.

We should not dismiss the Crustacea without saying a word about barnacles which are mentioned in every salty tale of the sea. The ancestors of these sessile animals were motile. Barnacles have acquired protection by the formation of calcareous shell-like plates that

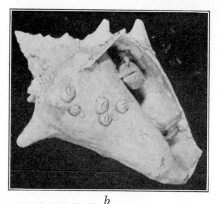
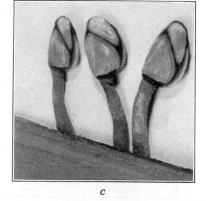

FIG. 183. Types of Arthropoda (Class Crustacea). *a,* spiny lobster; *b,* hermit crab in conch shell on which are a number of acorn barnacles; *c,* goose barnacles. *Photographs a, by John G. Shedd Aquarium, Chicago, Illinois; b and c by Erwin S. Koval.*

were responsible for the former inclusion of this group with the Mollusca. The goose barnacle is attached by a long fleshy stalk, but in the acorn barnacle the stalk is missing and the animal is attached by its shell. Barnacles are found in large numbers strongly attached to wharves, hulls of ships, and rocks along the shore.

From the standpoint of food, shrimp are probably the most important members of the Crustacea. The annual crop of shrimp for one year was over 180,000,000 pounds having a value of millions of dollars. The annual supply of crab meat represents a value exceeding three and a half million dollars. The crayfish, an almost exact model of the lobster, is likewise used more and more extensively for food. Lobsters thrive for the most part along the north Atlantic coast, where the Pilgrims found the Indians using them for food. Commercial lobsters vary in size from 2 to 5 pounds. The weight of the largest lobster on record was 34 pounds. Formerly in Canada alone more than 100,000,000 lobsters were caught in one year, and in the United States a two years' catch amounted to as much as 11,750,000 pounds. Naturally, the slaughter of any animal at such a rate soon means scarcity if not extinction. Now the government is making an effort to insure a continuous supply of lobsters by regulating the type of trap used, by licensing lobster fishermen, by protecting berried lobsters—i.e., females with eggs—and by rearing lobsters in hatcheries.

FIG. 184. A, millipede (Class Diplopoda); B, centipede (Class Chilopoda). *Photographs A furnished by Erwin S. Koval; B, by the General Biological Supply House.*

Class Chilopoda (*cheilos*—lip; *podos*—foot) and **Class Diplopoda** (*diploos*—double; *podos*). Most of us have seen centipedes and "thousand-legged worms" scurrying away when we overturned logs or stones. These animals have no typical **thorax** or **abdomen** but possess a rather distinct **head** with **antennas** and **simple eyes.** Their **segmentation, chitinous covering,** and **jointed appendages,** as well as their internal anatomy, definitely mark them as arthropods. The centipedes, class Chilopoda, with only one pair of appendages per segment, are active little animals that pursue and devour small insects and spiders after paralyzing them with a poisonous sting (Fig. 184). However, contrary to popular belief, the larger tropical forms do not inflict on man anything more serious than a painful wound. The millipedes, class Diplopoda, with two pairs of legs per segment, are rather slow-moving, non-poisonous vegetarians. They cause man little if any inconvenience.

Class Insecta (*insecare*—to cut in) or **Hexapoda** (*hex*—six; *podos*). It is doubtful if any group of animals is quite so varied in form, so interesting in life habits, and so vitally important economically as insects. From the earliest times to the present, there has been a conflict between man and insects. The warfare grows more and more intense because, in the struggle for a livelihood, each must have the same vital things at the same time, and often there is not enough for both. Howard, an entomologist, expressed the opinion that man's continued existence depends on his gaining control of the insects. He pointed out that insects have been on the earth for more than two hundred million years as compared to man's brief stay of approximately one million. Now, in 250,000,000 years, animals can become much specialized and, to a high degree, well adapted to their environment. Whether man can stay on earth will depend on his conquest of this mighty host, for it is a *mighty* host with probably more different species than all the other groups in the animal kingdom combined. However, not all insects are man's enemies, for, as will be seen later, he has some friends in the enemy's camp.

Insects differ from other arthropods in several distinctive features. Their bodies are divided into three main regions—**head, thorax,** and **abdomen.** They have **six legs,** all joined to the thorax. They breathe by means of air tubes called **tracheae,** and they usually have **membranous wings** supported by veins.

The grasshopper, an insect neither too primitive nor yet too specialized in form, is a desirable insect to study. Grasshoppers were the locusts that plagued the Egyptians, and grasshopper plagues still appear in various parts of the world. They feed on green plants, and some species may swarm over hundreds of square miles of territory leaving denuded fields as they pass along. The entire body is covered with hard, shell-like chitin, which makes a rather rigid head and thorax; but the abdomen is so constructed in jointed segments that it is fairly flexible.

On the head there is a pair of jointed tactile **antennas** in the basal regions of which are located the receptors of smell. A large **compound eye** stands out prominently on either side of the head. In addition to these, there are three simple eyes (**ocelli**) (Fig. 185). The mouth is located on the ventral region of the head and is surrounded by a number of mouth parts. There is a **labrum** or upper lip covering a pair of lateral "jaws" or **mandibles** with which the grasshopper nips off pieces of vegetables. The mandibles are assisted in their task by a pair of **maxillas** which have a pair of jointed sensory **palps.** The food is held in place for all this chewing by the lower lip or **labium,** likewise equipped with a pair of **palps.** The tonguelike prolongation of the floor of the mouth is the **hypopharynx.**

Attached to the thorax are three pairs of jointed **legs** and two pairs of **wings.** The last pair of legs, greatly elongated, is used in jumping. In running insects all the legs are similar, but in those that feed on other insects the legs may be adapted for holding the struggling prey. The wings are really chitinous evaginations or outgrowths from the

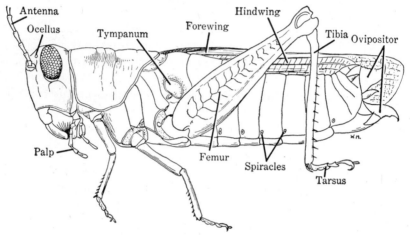

FIG. 185. External anatomy of the grasshopper.

body. Each begins as a saccular outpushing, the walls of which press together to form two thin membranes in contact with each other. Here and there appear thickened ridges called **veins,** which serve to strengthen the wings. The hardened and thickened forewings of the grasshopper fold over and protect the thinner, fanlike posterior pair. In flying, the forewings are extended rigidly like those of an airplane, and the animal is driven forward by the posterior pair. The wings vary in different insects. In some of the primitive forms like the springtails and silver fish the wings are missing. Flies and mosquitoes have only one pair. The butterflies and moths have their wings covered with beautifully formed scales. Other variations will be pointed out later.

Along the sides of the abdomen are small segmentally arranged paired openings called **spiracles,** through which air enters to the breathing tubes or **tracheae.** The posterior segments are modified in the female, forming an **ovipositor** (Fig. 185). This is used to make holes in the ground, in which eggs are laid. The ovipositor of some insects may punch a hole in woody twigs or even the trunk of a tree; in other insects it is modified into a sting. On each side of the first segment of the abdomen is a small oval membrane called the **tympanum** or eardrum. How much an insect really hears is a question.

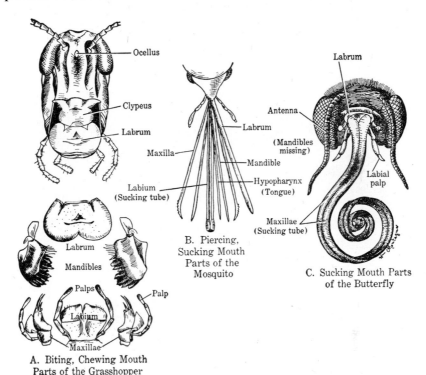

A. Biting, Chewing Mouth Parts of the Grasshopper

B. Piercing, Sucking Mouth Parts of the Mosquito

C. Sucking Mouth Parts of the Butterfly

Fig. 186. Insect mouth parts. *A*, grasshopper; *B*, mosquito; *C*, butterfly. *B and C, redrawn from Parker and Haswell, "Textbook of Zoology," Vol. I. By permission of the publisher, the Macmillan Co.*

Some grasshoppers make sounds with their hind wings, and crickets and katydids by rubbing together certain parts of the front wings.

The internal organs of the grasshopper and of all insects do not lie in a true coelom but in a blood-filled cavity known as a **hemocoele** (Fig. 187). An insect has all the systems represented that are present in man and other higher animals. The food after being chewed and mixed with saliva passes down the **esophagus** to the **crop,** a storage organ, and thence into the **gizzard,** where it is ground and mixed. It then passes into the **stomach,** where it is further digested. Extending from the anterior end of the stomach are fingerlike outpushings,

the **gastric caeca.**   The food is absorbed for the most part in the
stomach and caeca, which are modifications of the mid-gut region.   In
insects both the foregut region (esophagus, crop, and gizzard, when
present) and the hind-gut regions are lined with chitin.   The intestine is marked off into well-defined regions, the **small intestine**
and the **rectum.**   In some insects a crop is absent; a gizzard may be
missing.   In others which suck their food, the **pharynx** is modified
into a muscular suction pump.

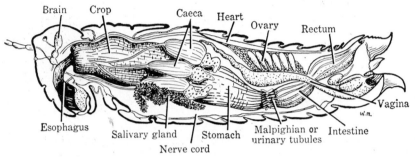

Brain   Crop   Caeca   Heart   Ovary   Rectum

Esophagus   Salivary gland   Stomach   Malpighian or   Intestine
                                                urinary tubules

Vagina

Nerve cord

FIG. 187.   Internal anatomy of the grasshopper.   The tracheal system, not shown
here, may be seen in Fig. 54.

We have already called attention to the peculiar respiratory system of insects (Fig. 54).   Grasshoppers breathe through the **spiracles,**
which lead into a vast system of many-branched, spiral-walled tubes
called **tracheae,** ultimately branching into the minute **tracheoles**
that reach every cell of the body.   This system provides for a much
more direct gaseous exchange than the blood stream.   The spiracles
may be guarded by hair, plugs (to exclude matter), or closed valves.
Some aquatic insects breathe by means of the gills; others carry under
the water air bubbles clinging to certain parts of their bodies.   The
main excretory system is made up of fine **Malpighian tubules,**
which lie in the blood sinuses and which extract nitrogenous wastes
from the blood, voiding them into the intestine near its junction with
the stomach.   Although radically different in structure the Malpighian tubules have the same function as the kidneys of other
animals.

The circulatory system of the grasshopper and other insects is very
simple.   The **heart** is merely a dorsal tube surrounded by blood which·
enters through **ostia.**   The blood is yellowish or greenish in color, has
no red corpuscles, and functions mainly in the distribution of food
and wastes; it is distributed through the body by a system of spaces

(hemocoeles). Various devices such as partitions serve to direct it in a fairly definite course through the animal.

The nervous system is very similar to that of the earthworm and crayfish, as well as other arthropods (Fig. 188). There is a dorsal brain joined to the doubled **ventral nerve cord** by a pair of connectives. The ventral nerve cord begins anteriorly with the **sub-**

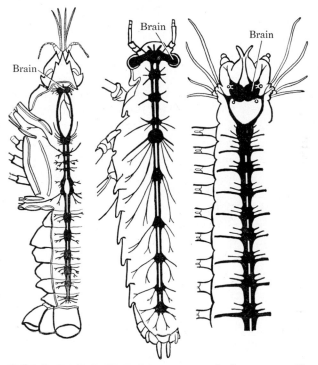

FIG. 188. Nervous systems of crayfish, insect, and clamworm. *Clamworm re-drawn, modified from Buchsbaum's "Animals Without Backbones," University of Chicago Press.*

esophageal ganglion, which controls most of the mouth parts. There are three **thoracic ganglia.** Much of the nervous activity of insects is of the reflex type. Apparently each ganglion has fairly independent control of a definite region of the animal. An insect whose brain has been removed lives, walks, and flies, but in a very erratic manner. We have previously described the functioning of the compound eyes and mentioned the fact that the antennas and mouth parts are the centers of taste and smell. The receptors of touch seem to be located in sensory hairs found on the body. Each of these special hairs has a tiny nerve fiber running to it. The "taste cells," or, more properly speaking, chemoreceptors, are thin-walled cones or plates which cover the sensory cells. They are kept moist by a secreting cell. Solid particles and gases are dissolved in the moist secretion, and the impulse is transmitted by nerve fibers. Insects are able to detect odors imperceptible to man. We have already called attention to the ears or tympana of the grasshopper. They apparently are set in vibration by sound waves. In the mosquito it is thought that certain whorls of hair on the antennas serve as organs of hearing.

All insects are either male or female. The male has two **testes.** Leading from them are two sperm ducts which fuse, forming a duct that opens to the outside. Various accessory glands may be present which aid in the transfer of spermatozoa from the male to the female. Female grasshoppers are readily distinguished from the males by the **ovipositor.** The eggs leave the **ovary** by the **oviducts,** which unite to form the **vagina.** This opens to the exterior through the **genital opening.** Above this opening is a tubular **seminal receptacle (spermatheca)** in which the male deposits the spermatozoa during copulation. The spermatozoa are released to fertilize the eggs as they are laid.

Metamorphosis of Insects. Many of the insects during their lives undergo remarkable changes in form; butterflies were once caterpillars, and shiny beetles developed from soft, wormlike grubs. The most striking changes of metamorphosis of insects occur in the external form of the body. Often there seems to be but little in common between the successive stages represented in the development of the same insect. On the basis of these differences four distinct types of development are recognized (Fig. 189):

Development without metamorphosis. The young insects just hatched are practically of the same form as the adults. This type of development is found among such primitive insects as silver fish and springtails.

Gradual metamorphosis. The young insects, **nymphs,** resemble the adults in general form of the body and mode of life. The changes that do take place—growing of the body, wings, and genital appendages—are very gradual and never conspicuous between two successive **molts.** A young grasshopper undergoing gradual metamorphosis is wingless. Grasshoppers, cicadas, earwigs, and true bugs have this type of metamorphosis.

Incomplete metamorphosis. The changes that take place are greater than those occurring in gradual metamorphosis and fewer than those of complete metamorphosis. The young insects (sometimes called **naiads**) differ markedly from the adults in form of body and mode of life. The naiads are adapted for an aquatic life, whereas the adults are terrestrial. Dragonflies, mayflies, and stoneflies have this type of metamorphosis.

Complete metamorphosis. Insects that exhibit this type of metamorphosis undergo astounding changes in their young stages, and the

Egg   Nymph 1   Nymph 2   Nymph 3   Adult

Gradual metamorphosis of the grasshopper

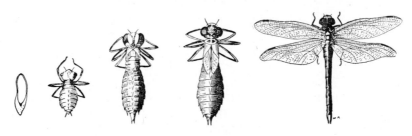

Incomplete metamorphosis of the dragon-fly

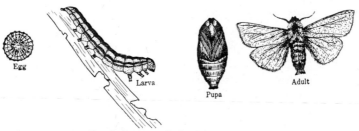

Egg

Larva   Pupa   Adult

Complete metamorphosis of the army worm

Fig. 189.   Metamorphosis of insects.

young do not even remotely resemble the adults. The classic example is the butterfly, which hatches from the egg as a caterpillar that transforms into a **chrysalis** or **pupa** from which it emerges as an adult insect. The pupa may be enclosed in a cocoon of spun fibers. Since so many different kinds of insects have this type of metamorphosis, the young stages are given different names: a young butterfly is a larva, a young beetle is a grub, and a young fly is a maggot. The term larva, in a broader sense, is used to denote immature insects of all kinds.

With these general facts in mind, we shall study some of the more important and interesting orders of insects.

Order Orthoptera (*orthos*—straight; *pteron*—wing). This group of insects brings together some very "queer" and dissimilar specimens. Here we find roaches, grasshoppers, crickets, katydids, and such curious forms as the walking-stick and the praying mantis (Fig. 190). These insects have chewing mouth parts. The males of some of the species are noisemakers. Apparently the silent females can hear. We have already said something about grasshoppers and how they can clear a countryside of everything green. In 1913 there was a plague of these insects in the western part of the United States. They were so numerous that railroad trains were stopped because the rails became slippery with the crushed bodies of so many insects. Grass on an area of more than 500 square miles was destroyed in this plague. Roaches are running orthopterans which prefer the warm indoors. They frequent all sorts of filthy and dusty places and may carry disease germs. They are fond of various foods and will chew also at woolen goods, leather, and anything starchy. They ruin the food they do not eat by perfuming it with their disagreeable roachy odor. Crickets do not bother us much unless their cheerful chirping becomes too monotonous. Walking-sticks injure trees by eating the leaves. They have a curious appearance resembling the twigs of a tree. The female drops her eggs from the trees to the ground, and there parental care ceases. The praying mantis is a curious orthopteran that holds up the body and the front legs as though in a reverent attitude. However, this attitude is its proper posture for catching and crushing other insects.

Order Coleoptera (*koleos*—sheath; *pteron*—wing). Coleoptera is the largest order of Insecta, with over 175,000 species. In fact, two-fifths of all kinds of known insects are beetles. Beetles are extremely important, for they feed on practically all kinds of plants, stored food, and other materials. They are readily recognized by their horny, non-veined forewings (**elytra**), which serve as shields or sheaths to cover the membranous hindwings, hence the name Coleoptera. The mouth parts are of the chewing type like those of the Orthoptera. The Coleoptera have a complete metamorphosis, and the larvas are known as grubs and borers (Plate XII).

A number of beetles are very injurious. The potato beetles, erroneously called "potato bugs," came from Mexico and then spread east and west until they are now widely distributed. Nor should we overlook another Mexican immigrant, the Mexican bean beetle, whose insatiable appetite for green beans and bean plants has caused

Walking-stick   Katydid

Praying mantis   Grasshopper

Cricket

FIG. 190. Orthoptera.

many amateur gardeners to forsake bean culture. Volumes could be written about the depredations of various beetles, but we shall merely list a few more. The larvas of pea and bean weevils bore through and ruin peas and beans. The cotton boll weevils caused cotton interests in the United States a loss of $470,000,000 in 1949. The larvas of the locust borer, the apple-tree borer, the sugar-maple borer, and other insect borers do their share of damage. It is estimated that bark beetles annually destroy trees worth $100,000,000. One of the best known of the destructive beetles is the Japanese beetle which landed on our New Jersey shores about 1916. From here it has spread to many parts of the United States. Some areas are more infested than others. These beetles eat both foliage and fruit, and their larvas (grubs) may injure the roots of plants by feeding on them.

But not all beetles are so unfriendly. Some are really beneficial and extremely interesting, among them being the carnivorous tiger beetles and certain ground beetles which spend most of the time busily hunting other insects. Scavenger beetles eat or bury decaying matter. The "tumblebug," really one of the scarab beetles, lays its egg in a ball of dung and then buries it. The young larva feeds on the dung that the provident parent has provided. We should not fail to mention the ladybird beetles, many of which, both as larva and adult, feed on plant lice and scale insects. Dead, dried, and pulverized blister beetles are applied by physicians in plasters to raise blisters on the skin.

Fireflies are not flies but beetles, and the females are wingless (glowworms). Junebugs are really not bugs; they are beetles.

Order Lepidoptera (*lepis*—scale; *pteron*). Lepidoptera is a very large order, including some of the most destructive as well as the most beautiful insects such as moths, butterflies, and skippers. They have four membranous wings which are shingled over with scales, hence the name Lepidoptera. In fact, scales cover most of the body and readily rub off on the fingers in the form of dust, hence the common name "miller" is applied to some of these insects, especially the moths. The scales are of various shapes and contain the pigment responsible for the beautiful colors of moths and butterflies. The surface of the scales is creased with fine ridges or striae, as many as 35,000 to the inch, through which the light rays are diffracted. In some Lepidoptera this diffraction produces a beautiful iridescence.

Lepidoptera have highly specialized mouth parts adapted for sucking. Adult moths and butterflies feed mostly on nectar, hidden away at the bottom of the corolla of the flowers. Along the sides of the mouth is a pair of hairy or scaly palps, between which arises a slender tube, called a **proboscis,** used for siphoning the liquid food of the moth or butterfly. Usually the length of the proboscis is about the same as the depth of the corolla, sometimes reaching a length of ten inches. When not in use such a long proboscis is coiled up like a watchspring. Flower visitation by moths and butterflies assists in cross-pollination.

To the average observer butterflies and moths are indistinguishable (Plate XIII). However, several differences, not all infallible, serve to separate the two subgroups. The antennas of butterflies are knobbed, but those of moths are feathery or hairlike. Butterflies usually fly by day and moths by night. When resting, butterflies usually hold their wings in a vertical position; moths hold theirs horizontally or spread out.

Lepidoptera have a complete metamorphosis in which the larval or caterpillar stage is the most destructive. The white butterfly with black spots on the wings, a very common form, is called the cabbage butterfly because its green larvas "riddle" cabbage leaves. Other interesting butterflies are the swallowtails, the mourning cloak, and the monarch. Larvas of moths are the most destructive Lepidoptera. We need only to mention the tent caterpillars and the webworms which eat the leaves of shrubs and trees, the coddling moth whose larvas make such interesting and ruinous tracings in the apple, and the army worm which "marches" in countless numbers from field to field to destroy the green vegetation in its path. The brown-tailed moth, introduced into New England, not only is a pest on shade trees but also its hairs, shed during molting, are very irritating to the skin of certain people. The gypsy moth, accidentally introduced from Europe, has caused serious havoc with all types of trees. It is a real menace to our forests. The clothing moth causes untold damage to wearing apparel and other fabrics. The European corn borer is responsible for heavy losses in the corn crop of certain regions.

However, there are some helpful Lepidoptera. For example, the silkworm moth was domesticated in China many centuries before Christ. The larvas at the age of forty days spin cocoons of a single silken thread more than 1,000 feet long. Man then kills the larvas with heat and unwinds the thread for his own use.

Order Diptera (*dis*—twice; *pteron*). The Diptera are the flies, mosquitoes, gnats, and the midges (Fig. 191). True to their name, they have only two wings, the forewings, the hindwings being reduced to a pair of short, slender threads with knobs on the end. These threads, called **halteres** or **balancers,** may be organs of equilibrium. The wings are small, gauzy, and adapted for very swift flight. The mouth parts are of the piercing-sucking type. Many Diptera feed on nectar and pollen; others on decaying flesh; some on blood; and still others dissolve and then suck up solid substances, as the housefly sucks up the icing of a cake.

The Diptera have a complete metamorphosis. Many larval flies are known as maggots and are found in decaying animal or vegetable matter. The larvas of certain gallflies feed on living plants. Some of the flies are viviparous, and in rare instances the larvas reproduce

Robber Fly (*Erax*) Peacock Fly (*Euaresta*) House Fly (*Musca*) Systropus

FIG. 191. Types of flies. Order Diptera.

young. This production of young by animals sexually mature but in other respects immature, such as larvas, is called **paedogenesis** (*pais* —child; *genesis*—descent).

Horseflies are pests of horses and cattle. Here the "female of the species is more deadly than the male," for she sucks blood and he lives on nectar. Botflies cause great losses in domestic cattle. The female botfly fastens her eggs to the hair on the legs or shoulders of a cow or horse. When the host licks them off, they hatch. The young larvas are swallowed by the host and live in the walls of its stomach until in the pupa stage they are voided with the feces. Oxwarble, whose larvas live under the skin, alone causes an annual damage estimated at $100,000,000, by boring through and ruining the hides of cattle. The Hessian fly, the insect most destructive to wheat, causes an annual damage estimated at $100,000,000. It feeds on the stems, weakening them and causing them to ripen prematurely or even to break over so that maturation of the grain is prevented or reduced. The apple maggot, the larval stage of a dipteran, bores through the pulp in all directions. The tachina flies are among the beneficial Diptera. They lay their eggs in grasshoppers and various caterpillars. When the egg hatches, the larva feeds on the host in which the egg was laid. Robber flies feed on other insects.

Order Hymenoptera (*hymen*—skin; *pteron*). Most of us readily recognize three kinds of Hymenoptera—ants, bees, and wasps (Fig. 192); but perhaps we do not know some of the other members, such as the gall wasps, the parasitic wasps, and the sawflies. Hymenoptera should top the list of invertebrate orders, for they exhibit a high degree of social organization and complex behavior. Many bees, ants, and wasps exhibit parental care, daily bringing food to the larvas, cleaning the nests, and guarding them. Other Hymenoptera, such as the many solitary bees, wasps, and gall-making species, merely lay their eggs where food is abundant.

Ant (*Tetramorium*)

Bumblebee (*Bombus*)

Hymenoptera have two pairs of small, scantily veined, membranous wings. Often the hindwings are fastened to the margin of the forewings by tiny hooks. The mouth parts vary from the chewing-lapping plan to the chewing type. Hymenoptera have a complete metamorphosis in their life history. Another peculiarity is that the ovipositor is often modified to form a sting; consequently only the females sting. As most of us know, the honeybee usually loses her sting in the wound because the nine or ten hooks on each dart which makes up the sting are pushed far into the wound. Some poison is added from the poison glands, making the wound more painful. Other Hymenoptera do not lose their sting and so can repeat the job. The sting with its poison is often used to stupefy other insects upon or in which eggs are laid, and then the victims are sealed up in the nest where they may serve as food for the young Hymenoptera.

Wasp (*Chlorion*)

Hornet (*Monobia*)

Fig. 192. Ants, bees, and wasps. Order Hymenoptera.

The sawflies are really Hymenoptera. They are so named because the female has a long, sawlike ovipositor which she uses to make holes in plants in which she deposits her eggs. The eggs hatch into larvas which carry on serious depredations on currant bushes, willow trees, and other trees. Closely related are the gallflies, which puncture and lay their eggs in such plants as roses and oaks. The injury and the developing larvas cause the wounded part to produce excessive growths or galls which have various characteristic forms (Fig. 193). The larvas feed on this excessive wound tissue. Sometimes the true owners of the galls may entertain guests of the same superfamily and

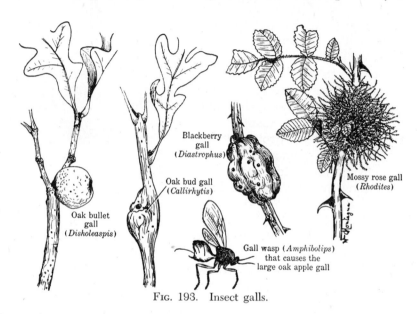

Blackberry
gall
(*Diastrophus*)

Oak bud gall
(*Callirhytis*)

Mossy rose gall
(*Rhodites*)

Oak bullet
gall
(*Disholeaspis*)

Gall wasp (*Amphibolips*)
that causes the
large oak apple gall

FIG. 193.   Insect galls.

numerous parasites. One oak gall contained guests of ten different species as well as forty-one species of parasites besides, of course, the gall maker! The chalcid "flies" are small Hymenoptera about one-fiftieth of an inch long. There are thousands of species of these flies, many of which are helpful in parasitizing the eggs, larvas, and pupas of harmful insects. They also make fig culture possible in this country.

Wasps are interesting Hymenoptera; some of them live in the ground, and others build nests of wood or mud. Many wasps make nests by excavating burrows in the ground. They lay their eggs and then provision the nest with paralyzed spiders, caterpillars, and other insects on which they lay their eggs. Some wasps often capture insects which are too large for them to transport by flying to the nest. They have to push and drag the prey over the ground. The paralyzed hosts are sealed in the nest, and when the eggs hatch the young larval wasps have a plentiful food supply.

The honeybee is a social insect. In other words, a number of bees live together in a social group where there are different castes and division of labor (Fig. 194). In a hive of bees we find a queen whose job is to lay eggs. The workers, which are sterile females, do a num-

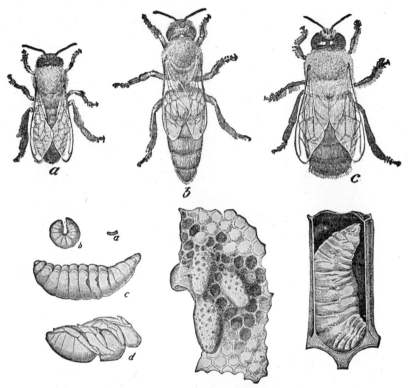

FIG. 194. Castes of the honeybee and some stages in their life history. *Above, a,* worker, or sexually immature female; *b,* queen, or sexually mature female; *c,* drone, or male. *Below, left,* egg (*a*), larval stages (*b* and *c*), and pupa (*d*); *center,* comb, showing some larger queen cells; *right,* side view of late larval stage within a cell. *From Curtis and Guthrie, "Textbook of General Zoology."* (*After White and Phillips, U. S. Department of Agriculture.*)

ber of different jobs in the community. They gather nectar and pollen from the flowers. The nectar mixed with saliva is carried home in the honey sac, a modification of the crop (Fig. 195). The pollen is carried on brushlike structures (pollen baskets) on the legs. The nectar mixture is regurgitated into the hexagonal cells in the waxy honeycomb, where, by the aid of the fanning wings of other workers, it is evaporated to the syrupy honey consistency. The cell is then sealed up. These cells were made from wax produced by wax glands.

The wax is carefully chewed and kneaded by the mandibles before it is placed in the comb. It has been estimated that between 40,000 and 80,000 trips, or more, are necessary to collect enough nectar to

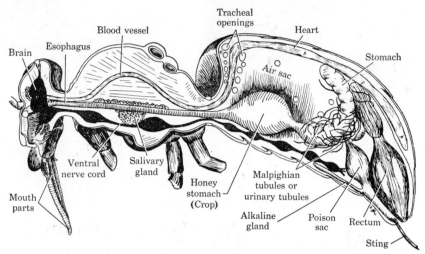

Fig. 195. Anatomy of the honeybee (worker).

make a pound of honey. If a single bee did this it would travel a distance equal to twice around the world.

Some workers create currents of air in the hive to aid in condensation of the honey; others clean the hive; and still others care for the

Fig. 196. A swarm of bees. *Photograph by Frank C. Pellet.*

young bees. The males do no other work than to fertilize the virgin queen in her nuptial flight. Bees "swarm" when a queen leaves the parent hive and takes with her many of the workers and drones to found a new community (Fig. 196). Bees produce annually more than $20,500,000 worth of honey and wax. In addition they make an invaluable contribution to plant pollination. Few people realize that in addition to the social bees there are a number of species of solitary bees.

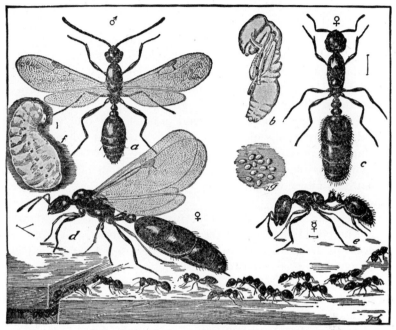

Fig. 197. Castes of the little black ant *Monomorium*. Order Hymenoptera. *a*, male; *b*, pupa; *c*, wingless female; *d*, winged female; *e*, worker, or sexually immature female; *f*, larva; *g*, eggs; group of workers in line of march below. *From Sanderson and Peairs, "Insect Pests of Farm, Garden, and Orchard." (After Marlatt, U. S. Department of Agriculture.)*

Ants, widely distributed over the world, may be the most abundant insects from the standpoint of numbers. Ants feed on a variety of foods. They may eat dead or helpless insects or keep aphids as slaves and feed on their sweet excretion, called honeydew. They also find stored sweet foods quite satisfactory. Socially ants are even further developed than bees (Fig. 197). As in the bee colony, the queen founds the colony and the male's function is to fertilize the queen. All the workers are sterile females. Among the workers may be found large and small individuals, soldiers, gardeners, and attendants for the queen. In the ant colony the queen produces eggs and larvas, often numbering thousands, which are cared for by the workers. The queen's sole task is egg laying.

The male and female ants are winged and mate while in flight. After the nuptial flight the males die; the queen breaks off her wings and seeks out a cavity or makes one in the ground. She then closes the opening of the cavity and remains isolated for a period of days, weeks, or months. When the eggs in the ovary have matured they are fertilized by the spermatozoa she received from the male. The eggs are then laid. They soon hatch, and the queen takes care of the young by feeding them from her own saliva. After the young are mature they take over all the duties of the colony except egg laying.

Order Hemiptera (*hemi*—half; *pteron*—wing). The Hemiptera are the true bugs. They have piercing and sucking mouth parts which enable them to pierce both plants and animals and suck out the sap or blood. Some groups of these insects are without wings, but as a rule wings are present. The front wings have two regions: the anterior portion is hard and horny, the posterior thin and transparent. Between the bases of the wings there is usually a characteristic triangular plate.

This group includes a number of insects injurious to man (Plate XIV). The chinchbug, one of the worst pests, feeds on small grains and corn. In the Mississippi valley, in a single season, it caused damage estimated at $100,000,000. These bugs are kept partially under control by a fungus disease. The tarnished plant bugs feed on more than fifty kinds of plants. They attack fruit trees in bud, flower buds, and the leaves of potatoes and beets. The bedbug, a blood sucker, belongs in this group.

However, we do have some friends in this group. There are the ambush bugs which hide in plant blossoms and capture insects as they visit the plant. Other bugs delight in a diet of bedbugs. The water-striders are often seen scooting over the quiet surface of the water in some pond or sluggish stream, and associated with them are small, greenish black water boatmen. On the bottom of the pond there may be giant waterbugs two or three inches in length. All these are carnivorous and feed on other insects.

Order Homoptera (*homos*—same; *pteron*). The mouth apparatus of this order is about the same as that in Hemiptera, but the beak is attached to the head differently. The wings may be lacking, but when present they are similar in texture throughout (Plate XIV). When the insect is at rest the wings are usually held folded over the back, resembling the roof of a house. There is quite a difference in the appearance of the members of this order, which includes such extremes

Fig. 198. Leaf hoppers. (Order Homoptera). *Photographs by Cornelia Clarke, courtesy of* Nature Magazine.

as the cicadas, the leaf hoppers and tree hoppers, plant lice, scale insects, and others.

The seventeen-year locust is really an interesting homopteran, a cicada. The female using her ovipositor gouges a series of grooves in the twig of a tree and lays her eggs in them. The twig dies. In about six weeks the eggs hatch; the nymphs fall to the ground and dig in to live seventeen years as nymphs. During this period they secure their food by sucking the juice from roots. After seventeen years of this secluded life, they leave the soil, crawl up on a plant, shed their last nymphal skin, and emerge as adult cicadas to make the summer air hideous with their rasping, discordant songs.

The leaf hoppers assume many bizarre forms (Fig. 198). The adults cause most of the damage when they puncture the twigs of plants in laying their eggs. Another interesting group of the hoppers are the "spittle" insects, whose nymphs hide in a mass of froth on the grass or other plant in which they may be feeding.

The aphids or plant lice bury their beaks in a plant and suck the sap. One species of aphid attacked the grapes of Europe and destroyed over 2,000,000 acres of grapes before it could be checked. The tiny scale insects do much damage to plants. The female anchors herself by pushing her beak into a plant, covers herself with a scale, and is fixed for life, while the male roves around freely. Some of the scale insects are important economically. Shellac, cochineal, and china wax, one of the ingredients of furniture polish, are made from the dried scales of some of these insects. One of the worst pests of this group has been the San Jose scale, which was introduced from China or Japan and is very destructive of fruit trees.

Order Odonata (*odontos*—tooth). The Odonata are the dragonflies, devil's darning-needles, or snake doctors, as they are variously called. Damselflies also belong to this order. These insects have well-developed jaws, biting mouth parts, and huge bulging compound eyes, some of which have as many as 30,000 facets. They are carnivorous, feeding on smaller insects, both friend and foe from man's standpoint. The young nymphs live in water and destroy many mosquito larvas. The nymphs also form an important item of fish food (Fig. 199).

Order Isoptera (*isos*—equal; *pteron*). The Isoptera are the so-called white ants or termites. They are often found in decaying trees or in the woodwork and supports of dwellings, where they do considerable damage. They are strongly negative to light and will build covered runways of soil mixed with secretions to get from one working place to another. They resemble ants in their social organization, although they have an even more complicated caste system. There are kings, queens, soldiers, policemen, and workers of several types. In fact, in some colonies there are as many as eight different castes. The queen tears off her wings after mating and becomes greatly en-

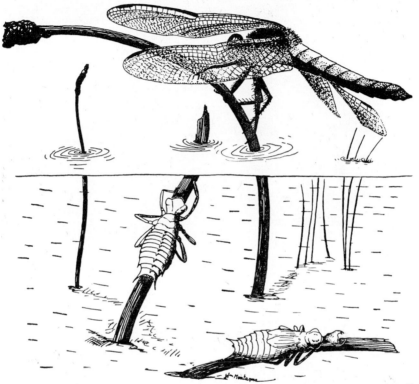

FIG. 199. Dragonfly and nymphs (Order Odonata). Note the aquatic habitat of the nymph.

larged, sometimes almost a thousand times as large as her consort. Her sole function is to produce eggs. She then becomes so helpless that she requires the services of nurses to feed her and keep her clean (Fig. 200).

Other orders of insects are:

Order Thysanura (*thysanos*—fringe; *oura*—tail). Springtails and silver fish which destroy starchy materials such as book bindings.

Order Ephemerida (*ephemeros*—lasting but a day). Adult mayflies live only to mate, lay their eggs, and die.

Order Plecoptera (*plekein*—to twine; *pteron*—wing). Stoneflies, whose nymphs make excellent fish food.

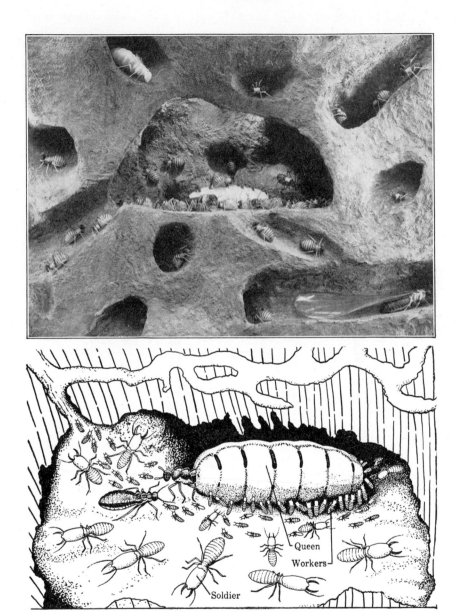

FIG. 200. Termites. Order Isoptera. *Above,* model of nest of termites and tunnels through the wood; *below,* drawing of various castes. *Photograph furnished by the Buffalo Museum of Science, Buffalo, New York.*

Order Corrodentia (*corrodeus*—gnawing).   Book and bark lice.

Order Mallophaga (*mallos*—a lock of wool; *phagein*—to eat).   Biting bird lice which eat hair, feathers, and epidermal scales.   They are not fatal but very annoying to chickens and other birds.

Order Thysanoptera (*thysanos*—fringe; *pteron*).   Thrips, which are often destructive to citrus fruits.

Order Neuroptera (*neuron*—nerve; *pteron*).   Ant lions, which are carnivorous. Aphis lions live on aphids.   Larval ant lions, "doodlebugs," hide in their sandy pits where they capture and suck the blood of ants which happen to fall in.

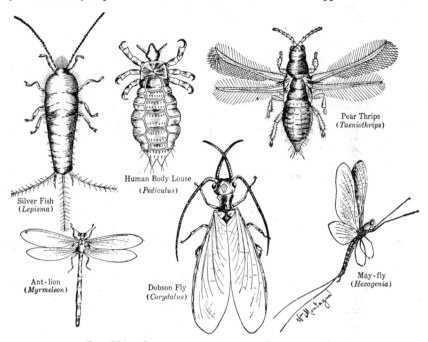

Pear Thrips
(*Taeniothrips*)

Human Body Louse
(*Pediculus*)

Silver Fish
(*Lepisma*)

Ant-lion
(*Myrmeleon*)

Dobson Fly
(*Corydalus*)

May-fly
(*Hexagenia*)

Fig. 201.   Some common insects of various orders.

Order Megaloptera (*megas*—large; *pteron*).   Dobson flies, whose larvas, familiar to many as the "hellgramites," are used for fish bait.

Order Mecoptera (*melsos*—length; *pteron*).   Scorpion flies.

Order Trichoptera (*trichos*—hair; *pteron*).   Caddice flies, whose aquatic larvas build a case of bits of leaves, grass, or sand for protection.

Order Siphonaptera (*siphon*—tube; *a*—without; *pteron*).   Degenerate fleas, which have lost their wings and have sucking mouth parts.   Their bodies are laterally flattened, and the legs are adapted for jumping.   They are found in the fur and feathers of animals.

INSECTS AND DISEASE

Contrary to oft-repeated accusations there has been no clear case against the bedbug as an important **vector** (*vectum*—borne) in disease. Excessive biting by the bugs may cause anemia, nervousness, and "influenzalike" symptoms. The sucking lice (Anoplura) are most important as disease vectors; they transmit typhus fever and trench fever, two diseases that may assume epidemic proportions in wartimes and famine. Lice do not transmit the disease by biting but only by contamination with their excreta or from their crushed bodies. The infectious parasite *Rickettsia* may live for several weeks in the dried dead bodies and feces of the lice. Relapsing fever, caused by spirochetes, is transmitted only by broken and crushed lice. Lice

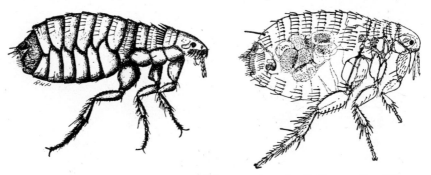

FIG. 202. *Left,* a dog flea (*Ctenocephalus canis*); *right,* Indian rat flea (*Xenopsylla cheopis*), a vector of bubonic plague. *Dog flea from Peairs, "Insect Pests of Farm, Garden, and Orchard," published by John Wiley & Sons. Rat flea from Thomas T. Mackie et al., "Manual of Tropical Medicine," W. B. Saunders, 1945.*

may also transmit bubonic plague and certain other bacterial diseases. The remedy is cleanliness and proper sanitation for all the people in a community. Lice and typhus are the companions of war, famine, poverty, and personal neglect.

On the basis of their hosts, fleas fall into three groups: human fleas, cat and dog fleas, and mouse and rat fleas (Fig. 202). Most fleas are neither strictly host parasites, that is, parasites which live exclusively on the host, nor nest parasites, like the bedbugs. The human flea lays its eggs in the dust and debris in the cracks of the floor, under the carpets, in the crevices of the wallpaper, or like places. The young larvas feed upon such material as hairs, mouse excreta, and excrement of adult fleas.

Fleas are blood-sucking parasites. They transmit such diseases as bubonic plague and certain forms of typhus. They are important vectors of **tularemia.** At the present time, bubonic plague is found mostly in tropical countries such as India, where each year over one-half million people die from it. The organism is found in the blood of rodents and is transmitted by the rat flea (*Xenopsylla cheopis*) which has fed on the blood of an infected animal. Fleas also are carriers of typhus, a disease found in the blood of rodents. Apparently it is transmitted to man from the feces and crushed bodies of the fleas. Fleas have also been suspected of being the carriers of relapsing fever. The remedy for fleas is to clean thoroughly the premises and sprinkle the flooring or ground with a good insecticide.

The flies, midges, and mosquitoes (Order Diptera) are more important than all the other arthropods as disease vectors. The sandflies (*Phlebotomus*) are small midges which can easily penetrate the meshes of ordinary netting. Some of the species feed exclusively on blood and are of great importance as transmitters of various types of leishmaniasis. They also transmit a virus disease known as three-day fever. In Peru they have been shown to be the vectors of Oroya fever. In the guts of these insects have been found the parasites causing Oriental sore, espundia, and kala-azar. The most important mode of transmission involves the crushing of the bodies of the vectors on the skin. There is some evidence that they may transmit disease by biting. The best protection against sandflies is an electric fan and oil sprays. The midges have been accused of transmitting a form of dermal leishmaniasis, and they also serve as intermediate hosts of two human filarial roundworm parasites.

The horseflies or tabanids are also blood suckers. Some of them cause trypanosome diseases of domestic animals such as surra in horses, camels, and cattle. They may even occasionally transmit the trypanosome of human sleeping sickness. Certain stable flies may transmit anthrax. Other species of these flies (*Chrysops*) have been found to be transmitters of tularemia and the roundworm *Loa loa*. The only means of fighting these flies is by repellents.

Tsetse flies have already been mentioned as the vectors of sleeping sickness, a trypanosome disease. They are limited in their range, however, to the middle portion of the African continent. It has been suggested that sleeping sickness could be controlled by the elimination of certain African game animals which harbor the parasites in their blood. However, this would be a gigantic task, and evidence would seem to indicate that the results would not justify such a course.

The eye flies (*Oscinidae*) in Florida may cause "pink eye." Other species in the West Indies may be responsible for the majority of the cases of yaws, because the spirochetes of yaws have been found motile in the pharynx and digestive tracts of certain of these species. Infection occurs when the flies regurgitate fluid from their digestive tract after feeding.

Mosquitoes are probably the worst of all insect pests. This is one pest which is more abundant in the cold northern countries than in the tropics. However, the northern mosquitoes are not disease carriers. Four human diseases are transmitted by mosquitoes exclusively: malaria, yellow fever, dengue, and filariasis. The eggs of the South American fly, which in the larval stage affects man, are also carried by mosquitoes. Contrary to popular opinion, mosquitoes feed to a large extent on plant juices, honey, and other products. All the males are vegetarians; the females are the blood suckers. The genus *Anopheles,* which is a vector of the malarial parasite, is widely distributed, not only in the northern sections of the world but in the jungles and forests of the tropics as well. Most *Anopheles* mosquitoes feed in the evening; therefore one is not so likely to receive a bite and consequent infection during the day.

Yellow fever is transmitted by a mosquito called *Aëdes aegypti.* This mosquito lives in and around houses; in fact, it seldom leaves the room of a house except to find a breeding place, which may be a rain barrel, water-filled tin cans, sagging roof gutters, flower vases, in fact, any small body of water. The yellow-fever mosquito is widely distributed, and, since it stows away quite readily in clothing, one can readily appreciate how easily these insects with their disease-producing guests may be scattered throughout the world.

Mosquito control may utilize the following methods: use of repellents and protective clothing; elimination and exclusion of mosquitoes from dwellings; and, finally, the destruction of breeding places and larvas. In mosquito-infected areas all pools of water should be eliminated or the surface covered with oil, which kills the larvas. Certain species of fish that feed on mosquito larvas have been found useful.

Myiasis is a term used to describe a human infection by fly maggots. The so-called muscoid flies are most frequently involved in myiasis. The botfly larvas are entirely parasitic in the larval stage. Fly myiasis may be of four types: the larvas may live outside the body and suck blood by puncturing the skin; the larvas may burrow into the skin and develop under it; eggs or young larvas may infect the wounds or the natural cavities of the body such as the nose or ear; and some larvas live in or pass through the intestine or urinary passages.

The Congo floor maggot (*Aucheromyia*) lies buried in the dust under sleeping mats during the day and comes out at night to suck blood from sleepers. The larvas of two species of flies live under the skin of animals where they cause nodules or boil-like lesions frequently called warbles. They attack cattle and other domestic animals more often than man. A domestic animal may become infested with thousands of the larvas; the hides of animals are often so riddled by their perforations as to be worthless. Man often attempts to remove the maggot, but unless he is careful a serious and even fatal secondary infection may occur.

The African skin maggot is the larva of a yellowish brown fly found in tropical Africa. The eggs are laid on exposed clothing or dry sand about which there may be some body odor. When stimulated by heat, as when one puts on a garment, the activated larva soon buries itself under the surface of the skin. The lesions that are produced enlarge, and in heavy infections death may result.

As was pointed out before, the larvas of certain flies attack wounds. Even a scratch may afford the stimulus or point of attack for myiasis. These maggots may also attack the natural cavities of the body. Severe infections of man may lead to death. One member of the screw-worm family found in southeastern Europe breeds in open wounds. The larvas need to be removed as soon as possible, and the wounds made by their removal must be carefully cared for by antiseptic methods.

In this very brief presentation of the insect parasites, it has been possible to mention only a small fraction of the different species of animals involved. Further, very little has been said of the losses to man of his domestic animals through the attacks of these parasites.

Battling the Insects

We have just seen that insects are injurious in various ways. They are the vectors of various parasites which seriously injure man and his domestic animals. Moreover, they destroy man's clothing and often his habitation. They threaten his food supply, both animal and vegetable. Some ruin plants by chewing; others content themselves by sticking in their beaks and sucking the sap. Some work into the inside of plants and tunnel about through the tissues. Even the heartwood of large trees is often tunneled and ruined by insects. No part of a plant is immune from the insects; root, stem, leaves, and fruit are all liable to attack. The damage done directly by insects is bad enough, but, in addition, insects carry the spores of various plant diseases which find entrance into the plant through the wounds they make.

Man fights the insects in various ways. Sometimes he resorts to chemical warfare and sprays the herbs, trees, and shrubs. When in-

FIG. 203. Destruction caused by insects. *Photographs furnished by the Bureau of Entomology and Plant Quarantine, U. S. Department of Agriculture.*

sects eat plant material sprayed or mixed with certain arsenicals, the poison sets up an inflammation in their stomachs and the insects die. This method is effective with insects equipped with chewing mouth parts such as certain Orthoptera and beetles. Contact poisons kill the insects without being swallowed. Sometimes a lethal gas such as nicotine may enter the spiracles and cause suffocation. In some cases the compound may affect the nervous system. Since 1940 such new synthetic compounds as DDT, methoxychlor, and others have come into extensive use. However, insects may develop an immunity against DDT. Contact poisons are very effective against insects having sucking mouth parts and those equipped with chewing mouth parts also. The airplane is often utilized for dusting large areas of crops.

Often fumigants such as hydrocyanic acids, nicotine, and others are employed to rid houses, warehouses, grain elevators, and clothing of insect pests. In California citrus trees have been enclosed in gas-tight tents and fumigated with hydrocyanic acid.

Man uses mechanical means as well as chemical. He often picks the insects or the larvas from his plants or wields a swatter effectively. Bands of screen, gauze, or sticky substances put around tree trunks prevent the crawling ascent of destructive larvas. Mechanical barriers such as furrows in the soil or wooden barriers stop the march of such wingless insects as the Mormon cricket or the chinch bug (Fig. 204). Ingenious traps and collecting machines have been developed. One of them, called a hopperdozer, is a trough-shaped affair with a high back screen. It is drawn by horses over a field, and the aroused insects, mostly grasshoppers, as they fly up, hit the back of the screen and fall into the trough. They may then be killed by a kerosene solution, or allowed to accumulate. They may be sacked, dried, ground, and used for hog or chicken feed. From 4 to 8 bushels per acre has been collected with these machines.

Some insect pests can be controlled by crop rotation and by varying the time of planting and harvesting. It has been found that the Hessian fly, a serious wheat pest, can be successfully controlled if winter wheat is planted after the egg-laying period of the adult flies which live only three or four days. All soil should be kept as free as possible from weeds and such crop residues as corn stalks and wheat stubbles, which serve either as hosts or as breeding places for insects. Pruning or thinning trees and shrubbery often helps to control insects.

Efforts have been made to kill certain insects by inoculating some captured individuals with a fatal fungus or bacterial disease and then releasing them to spread the disease. Often predatory insects are

Fig. 204. Fighting insects. *Photographs furnished by: Top, Root Manuf. Co.; Center, W. S. Hough, Winchester, Va.; Bottom,* Metal barriers for Mormon cricket control, *Geo. M. List, Colo. Agr. Exp. Sta.*

introduced to prey upon injurious forms. At one time the cottony cushion scale, which was accidentally introduced from Australia and New Zealand, threatened to kill all the orange trees in California. Five hundred lady beetles were brought from Australia and released. Within a comparatively short period, the lady beetles brought the scale insects under control throughout the entire state. This is a good example of what happens when the relationships in a community of living organisms are destroyed and then restored. Parasitic insects have been most useful agents in insect control. We must not forget that there are many other insectivorous insects, such as wasps, certain diptera, dragonflies, various beetles, and bugs. Spiders also are man's partners in these wars. We shall call attention to the services of the Amphibia, certain snakes, lizards, and the birds. We cannot emphasize too strongly the need for bird protection as well as assistance in building up bird refuges, breeding places, and the like.

Class Arachnida (*arachne*—spider). The animals of this class are familiar to us as spiders, but there are others as well, such as the scorpions, daddy longlegs or harvest men, mites, and ticks. The head and thorax are fused to form a **cephalothorax,** and the abdomen is unsegmented. Both the cephalothorax and abdomen are covered with chitin. The arachnids have neither antennas nor mandibles. In front of the mouth arachnids have a pair of appendages, in the form of either pincers or sharp claws called **cheliceras.** Behind the mouth and the cheliceras is a pair of appendages called **pedipalps,** which in spiders are sensory in function but in scorpions are used for seizing prey. Arachnids have four pairs of walking legs and no compound eyes.

The spiders usually have eight simple eyes (Fig. 205). On the abdomen of most spiders there are no appendages except the three pairs of tiny little spinning glands called **spinnerets,** which secrete a sticky fluid that hardens, on exposure to the air, into relatively tough, flexible threads often arranged in beautifully designed webs. The spider waits in the web until some insect, probably a fly or grasshopper, becomes slightly entangled. It then pierces the prey with the pedipalps and injects a poison. If the captured animal is too large the spider weaves a silken net to hold the struggling victim. The spider sucks the juice from its victim, after which it throws the shrunken body out of the web. The food is sucked into the stomach and thence into the intestine, whose surface is increased by a number of pouches or caeca. The caeca enable the spider to tide over long periods between meals. The food is absorbed into and distributed by the blood, which is driven by the tubular heart through the vessels and hemocoeles. This colorless fluid is a carrier of oxygen and carbon dioxide also. The exchange of gases takes place in the special breathing organs called "book lungs," tracheae, or both. The urinary wastes are eliminated by the Malpighian tubules as in the insects.

Spiders are of separate sexes. The female is often much larger than the male, who courts her in her web by striking fantastic poses and by doing a dance. If he is accepted he may be eaten, even before the marriage, by the female. The eggs are laid in cocoons, which

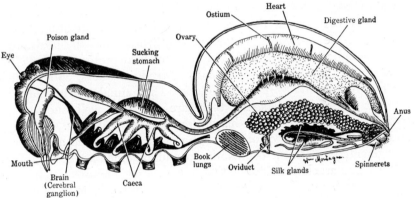

Fig. 205. Diagram of the internal anatomy of the spider. *Modified from various sources.*

may be fastened to various objects or carried around by the spider. After some months the young come out of the cocoon and spin a strand of silk on which they are carried around by the wind to new homes, often many miles away. There are various types of weaving spiders, but not all spiders spin webs. Some merely run around; others are able to jump.

Spiders are very interesting and much-maligned animals. They are of positive value to man, for they feed almost entirely on insects. Most of them have poison glands, and their bite is fatal to many smaller animals but not to man as a rule. The spiders most to be feared by man belong to the genus *Lactrodectus*. The bite of one species is dangerous to horses and camels. A few authentic cases of human death from spider bites are known, but generally the result is discomfort for a period of a few hours to ten days, followed by recovery. The species most dreaded in America is the black-widow spider, whose bite, although not so deadly as popularly believed, may cause intense agony, and rarely death.

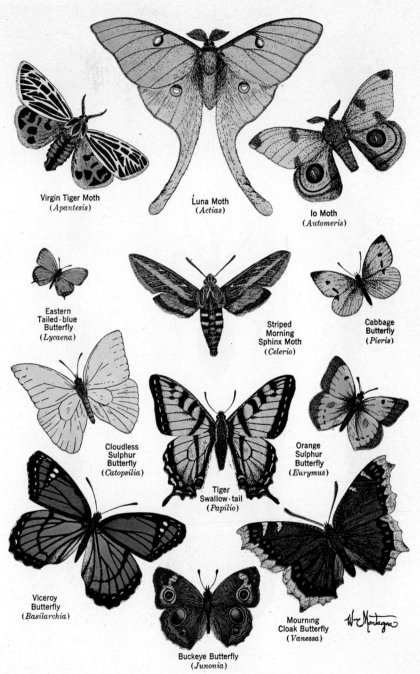

Virgin Tiger Moth
(*Apantesis*)

Luna Moth
(*Actias*)

Io Moth
(*Automeris*)

Eastern
Tailed - blue
Butterfly
(*Lycaena*)

Striped
Morning
Sphinx Moth
(*Celerio*)

Cabbage
Butterfly
(*Pieris*)

Cloudless
Sulphur
Butterfly
(*Catopsilia*)

Orange
Sulphur
Butterfly
(*Eurymus*)

Tiger
Swallow - tail
(*Papilio*)

Viceroy
Butterfly
(*Basilarchia*)

Mourning
Cloak Butterfly
(*Vanessa*)

Buckeye Butterfly
(*Junonia*)

PLATE XIII. Types of Lepidoptera.

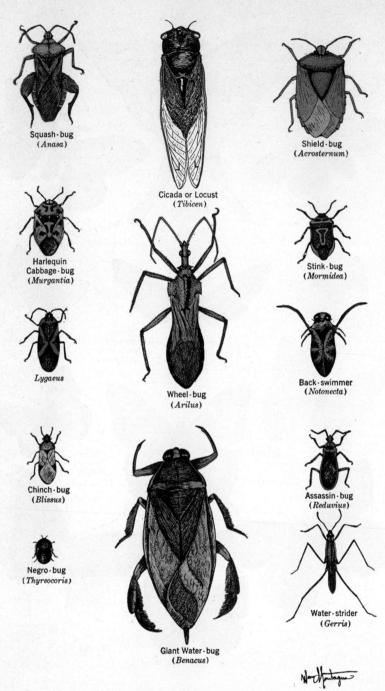

Squash-bug
(*Anasa*)

Cicada or Locust
(*Tibicen*)

Shield-bug
(*Acrosternum*)

Harlequin
Cabbage-bug
(*Murgantia*)

Stink-bug
(*Mormidea*)

Lygaeus

Wheel-bug
(*Arilus*)

Back-swimmer
(*Notonecta*)

Chinch-bug
(*Blissus*)

Assassin-bug
(*Reduvius*)

Negro-bug
(*Thyreocoris*)

Water-strider
(*Gerris*)

Giant Water-bug
(*Benacus*)

PLATE XIV. Types of Hemiptera and Homoptera.

Fig. 206. Types of Arachnids: *a*, tarantula; *b*, scorpion; *c*, black widow spider. *Photographs a and b furnished by Bureau of Entomology and Plant Quarantine, U. S. Department of Agriculture; c furnished by* Nature Magazine.

Most of us have seen the daddy longlegs but have usually thought of them as insects. They are arachnids, and they use their eight slender elongated legs in chasing insects. Scorpions are found mostly in tropical countries. They are carnivorous and have on the tip of the abdomen a slender poisonous sting which they use in capturing their prey. The sting may be serious to man, sometimes resulting in death. Anti-scorpion serum has been found effective.

Most **mites** are round or oval in shape with head, thorax, and abdomen fused. When certain mites burrow beneath the skin, they cause itch, mange, and "scab" in man and other animals. The female makes a burrow in the epidermis and lays her eggs. The young hatch and in turn make burrows of their own. The infection may hang on for some time and become known as the "seven-year itch."

Ticks are transmitters of many diseases of man and domestic animals. They cause much sickness and death and enormous economic losses. All ticks are parasitic at some time in their lives. They suck the blood of the host.

Ticks have an interesting life history, which is more or less similar for all species. The eggs, and there may be as many as 10,000 from one female, are deposited on or near the surface of the ground. Here they develop into larvas, popularly known as "seed ticks," which climb up on a blade of grass from which they may attack their host and feed on his blood for several days. Then they drop off, undergo further development, and often attack the host again. After the second feast they again drop off and finally become mature ticks which must contact the final host.

Ticks are widely scattered over the world, and wherever they go they have the reputation for spreading disease. Members of one genus (*Dermacentor*) in the United States are credited with carrying spotted fever, tularemia, Colorado tick fever, "nine-mile fever," tick paralysis, and several viruses (Fig. 207).

In addition to carrying diseases, ticks themselves are dangerous to man. Wounds made by tick bites often become infected and result in rather extended sores and ulcers. In some domestic animals they have caused serious and even fatal anemia. Sometimes female ticks, attaching themselves to the back of the neck or the base of the skull and gorging on the blood of an individual, may cause paralysis. The individual recovers in six to eight days unless the heart and respiration become affected. Sometimes paralysis of the heart and respiratory muscles ensues, followed by death.

The control and eradication of ticks present a difficult task. Clearing away the brush and burning over tick-infested lands are common control measures. Certain domestic animals are dipped in vats containing a fluid that kills the ticks. Certain rodents serve as reservoirs for many of the diseases carried by ticks. In Montana, for instance, quite a campaign has been conducted for the elimination of ground

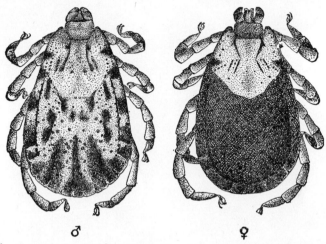

♂ ♀

FIG. 207. Spotted fever tick. *From Chandler, "Introduction to Parasitology." By permission of Asa C. Chandler and of John Wiley & Sons.*

squirrels, which are the hosts for immature ticks. Meadow mice and white-footed mice also serve as refuges for ticks in their immature stages.

Class Merostomata. The only living representative of the class is the king crab, *Xiphosurus* (*Limulus*). It resembles so closely certain extinct arthropods that it has been called "a living fossil." It is marine and lives on sandy or muddy bottoms, where it feeds on worms and mollusks. It has five pairs of typical arthropod appendages and a respiratory organ made up of flattened plates and known as a **gill book.** The animals are of little economic value.

PHYLUM ONYCHOPHORA
(*onychos*—claw; *phoros*)

These are soft-bodied caterpillarlike animals 2 to 5 inches long. They live in moist habitats in widely scattered regions in Australia, Africa, Asia, and South America. One of the best-known animals of the group is called *Peripatus*. *Peripatus* is segmented internally but not externally (Fig. 208). There is a pair of legs for each internal segment. The legs resemble those of arthropods but are unjointed. Each leg bears a claw which superficially resembles those of arthro-

pods. Three fused segments make up the head which is equipped
with a pair of annelidlike simple eyes, a pair of jaws, palps, and an-

FIG. 208. *Peripatus* (Phylum Onychophora). *Photograph furnished by Ralph S.
Buchsbaum.*

tennas. Internally *Peripatus* has a circulatory system and a respiratory system of tracheae like the arthropods. The simple digestive
tube, the pair of nephridia per segment, and the ciliated reproductive

organs are all annelid characteristics. The nervous system consists of a brain which is connected to the two widely separated non-ganglionated lateral nerve cords.

This mixture of annelid and arthropod anatomical features has resulted in *Peripatus* being placed by some biologists with the annelids and by others with the arthropods. It has finally been placed in a phylum of its own, phylum Onychophora. Many biologists refer to *Peripatus* as a "missing link" or, better, "a connecting link" between Annelida and Arthropoda. However, it is more nearly correct to conclude that *Peripatus* "suggests what the intermediate stage between the two phyla might have been like."

21

Mollusks and Echinoderms

PHYLUM MOLLUSCA
(*mollis*—soft)

Nearly everyone is more or less familiar with such mollusks as clams, oysters, and various types of snails, but most of us are much less familiar with certain marine members of the phylum: the squid, the octopus, and the chambered nautilus. This phylum is a large group of invertebrates, and its members are used extensively for food. Mollusks vary in size from small creatures the size of a grain of rice to huge clams weighing as much as 500 pounds. The giant squids may reach a length of 50 feet overall. Mollusks are found both in fresh and salt water and on land.

Mollusks have bilateral symmetry. There is usually a ventral muscular **foot** commonly used for locomotion. The main part of the body is enclosed in a fold of tissue called the **mantle,** surrounded in most of the animals by a hard **shell** of calcium carbonate. The three important classes of this phylum are the Pelecypoda, Gastropoda, and Cephalopoda.

Class Pelecypoda (*pelecys*—hatchet; *podos*—foot). These are oysters, clams, scallops, and mussels. They are characterized by having a hatchetlike foot, and a shell made up of two valves, hence the name bivalve. A brief study of a salt water clam will give a clear picture not only of this class but of the entire phylum as well. The "body" of the clam, that is, its vital structures, is enclosed within two shells or **valves** fastened together at the dorsal edge by a tough **hinge ligament** that will automatically hold the valves open (Fig. 209). Large **adductor muscles** attached to the valves are able to close them and hold them tightly together. Along the margins of the valves are a number of interlocking projections or **teeth** which assist in keeping the valves closed. The tightly closed valves afford the clam its only protection against enemies. Lining the valves and enclosing the soft body parts are the two **mantle lobes,** which serve not only to protect the delicate soft body but also to secrete the shell.

At the posterior end of the clam the mantle lobes form two tubes leading into the **mantle cavity,** the space between the mantle lobes and surrounding the body proper. The dorsal tube is called the **exhalent siphon,** and the ventral one the **inhalent siphon.**

Let us now examine the most important structures enclosed by the mantle. These, for the sake of description, we have called the "body." The most ventral region is made up of the **muscular foot,** which

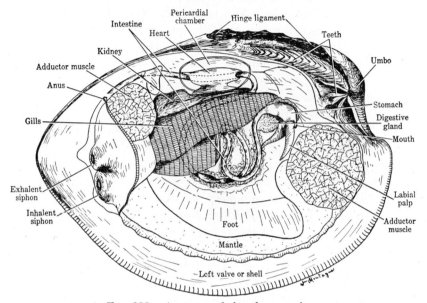

FIG. 209. Anatomy of the clam, quahog.

protrudes between the valves and slowly plows its way through the mud, pulling the animal along. Dorsal to the foot are the thin, leaflike gills covered with cilia whose beating brings water through the incurrent siphon into the mantle cavity. The gills are perforated by numerous pores through which the water enters. Water then passes upward through the gills, to the dorsal gill passages and out through the excurrent siphon, carrying with it carbon dioxide and also excreta from the intestine (Fig. 209). In certain marine clams and oysters water passes through the mantle cavity at the rate of approximately 3 quarts an hour.

The clam has no head. The **mouth** is found at the anterior end between triangular flaps called **labial palps.** The food particles entangled in mucus secreted by the gills are moved toward the labial palps by ciliary action. The cilia of the labial palps direct the food into the mouth.   Ciliary action carries it on to the **stomach** and through the **intestine.**   The much-coiled intestine passes dorsally through the pericardial cavity and ends above the excurrent siphon. Associated with the stomach is a **digestive gland** that aids in the digestion and absorption of food.

The clam has a well-defined circulatory system made up of blood vessels and certain spaces or **sinuses** in the body through which the colorless blood is pumped both forward and backward by the **heart.** The heart has two **auricles** and a **ventricle.**   The blood in its course of circulation passes through the kidneys and the gills, where the wastes are extracted.   In the gills and the mantle, oxygen is acquired and carbon dioxide is eliminated.   In certain mollusks the mantle is a more important respiratory organ than the gills (Fig. 209).

The rather simple nervous system consists of three main pairs of ganglia.   The **cerebral ganglia** ("brain") are located above the mouth.   They are connected by nerve cords with the **pedal ganglia** in the foot and the **visceral ganglia** far back in the body.   A pair of **statocysts** function as balancing organs, and a sensory organ (the **osphradium**) is thought to test water entering the mantle cavity.

The fresh-water mussel produces a large number of eggs.   The eggs are collected in the gills, where they are fertilized by sperm entering the mantle cavity of the female with the incoming current of water.   Here they remain until they develop into small bivalved larvas called **glochidia,** whose shells are usually equipped with small, rather sharp teeth.   The glochidia leave the parent via the excurrent siphon and settle to the bottom of a pond or stream.   Then, if some passing fish happens to brush them, they hook on, bore into the passerby, and live parasitically for a time.   Within a few weeks, they undergo a remarkable transformation and finally drop out of the foster parent as young mussels.   Meantime, the fish may have carried the young mussel quite a distance from its original home.

The Pelecypoda are of great importance to man.   The value of various clams, oysters, scallops, and others used for food amounts to millions of dollars.   The government reports for 1945 reveal that the annual crop of clams and oysters had a total value of $13,492,000. The shells of the fresh-water mussel are used extensively in the manufacture of pearl buttons.   The 1945 reports show that the annual production of pearl buttons and pearl novelties such as knife handles, dolls, and lamps from the shells of mollusks amounted to $9,225,261.

The shipworm, really a pelecypod mollusk, using its shell as an auger, bores into ships and piling along the ocean, causing a loss of

Fig. 210. Class Pelecypoda (Phylum Mollusca): *a*, fresh-water mussel from which blanks for pearl buttons have been cut; *b*, hard-shell clam; *c*, fresh-water mussel; *d*, oyster; *e*, *Pholas*; *f*, *Pecten*; *g*, *Mytilus*; *h*, borings of the shipworm, a molluscan. *Photographs by Erwin S. Koval.*

thousands of dollars. Nor should it be overlooked that some of the Pelecypoda form pearls.

A pearl is formed when a grain of sand or a dead parasite gets between the valve and the mantle. The irritation causes the mantle to cover the foreign object with smooth, non-irritating mother-of-pearl, and the end result is a pearl. Sometimes little metal images of Buddha have been introduced into a clam and the animal returned to the water. In due time the supposedly miraculous pearly Buddhas are removed and sold to the believers.

Class Gastropoda (*gaster*–stomach; *podos*). This group of mollusks includes those animals which usually have a spirally coiled shell

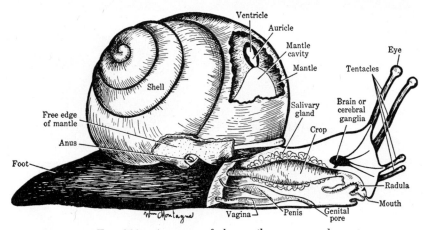

FIG. 211. Anatomy of the snail, a gastropod.

containing the dorsally placed visceral mass and a flattened oval foot. In some forms the shell is missing. Gastropods are found in both fresh and salt water, and on land. Probably most of us have seen a snail with its shell on its back, on the sides of an aquarium or in the garden, moving slowly along by a series of wavy muscular contractions of the broad ventral foot. Snails smooth their pathway by laying down a very necessary layer of slime, which pours from an opening on the anterior end of the foot.

The foot is not the only prominent organ in the members of this class, for there is also a very definite head region with **eyes** located on the tips of projecting **tentacles** (Fig. 211). Other tentacles may be present near the mouth. The mouth is equipped with a tongue, which is modified to form a flexible file-like rasping organ called a **radula** (*radere*–to scrape). Mollusca is the only group in the animal kingdom where this structure appears. This device plays havoc with garden vegetables, and the radula of a marine mollusk, the oyster-

FIG. 212. Gastropods. *a, b, c, d, e,* and *g furnished by the General Biological Supply House. f, photograph of living snail furnished by Ervin S. Koval.*

drill, bores right through the hard shell into the soft tissue of the oyster.

Gastropods have digestive, nervous, excretory, and reproductive systems resembling, in a general way, those of the clam (Fig. 211). Of rather special interest are the breathing devices of this group. Some gastropods get their oxygen by means of gills. Others use not only the gills but also the mantle, which, in some of the land forms, is the sole breathing mechanism. Thus the mantle and its cavity serve as a "lung." Some snails are practically amphibious and may live submerged in the water or may be found perched on the emergent top of some aquatic plant.

We have already mentioned that some gastropods eat oysters and clams, and that slugs and other snails may be great pests of the garden and field. From the standpoint of disease, we have already noted that certain snails serve as intermediate hosts of parasites. Many snails are used as food, particularly abroad. It is estimated that as many as 200,000,000 snails have been consumed in Paris alone in a single season!

Class Cephalopoda (*kephale*—head; *podos*). The Cephalopoda are the most highly developed of the mollusks. Some members of the group possess an eye which is very similar to the vertebrate eye and may be image perceiving. The well-defined head of the animals in this group is really a grand combination of both foot and head. The mouth is located in the center of the foot! It is surrounded by a circlet of **arms** which are, in a sense, the fringe of the foot (Fig. 213). The mouth has not only a radula but also two horny, parrotlike jaws. Cephalopods capture their prey by means of the long arms, which, equipped with a series of **suckers**, grasp the prey, such as a fish, and pull it into the mouth. Here the jaws and the radula do a finished job of tearing off pieces to be swallowed.

The shell is practically missing in this group except in the nautiloids. Partly for this reason most of the cephalopods are anything but sluggish. The bare muscular mantle of the squid and cuttlefish covers the body except for the head. The squid draws water into the mantle cavity and then shoots it out very forcibly through a small funnel (**siphon**), propelling the animal through the water like an exploding rocket through the air. A **lobed fin** aids in directing the movements. The octopus is more sluggish and crawls rather than swims. When these animals are attacked by fishes and whales, they may shoot a cloud of ink out into the water and under cover of this "smoke screen" make their escape.

The Cephalopoda are of some economic importance. Despite many tales to the contrary, few of them attack man. Squids destroy the young fry of certain food fishes, but they in turn are often eaten by man. The cuttle bone in the cage of the pet bird came from a cephalopod called *Sepia*.

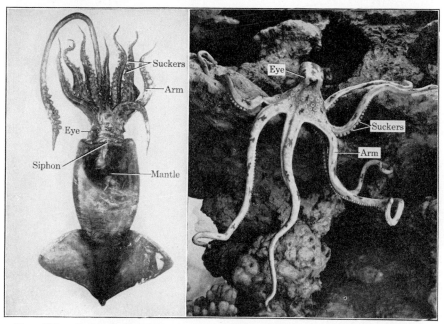

FIG. 213.   *Left,* squid; *right,* octopus (Class Cephalopoda).   *Photographs furnished by the American Museum of Natural History.*

Class Scaphopoda (*skaphos*—hollow; *podos*). The members of this small class of mollusks are commonly known as the "tooth shells," since the miniature shell resembles an elephant's tusk. The animals are of little economic importance.

Class Amphineura (*amphi*—double; *neuron*—a nerve). Included in this class are mollusks known as the chitons. These are sluggish marine animals which are found browsing on algae growing on the rocks along the coast. They are considered the most primitive of all of the mollusks. The ventral surface of a chiton is made up of the flattened muscular **foot** above which lies a **visceral mass** which is completely covered by the **mantle**. The upper surface of the animal is protected by a **shell** which usually consists of eight separate overlapping plates (Fig. 214). The head is poorly developed but there is a definite anterior end. The **mouth** opens into the muscular **pharynx**

which is equipped with a **radula.** The digestive tract extends from the anterior to a definite posterior end. The colorless blood is pumped through a circulatory system by the **heart.** A pair of **kidneys** is

Fig. 214. *Chiton* (Class Amphineura). *Photograph by Ralph Buchsbaum, from* Animals Without Backbones, *University of Chicago Press.*

present for the elimination of nitrogenous wastes. The nervous system is rather interesting since it is of the ladder type so characteristic of the flatworms.

PHYLUM ECHINODERMATA
(*echinos*—hedgehog; *derma*—skin)

This phylum numbers among its members the starfishes, sea urchins, sea cucumbers, and others, all of which live in the salt water. Some echinoderms are found crawling slowly around in the shallow water along the shore or partially concealed in the crevices of the rocks.

Others live in the deep parts of the ocean. Among them are the crinoids or sea lilies, most of which are attached.

Echinoderms begin life with bilateral symmetry but gradually change until in the adult they have **radial symmetry.** Most of them have an **endoskeleton** made up of plates of calcium carbonate, embedded in the body wall. Many of the plates are equipped with **spines,** a condition which is responsible for the name of the phylum.

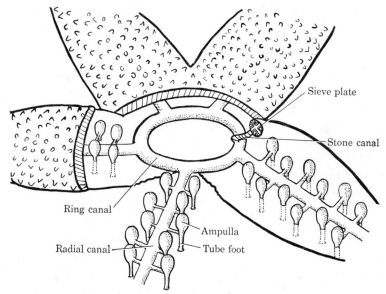

FIG. 215. Water vascular system of the starfish.

Another interesting and characteristic feature of the Echinodermata is a peculiar apparatus known as a **water vascular system.** It is used principally for locomotion and usually consists of a series of water-filled tubes radiating from a **ring canal** which surrounds the mouth region (Fig. 215). Attached to the radiating tubes are numerous small **tube feet.** When they are projected, little reservoirs, filled with water and called **ampullas,** contract, forcing the water into the elastic tube feet which extend and attach themselves by suction to some object. Then the tube feet shorten by muscular contraction, and the animal is slowly pulled in that direction. The tube feet may then release their hold, elongate, and attach themselves again, and so the process continues. The water vascular system and tube feet may be modified in various members of the phylum. Most echinoderms have

remarkable powers of regeneration as previously described for the
starfish and sea cucumber.

The reader will probably be surprised to learn that zoologists consider Echinodermata the invertebrate phylum most closely related to
man and other vertebrates. This conclusion is based mainly on the
similarity in early embryonic development. The mesoderm and the
coelom of echinoderms and vertebrates have a similar origin. (See
page 517.) Certain chemical tests show that the proteins of the echinoderms and the lowest chordates resemble each other in their reactions.
The echinoderms are not particularly important economically.

Class Asteroidea (*aster*—star; *eidos*—form). The starfish, the most
widely known member of the echinoderms, belongs to this class.
There are over one thousand species in class Asteroidea. The starfish is made up of a simple **disk** from which radiate a variable number of **arms**. The skeleton is made up of a large number of calcareous
plates from which project numerous **spines**. Plates are so arranged
that the animal possesses much more flexibility than one would expect from an examination of a dried specimen. We have already described the water vascular system and tube feet. In the starfish water
enters this system through the **sieve plate** on the upper surface of the
animal and passes down a canal (**stone canal**) to the **ring canal.**
In the starfish the tube feet are arranged in rows on the under surface
of the arms of the animal (Fig. 215). The **mouth** of the starfish
leads into the **stomach** which is made up of two parts, a **cardiac
region** and an inner **pyloric region.** Attached to the **pyloric stomach** are pairs of much branched **digestive glands** (Fig. 216). Starfishes live on clams and oysters. In securing its prey the starfish
"humps" over a clam or an oyster and attaches its tube feet to the
two valves. Then the tube feet, working in relays, begin a constant
pull which is maintained until the adductor muscles which hold the
valves together finally become fatigued and relax. When the shells
gape the starfish pushes its cardiac stomach through its mouth onto
the soft parts of the clam and digests it. If the shellfish happens to
be fairly small the starfish simply takes it up into its stomach, digests
the soft parts, and then later ejects the shells through the mouth.
The starfish consumes great quantities of oysters and clams and so
comes in for plenty of attention from the oysterman.

There is no definite circulatory system in the starfish. However, the
large coelom is filled with a fluid which bathes all the internal organs
and extends out into many small fingerlike projections called "skin
gills" (**dermal branchiae**). The oxygen-carbon dioxide exchange

takes place not only through these skin gills but also through the tube feet. The external surface is equipped with small pincers called **pedicellarias** which serve to grasp any foreign material and thus keep the skin gills free from any debris. The nervous system is fairly simple. There is a ring of nerve tissue around the mouth and five radial nerves extending into the arms—one to each arm.

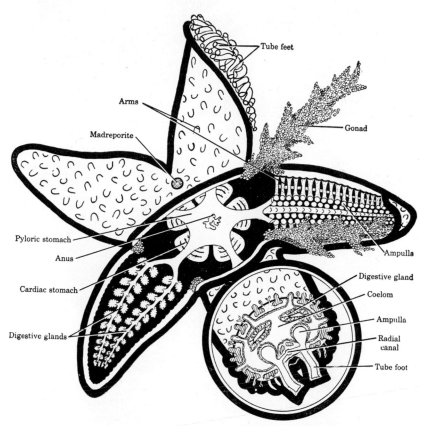

FIG. 216. Internal anatomy of the starfish. *Redrawn, modified from Buchsbaum's "Animals Without Backbones," University of Chicago Press.*

The sexes are separate in the starfish, and the eggs and spermatozoa are shed directly into the water, where fertilization takes place.

Class Ophiuroidea (*ophis*—serpent; *oura*—tail; *eidos*). Brittle stars. The arms of these forms are sharply marked off from the disk.

Class Echinoidea (*echinos*—hedgehog; *eidos*). Sea urchins and sand dollars. They have no arms but are globular or disk-shaped animals covered with spines. The eggs of some of the sea urchins are sold for food.

Class Holothuroidea (*holothurium*—water polyp; *eidos*). Sea cucumbers. Exoskeleton with spines missing. Body wall is muscular and contains small

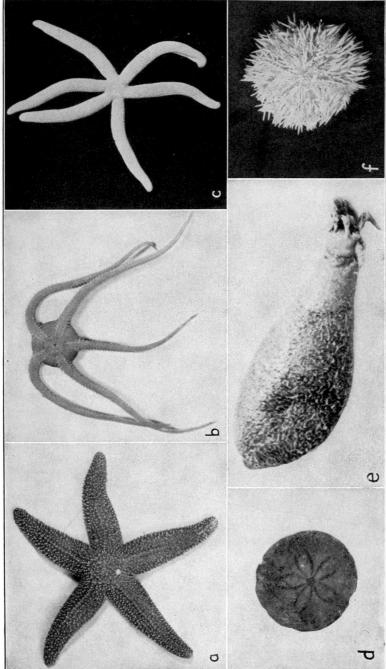

Fig. 217. Echinodermata: a, starfish (Asterias); b, serpent stars; c, starfish (Echinaster); d, sand dollar; e, sea cucumber; f, sea urchin. Photographs a, b, c, d, and f, by Erwin S. Koval; e, by David Huntsberger.

calcareous plates. The Chinese and other people of the Orient are very fond of dried sea cucumbers, which are sold as trepang. It is made into soup and other choice dishes.

Class Crinoidea (*krinon*—lily; *eidos*). Sea lilies. The arms are usually branched, and the animal may be temporarily or permanently attached by a stalk. They were very abundant in geologically ancient times.

22

Chordates

PHYLUM CHORDATA
(*chordos*–a string)

In this last great group we find animals which have at some time in their life a **dorsal, tubular nerve cord** and a supporting endoskeleton. The first indication of the endoskeleton is a gristlelike rod called a **notochord** extending the length of the body dorsal to the intestine. **Pharyngeal pouches** are always present. There are a number of these paired pouches which, pushing out from the pharynx, may break

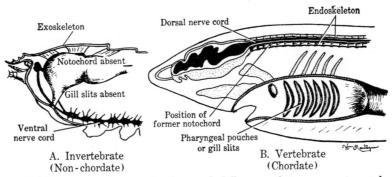

FIG. 218. Diagrams showing fundamental differences between an invertebrate and a vertebrate animal.

through to the exterior. We might say in passing that the notochord of human beings and of other higher animals has disappeared in the adult, having been replaced by a backbone. However, one of the pharyngeal pouches still persists as the Eustachian tube (Fig. 218).

We have just reviewed a number of phyla of animals which showed an extremely wide variation in size, shape, and structure. Nevertheless in this varied assemblage we have found a few rather constant characteristics. Thus, invertebrates (except the lowest chordates) never have a dorsal tubular nerve cord, a notochord, or pharyngeal pouches. So we see that the invertebrates are quite distinct from the great majority of the chordates, the bulk of whose membership consists primarily of the vertebrates. Man, birds, snakes, frogs, and many other animals, although chordates, are known as **vertebrates** (*verte-bra*—joint) because they have a jointed vertebral **column** or **backbone.**

PRIMITIVE CHORDATES

It so happens that there are some animals which, although they have no backbone, possess chordate characteristics, i.e., notochord, pharyngeal pouches, and a dorsal, tubular nerve cord. In most of these animals the notochord persists throughout life and is the sole endoskeletal structure.

Amphioxus (Subphylum Cephalochordata). Probably the best known of the primitive chordates is *Amphioxus*, a small fishlike, semi-

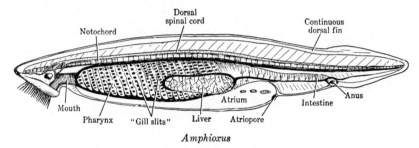

Amphioxus

FIG. 219. *Amphioxus*, a primitive chordate (Subphylum Cephalochordata).

transparent chordate found in shallow marine waters all over the world. It is capable of swimming by undulations of the body but spends most of the time buried in the sand.

Amphioxus has received much attention because of a suspicion that it might be one of the ancestors of the vertebrates. It has a **notochord** which persists throughout life and a typical tubular dorsal **nerve cord** (Fig. 219). However, there is no well-developed brain, and there are only "dubious traces" of a nose or eyes. Water passes into the mouth and is strained through the **gill slits** in the walls of the **pharynx** into a chamber known as the **atrium.** The water is expelled from the atrium through the **atriopore.** Oxygen and food are removed in the **pharynx.** As the food particles pass through the pharynx, some of them become entangled in sticky mucus produced by the glandular cells of a ciliated groove (**endostyle**) in the floor of the pharynx. The rope of mucus with its entangled food particles eventually passes into the **intestine** (Fig. 219). The muscles of the body wall are arranged in two longitudinal lines of bundles or **seg-**

ments. There is a continuous dorsal **finfold** which expands into a broad **tail fin** and continues a short distance ventrally, as the **ventral fin,** to the atriopore. In front of the ventral fin are two **lateral folds.** We have included this detailed description because this is the same general arrangement of fins found in the embryonic true fishes. However, as fins develop in fishes, the continuous dorsal finfold disappears in certain regions and from the lateral folds come the pectoral and pelvic fins, the forerunners of the paired fore and hind limbs of the higher vertebrates. In general *Amphioxus* shows a body plan resembling that of the vertebrates but much simpler in design. The larva of the lamprey, a very "low-level" vertebrate, shows marked similarities to *Amphioxus.*

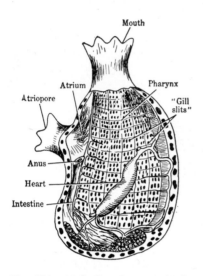

FIG. 220. *Molgula,* a tunicate (Subphylum Urochordata).

Tunicates. The tunicates or sea squirts are primitive chordates (Subphylum Urochordata) most of which are found growing attached to rocks and seaweeds, as formless sessile objects. Early in life they are active swimmers. Some species, however, eventually settle down and degenerate. Their bodies are surrounded and protected by a **tunic** whose chemical composition resembles that of cellulose which, as may be recalled, is found almost exclusively in the plant kingdom. Externally the animal shows little resemblance to the vertebrates. Internally most of the body is occupied by the large saclike **pharynx** which is perforated by many rows of **gill slits** (Fig. 220). There is present an **endostyle** as in *Amphioxus.* Water passes from the pharynx into a surrounding **atrium** from which it is forcibly expelled in "squirts" through the **atriopore.** The tubular **nerve cord** and **notochord,** present in the free-swimming larva, is missing in the adult. The tunicates are regarded by most biologists as a "degenerate side branch of the vertebrate ancestral line."

Acorn worms (Subphylum Hemichorda). This is a primitive chordate group which includes a small, wormlike form called *Saccoglossus,* which lives in the sand of the sea. It was formerly classified with the worms until biologists discovered its notochord, dorsal nerve cord, and pharyngeal pouches (Fig. 221). Further interest attaches to this animal because its larval stage resembles that of the echinoderms, mollusks, and annelids, a fact that has led some zoologists to think that perhaps chordates had their origin from the same common ancestors as these invertebrates. Some biologists today are inclined to return these animals to their former classification with the worms.

FIG. 221.   The acorn worm, *Saccoglossus* (Subphylum Hermichordata).

VERTEBRATES

We have already made a somewhat intensive study of vertebrates in our earlier discussions of anatomy and physiology. These discussions dealt with general fundamental principles that will help us to understand the variations in form and structure found in the different classes. The following review may be helpful. In vertebrates there is always present a jointed **dorsal vertebral column** or backbone of either bone or cartilage which supports the animal and protects the **dorsal nerve cord.** Along the sides of the **vertebras** making up the backbone are attached ribs and usually two pairs of locomotor organs—**fins, legs,** or **wings.** In front the skull protects the brain. The ribs support the body wall, which in turn encloses the coelom or body cavity in which are found the digestive system, the heart, and often the breathing mechanism. Breathing is done by gills or lungs, sometimes by both. The nervous system is made up of a well-defined brain and spinal cord. We shall now examine some of the most important groups of vertebrates.

Class Agnatha (*a*—without; *gnathos*—jaw). This most primitive vertebrate class includes the fishlike lampreys and hagfishes, animals living in both salt and fresh water. They lack a lower jaw and paired appendages. The notochord persists throughout life, the vertebras are rudimentary, and the cranium does not completely enclose the brain. The skeleton is completely cartilaginous. The animals attach themselves by their suckerlike mouths to the surface of a fish and rasp off the flesh of the victim. They are of no great economic importance.

Fish.   Formerly all fishlike animals were grouped under Class **Pisces** (*piscis*—fish). We shall give a general description of fish and then a somewhat more detailed discussion of two of the classes.

Fish are vertebrates which spend their entire lifetime in the water. The usually pointed head is united directly to the smooth, scaly body, which is driven easily and rapidly through the water by the graceful waving of the tail. Unpaired **dorsal** and **ventral fins,** as well as paired **pectoral** and **pelvic fins,** are usually present to assist in guiding the fish in its course and to aid in swimming (Fig. 222). Sometimes these pectoral and pelvic fins serve to support the animal as it rests on the bottom—a foreshadowing of the future limbs of the higher vertebrates. In some fishes there is present an aïr sac or **swim**

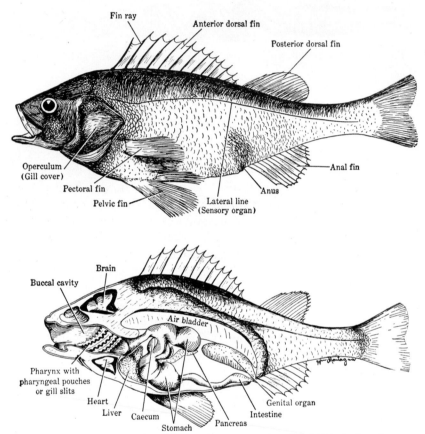

Fin ray

Anterior dorsal fin

Posterior dorsal fin

Operculum
(Gill cover)

Pectoral fin

Pelvic fin

Lateral line
(Sensory organ)

Anus

Anal fin

Brain

Buccal cavity

Air bladder

Pharynx with
pharyngeal pouches
or gill slits

Heart

Liver　Caecum

Stomach

Pancreas

Intestine

Genital organ

FIG. 222.　External and internal anatomy of a bony fish (teleost).

bladder located in the middorsal region of the body cavity. This assists the fish in maintaining a position at various levels in the water (Fig. 222). The amount of gas present in the swim bladder is regulated to some extent by the fish, but when fish from moderate depths of the sea are exposed to the relatively low surface pressure their air bladders become so distended that they cannot sink again.

Not all fish move by the customary mode of swimming. Some tropical forms may work their way along the shore by means of their pectoral fins and tail. The climbing perch may be found on roots of trees along the water, and certain flying fish may jump from the water, spread their pectoral fins, and soar along for several hundred yards before submerging again.

The different kinds of fish consume a great variety of foods. The black-swallowers eat fish larger than themselves, and others, such as the herring, eat annelids and various plants. It has been said that the herring catch can be estimated from the number of sunshiny days, so important is plant life in their diet. Many food fish depend entirely on very small plants and animals that live near the surface of the water of lakes, ponds, and seas, known collectively as **plankton.**

Most of us know that a fish breathes by means of **gills.** Gills are readily seen as J-shaped rows of filaments attached to the **gill arches,** which are the walls separating the gill slits. Water containing oxygen is gulped in through the mouth. It passes out through the four or five gill slits and bathes the thin-walled gills, which are well supplied with blood. Oxygen enters the blood and carbon dioxide is given off.

Fish are cold blooded. The heart receives and pumps only venous blood, which enters the single auricle and passes to the lone ventricle that forces it out through paired **afferent arteries** into the gill arches and the gills. The blood, oxygenated in the gills, leaves by the **efferent branchial arteries,** which lead into the aorta (Plate V and Fig. 222). A pair of kidneys removes the nitrogenous wastes from the blood.

Class Chondrichthyes (*chondros*—cartilage; *icthys*—fish). The Chondrichthyes are marine animals and include the sharks and the very much flattened rays. They have a skeleton of cartilage and usually a ventral mouth. Some sharks may reach a length of thirty to forty feet. Sharks are voracious feeders on fish and other animals. Authentic instances are on record of sharks attacking man, but the greatest damage incurred by man from sharks and dogfish is the tearing of his nets and fishing gear. In a single year, the New England fisheries sustained a loss of $400,000 as a result of the damage wrought by these fish. Some of the rays inflict painful and often poisonous wounds by the lashing of their spiny tails. The torpedo or electric ray is able to generate a charge of electricity which may disable a man for as much as a day.

In America and abroad these fish are used to some extent for food. Some of the flesh is canned and sold under a trade name. They are also used for fertilizer and oil. A basking shark may yield as much as a ton of oil, most of which is extracted from the liver.

Class Osteichthyes (*osteon*—bone; *ichthys*). The Osteichthyes are known as the bony fish or true fish. Most of them have a complete bony skeleton and air bladder. The mouth is terminal. More than 12,000 different species are distributed through waters everywhere and are familiar to us as various types of game and food fish.

Fig. 223.   Fish: *a*, lake sturgeon; *b*, alligator gar; *c*, sea robin. *Photographs furnished by the John G. Shedd Aquarium, Chicago, Illinois.*

Osteichthyes are extremely valuable to man as a source of food, and fishing is an important occupation. It is estimated that more than 10,000,000,000 herring alone are caught annually by British and American fishermen to be smoked, salted, and packed for distribution. In France 100 sardine canneries have turned out more than 5,000,000 cans annually, and in Maine more than 3,000,000 cases was the 1948 output. When we attempt to estimate the amount of money invested and the number of people employed in cod fishing, salmon canning, mackerel fishing, and countless other related activities, we realize that here is a biological industry involving billions of dollars and millions of people.

In the light of what has just been said, we can understand at once that measures must be taken to ensure a continuing supply of fish. *Nature's store of living creatures is never inexhaustible.* So now we

Fig. 224. Fish: *a*, mud springer; *b*, Australian lung fish; *c*, catfish; *d*, sand shark.
Photographs furnished by the John G. Shedd Aquarium, Chicago, Illinois.

are not only catching fish but also rearing them. Fish culture was practiced by the Chinese and the Romans, but we did not start it in the United States until about 1865, when the Bureau of Fisheries was established. This bureau is supplemented today by many state and private hatcheries. The government hatcheries not only make studies of the food habits, breeding habits, and habitat relations of fish but also rear young fish.

FIG. 225. African lung fish. *Photograph furnished by the General Biological Supply House.*

In the hatcheries the eggs are stripped from the females and fertilized by mixing with spermatozoa from the male. The zygotes are carefully kept in pure aerated water at proper temperature for their development. The young fish are reared under favorable conditions and protected from their natural enemies. In this way millions of eggs and young fish are saved which otherwise might be destroyed. When the fish reach a certain size they are shipped in large cans to certain points for the restocking of streams, ponds, or lakes. In shipping, special care is taken to keep the water cool and well aerated.

Included among Osteichthyes is the lung fish, found in Australia, Africa, and South America. They breathe not only by means of gills, which may be either external or internal, but also by lungs which are developed from the air bladder, hence the name "double-breather." When the ponds and streams dry up, certain of these fish burrow into the mud and form a mucus-lined cocoon. Here they exist during the hot, dry season; in other words, they **estivate** (*aestas*—summer) until conditions favorable for active life return. Some of these fish are shipped to this country in a block of mud and, on arrival, are placed in water and "thawed out" (Fig. 225).

Class Amphibia (*amphi*—double; *bios*—life). In this class of vertebrates we find among other animals the frogs, toads, water dogs,
and newts. Amphibians are both aquatic and terrestrial. They spend
all or part of their life in the water, either as adults or as free-swimming fishlike tadpoles. The tadpoles breathe by means of gills which
may be later supplemented or even supplanted by lungs. Not only
is there an oxygen-carbon dioxide exchange through the gills and
lungs but the skin also plays an important role, hence the skin must
always be kept moist. Modern Amphibia have no scales, feathers, or
hair, and their limbs bear digits which have neither nails nor claws.
They have a heart made up of two auricles and a ventricle, and they
are cold blooded. In cold weather many of these animals **hibernate**
(*hibernus*—wintry) in the mud of ponds and streams. Amphibia hold
a peculiar interest for us because their anatomy and physiology throw
some light on the gradual shift from purely aquatic to land animals.

Order Caudata (*cauda*—tail) *or Urodela*. These Amphibia keep
their tails throughout life. In the order Caudata we find water dogs
or hellbenders, mud puppies, and other salamanders and newts. Salamanders and newts are often found under logs and stones, in moist
and swampy places, and around springs. The uninitiated call them
"lizards," but they can readily be distinguished from lizards by the
absence of claws on the toes or scales on the skin and by their choice
of moist living quarters. These little animals live on insects and
insect larvas for the most part. ⎮ Many of them are very pretty. Some
are vermilion spotted; others are jet black with ivory blotches; and
still others are beautifully striped. They are harmless. (Plate XV.)

The water dog or hellbender (*Cryptobranchus*) and the mud puppy
(*Necturus*)—not a young water dog—are found mostly in the Mississippi River and its tributaries, and these hellbenders may reach a
length of twenty or thirty inches. The hellbender of Japan, sometimes five feet in length, is used for food by the Japanese. The mud
puppy is about twelve inches long. All these animals are harmless to
man and are the scavengers of streams. The water dog may eat some
fish but it is of practically no economic importance from that angle,
yet the fisherman loathes these animals, claiming they are poisonous
and great killers of fish. In some localities enthusiastic but misguided
sportsmen hunt and slaughter them wholesale as vermin."

Order Salientia (*salio*—leap) *or Anura*. These are tailless Amphibia—our friends, the frogs and toads (Fig. 226). They start in life
usually as swimming, gill-breathing tadpoles but later metamorphose
into leaping, lung-breathing adults. Frogs and toads are almost com-

pletely insectivorous. They have a very flexible tongue attached in front. This they flip out, capture the moving insect, and pull the prey back into the mouth where it is swallowed without being chewed.

Frogs and toads usually lay their eggs in jellylike masses in pools and streams. Here the eggs hatch into small tadpoles which begin life as vegetarians but become carnivorous when adult. Toad tadpoles develop into tiny toads which often appear during a shower on their aquatic Emancipation Day, when they are seen in such numbers that many people think they were "rained down." Besides the ordi-

Fig. 226. Order Salientia. *Left,* tree frog; *right,* bull frog (*Rana*). *Photographs on left furnished by General Biological Supply House; photograph on right by R. L. Fricke, Carnegie Museum.*

nary frogs and toads there are tree frogs which, having toes equipped with sucking disks, climb without any difficulty. Some of the tropical tree frogs never leave the tree tops but lay their eggs in pools of water collected in the trees or leaves. One tree frog in Java rolls up a leaf to make a nest.

The Salientia are useful to man as insect destroyers. Kirkland found that 88 per cent of a toad's diet was insects and about 16 per cent was cutworms. He found further that a toad would eat four stomachfuls every 24 hours. At this rate one toad would account for almost 10,000 insects in three months! Frogs are useful not only as insect destroyers but also for food. The flesh is best in the autumn and winter. They are used extensively in experimental biological work.

Some attempts have been made to operate frog farms. One farm in Ontario in one year had an output of 5,000 pounds of dressed frog legs and 7,000 living frogs. However, there are difficulties for the frog farmers. Birds, turtles, snakes, and other animals eat tadpoles and even adult frogs. Moreover, since frogs will eat only moving insects, a natural pond with rank vegetation is one of the prime requisites for the venture.

Order Apoda (*a*—without; *podos*—foot). Apoda are degenerate, limbless, snake-like Amphibia found only in tropical countries; imbedded in the skin are scaly skeletal plates. The animals are unimportant economically.

Class Reptilia (*repere*—to crawl). When the word reptile is mentioned most of us think of snakes, for snake, unfortunately, is too often our only concept of a reptile. However, Reptilia include not only snakes but also turtles, lizards, crocodiles, alligators, and others. These animals are found either on land or in the water. We can

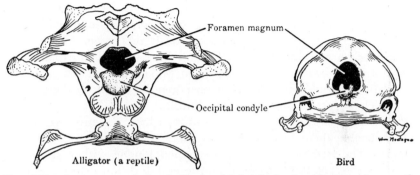

Foramen magnum

Occipital condyle

Alligator (a reptile)   Bird

FIG. 227. Comparison of the skull of a bird (chicken) with that of a reptile (alligator). Note the opening (foramen magnum) through which the spinal cord passes. Below this opening is the basioccipital bone on which is found a single protuberance known as an occipital condyle which articulates with the backbone.

readily identify reptiles because the body is covered with **scales** and, with the exception of snakes, the digits of the limbs have **claws.** They are **cold blooded,** and most of them have a heart made up of two auricles and two ventricles. In most reptiles the septum between the ventricles is not completely closed. Another peculiarity is the attachment of the skull to the backbone by one **condyle** on the base of the skull (Fig. 227).

Reptiles have become independent of the water as a necessary dwelling place for any part of their life. It is not necessary for them to return to the water to lay their eggs, since the developing embryo is inclosed in a water-filled sac called the **amnion.** Also an **allantois** is present to care for excess waste. As some one has put it, each individual embryo now has its own private pond. There is an increase in the respiratory surface of the lungs, owing to the development of folds which form additional chambers. Gills are absent from the list of reptile structures. The moist, soft skin such as that of the Amphibia is no longer necessary as an accessory respiratory organ. Instead, the dry and scaly skin of reptiles prevents the loss of water. The various adaptations just described make it possible for reptiles to live in dry sandy regions far removed from water. We shall now examine some of the most important orders of living Reptilia.

Order Squamata (*squama*—scale). The Squamata are lizards and snakes. Strange as it may seem, a snake in many respects is a lizard minus appendages. The lizards have a rather small head attached to the trunk by a neck. Usually a long tail is present. The body is often covered with colored scales arranged in different color patterns. The chameleon, a lizard, can change its color to harmonize with its surroundings—a mode of protection. Another very interesting protective feature possessed by some lizards is the power to break off certain regions of the tail automatically. It probably explains the fable of the "glass snake," which, when broken into pieces, was supposed to reassemble the pieces in proper order when all danger was past. The "glass snakes" are really limbless lizards.

Some of our tropical lizards are equipped with vacuum-cupped toes which enable them to chase insects along the walls and ceilings of rooms. The chameleon has a club-shaped tongue with a sticky tip, and it shoots out this tongue to an incredible distance to capture insects. The flying dragon is a rather small lizard which glides from tree to tree by means of its lateral "wings," made up of the rib-supported sides of the body. Another lizard we hear much about is the "horned toad," which burrows in the ground and is able to withstand extreme weather conditions. However, the report that it can remain alive when sealed in stone for a period of years is incredible. When cornered and in danger, the horned toads have the curious habit of shooting blood out of the eye to a distance of two feet or more.

The only poisonous lizards are the Gila monsters or beaded lizards found in southwestern United States, Mexico, and Central America. These lizards are covered with beadlike scales arranged in bright red and other colored bands around the body. The poison glands are in the lower jaw, and the animals are able to deliver a bite which Ditmars, an authority on reptiles, considered "dangerously poisonous to man."

Everyone readily recognizes a snake by its long, scaly, cylindrical, limbless body. Pythons and boas, however, have bones of vestigial limbs imbedded in the muscles under the skin. This, together with other evidence, seems to indicate that the ancestors of the snakes were four-footed, lizardlike animals. The willowy slenderness of the snake brings about curious adaptations. One lung has practically

Tiger Salamander: *Ambystoma tigrinum*

Green Salamander: *Aneides aeneus*

Eurycea lucifuga

Jordan's Salamander: *Plethodon jordani*

Marbled Salamander: *Ambystoma opacum*

Newt (Land stage) *Triturus viridescens*

PLATE XV.   Types of Caudata.

American Goldfinch

American Goldfinch

Cardinal

Indigo Bunting

Scarlet Tanager

Red-winged Blackbird

Black and White
Warbler

Downy Woodpecker

Barn Swallow

Screech Owl (Red Phase)

Green Heron

PLATE XVI. Representative birds.

Fig. 228. Lizards (Order Squamata). *Upper,* horned toad; *lower left,* giant amolis; *lower right,* gila monster. *Upper photograph furnished by General Biological Supply House; lower right and lower left, National Zoological Park.*

disappeared, the urinary bladder is missing, and the various other internal organs are peculiarly arranged.

One naturally wonders how these limbless animals crawl and swim, and the mechanism is quite interesting. The two or three hundred vertebras are joined in a flexible column by ball-and-socket joints. Attached to most vertebras is a pair of ribs fastened at the free end by muscles to the broad ventral scales. These muscles contract, causing the ventral plates to strike backward on the ground and help, with the wriggling of the body, to drive the animal forward.

Snakes never chew their food and quite often swallow animals much larger in diameter than themselves. The snake's lower jaws are attached very loosely to the skull and are held together in front by an elastic ligament. Thus the entire palate and lower jaw are very flexibly articulated so that a garter snake, for instance, can easily swallow a large toad. The teeth, also as fine and sharp as needles, curve backward, an arrangement that helps to keep the bulky food moving into the mouth and on down the throat. In the poisonous snakes some of the teeth are either grooved or hollow. They are the fangs through which the poison passes from the poison glands down into the wound. The little red, forked structure which darts out from the snake's mouth is the tongue and not the "fangs."

Snakes are either oviparous or viviparous. Oviparous snakes lay their eggs under stones, logs, or leaves or bury them in the soil. The eggs depend on the heat of the sun for incubation. The viviparous garter snakes retain the eggs within the body until they hatch.

Contrary to popular belief, most snakes are harmless. In fact, many snakes are man's friends. The little green grass snakes crawl up on weeds, hunting insects which they eat. Other insectivorous snakes are the brown or ground snakes, most of which live in the soil. They are dull brown above; ventrally they may be white, yellow, or pink. The rat snakes are very useful as rodent destroyers; among them are the fox snake, the spotted chicken snake, and the pilot blacksnake. The common blacksnake or blue racer is not only harmless but indeed very useful in destroying field mice, rats, and other rodents. In spite of reports to the contrary they do not wrap around a person and squeeze him to death. The garter snakes, although non-poisonous, are of negative value because they are great destroyers of frogs, toads, young birds, and bird eggs. The hog-nosed snakes are harmless snakes called blowing vipers and puff adders. They have a flat, somewhat triangular head resembling that of the poisonous snakes. The shape of the head and the habit they have of

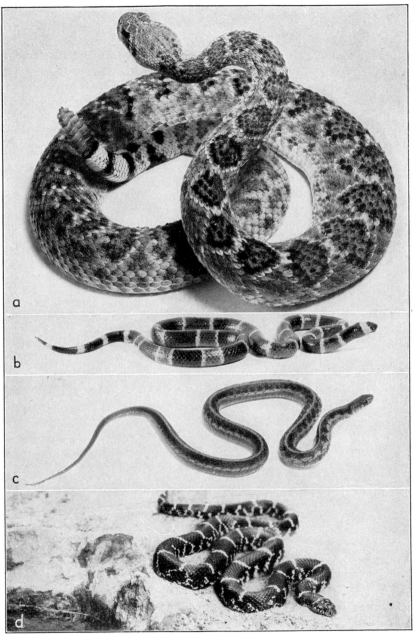

FIG. 229. Snakes (Order Squamata): *a*, rattlesnake; *b*, coral snake; *c*, garter snake; *d*, chain snake. *Photographs a, b, c, furnished by the Fish and Wildlife Service, U. S. Department of the Interior. Photograph d, furnished by the National Zoological Park, Washington, D. C.*

blowing and hissing when disturbed have led to the erroneous belief that they are very poisonous. The blowing and hissing are merely bluff.

No one actually knows how many people die every year from the bite of poisonous snakes, but estimates vary from 12 persons in Australia to 20,000 people in India. Pope thinks this last figure

Fig. 230.   King snake killing a cottonmouth snake.   *Photograph furnished by Ross Allen Reptile Institute, Silver Springs, Florida.*

grossly exaggerated, but it is estimated that in the United States alone the number is approximately 160. Of the people bitten in the United States who receive proper treatment only 3 or 4 per cent die, whereas 15 per cent of those untreated die.

The poisonous snakes responsible for most of the deaths in the United States are rattlesnakes and water moccasins, which belong

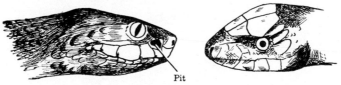

Pit

Fig. 231.   Comparison of the heads of a poisonous (pit viper) and a non-poisonous snake. On the poisonous snake note vertical pupil and "poison" pit. This pit is lacking in the non-poisonous snake, and the pupil of the eye is circular in outline.

to the pit-viper group. Another pit viper in the United States which is blamed for many deaths is the copperhead, but data show that less than 1 per cent of the people bitten by copperheads die. The other poisonous snakes in the United States are the coral snakes, but it is rarely that they inflict a bite that is fatal.

Three methods are found among snakes for the injection of poison into the wound. In some snakes the fangs are grooved and are the hindmost teeth of the upper jaw. Snakes thus equipped must hang on and chew in order to get the poison into the wound. The second type of fang, found in the cobras and their allies, is rather short and rigidly set. Although the tooth has a canal, there still remain strong traces of an external groove. The most efficient type of fang is found in the viperine group such as the water moccasin and rattlesnake. These fangs are rather long and slender and are found near the front of the mouth rigidly attached to a movable bone. Located near the eye is the poison gland drained by a duct opening into the hollow fang. This apparatus works like a hypodermic syringe.

Fresh snake venom is usually a yellow, occasionally colorless, liquid. It is tasteless and odorless. If exposed to ultraviolet light or treated with nitrate of silver or potassium permanganate it loses its poisonous qualities. In preparing antivenin, the dried venom is dissolved and a dilute solution is injected into horses in successive doses of increasing quantity (Fig. 49). After a few weeks there develops in the horse's blood a substance that neutralizes the poisonous effects of the venom. Antivenin reaches its highest concentration three or four months after the horse has been inoculated. Some of the serum is drawn off from the horse, and the antivenin in it is concentrated by a special process, measured for its antivenin reaction, and then put up for use in measured amounts in small syringes.

Snake venoms contain two types of harmful substances: one type destroys or paralyzes nerve cells, damages the blood vessels, and ruptures the walls of the capillaries; the other is made up of a group of substances and acts by "digesting" the living flesh. In the second type there is an antifibrin ferment which keeps the blood from clotting and consequently causes internal bleeding. The poisons of the pit vipers of the United States contain small amounts of the neurotoxin, whereas the venom of the cobras and their allies is made up chiefly of the nerve-affecting elements. Snake venom lowers the resistance of the blood to infections.

Treatment for Snake Bites. First-aid treatment recommended for snake bite includes the following steps: 1. Do not get frightened and lose your courage. 2. Apply a tourniquet above the bite just tight enough to permit circulation of the blood but not the lymph. 3. With a sharp sterile knife make short cuts across the fang wounds one-fourth of an inch deep and one-fourth of an inch long. 4. Suck the wound with mouth, if there are no cuts or sores present, or with mechanical suction apparatus, for twenty or thirty minutes. 5. Ad-

minister antivenin. 6. As swelling develops in a limb, make shallow
cuts one-eighth inch deep and about as long in a circle around the
badly swollen limb. Suck out as much fluid as possible. 7. Do not
give alcoholic drinks. 8. Do not cauterize with hot iron or apply the
viscera of a freshly killed chicken.

Fig. 232. Class Reptilia (Order Crocodilia): *a*, alligator; *b*, gavial. *Photograph
a furnished by the National Zoological Park; photograph b, by the New York
Zoological Society.*

Order Crocodilia (*krokodeilos*—crocodile). This group of carnivorous reptiles, having a worldwide distribution, includes crocodiles,
alligators, gavials, and caimans (Fig. 232). They are water-dwelling
reptiles having long jaws and webbed feet. Alligators and crocodiles
are found in the bayous and streams draining the southern part of the
United States. Alligators may attain a length of twelve to fourteen
feet. They lay their eggs in nests of decomposing vegetation, the heat

of which incubates the eggs. The skins of the animals are used for leather. The annual production of alligator hides amounts to more than 88,000 pounds.

Order Chelonia (*chelone*—turtle). Chelonia are turtles, terrapins, and tortoises. They are interesting reptiles having toothless jaws and a protective "shell" which is really a transformation of the vertebras, ribs, and sternum into bony plates. The bony plates, in turn, are shingled over by horny plates corresponding to the scales of other reptiles. Here is a group of animals whose hips and shoulder blades lie inside the ribs or, more properly speaking, inside the endoskeleton. How such a reversal came about is still a biological mystery. These reptiles are mostly carnivorous and aquatic. The eggs are laid in a shallow pocket made in the sand, and there, covered only by a thin layer of sand, they hatch. The young are left to shift for themselves.

Turtles are of interest to man not only because of their peculiar form and food habits but also because of their food value. Many of the fresh-water turtles are quite destructive of fish, frogs, and waterfowl, both young and old. The snappers—the southern alligator snapper may weigh as much as 140 pounds—are ferocious and will snap at almost anything. They are able to pull under the water and drown full-grown ducks. Speaking of size, we must not overlook the giant sea turtles which may weigh 500 pounds, and the giant land tortoises of the Galapagos Islands which may weigh more than 300 pounds. The giant tortoises are vegetarians. Sea turtles are taken when they come on land to lay their eggs, and are also captured at sea by harpooning. These as well as many other turtles are used for food. The diamond-back terrapin is considered quite a delicacy and is reared commercially on terrapin farms. Snapping turtles and soft-shelled turtles make excellent soup. In a single year turtle products in the United States alone were valued at more than $129,000.

The little land turtle or tortoise, properly speaking, is probably the most familiar of all the Chelonia. This turtle with its occasionally initialed and numeraled shell is found wandering about and feeding on berries, earthworms, and insects. The ventral shell or plastron is so hinged that the entire head and the pectoral appendages can be withdrawn into the shell and enclosed by the hinged ventral shell or **plastron** (*plastron*—breastplate).

Order Rhynchocephalia (*rhynchos*—snout; *cephale*—head). Here belongs a lizardlike reptile about two feet long found in New Zealand. It is a burrowing, nocturnal animal and interesting because it is apparently a primitive animal which has persisted up to the present. It has a single well-developed pineal eye in the

a

b

c

Fig. 233. Turtles (Order Testudinata): *a*, hawk's-billed turtle; *b*, Cumberland terrapin; *c*, soft-shelled turtle. *Photograph b furnished by the General Biological Supply House; a and c furnished by John G. Shedd Aquarium, Chicago, Illinois.*

roof of the skull and numerous other peculiarities of the skeleton that are found only in the fossil Reptilia.

Reptiles of the past. The different members of Reptilia that we have discussed so briefly are but a small sample of that mighty group which reached its zenith in variability and size millions of years ago. The record of the vast assemblage is preserved in the fossilized specimens found in the rocks. The state of Kansas at one time was covered by seas in which swam huge plesiosaurs and mosasaurs whose limbs were modified to form paddles somewhat like those of modern whales. Fishlike ichthyosaurs also inhabited these seas, while overhead flew great reptiles called pterodactyls, some of which had a wing spread of twenty feet.

In Wyoming, Utah, and adjacent states there were vast swamps with remarkably dense vegetation. In the swamps there lived huge dinosaurs ("terrible reptiles"), some of which were almost a hundred feet long from the tip of the relatively small head to the end of the long tail. These animals were mostly vegetarians. It is estimated that for a day's ration one of these creatures, which must have weighed many tons, required almost a thousand pounds of vegetation. Judged by the size of the cavities for the brain and the nerve cord, these gigantic reptiles must have been very stupid and sluggish. Their extinction was probably brought about by changing climatic conditions and by the great carnivorous dinosaurs whose jaws were equipped with seven-inch teeth and on whose toes were huge tearing claws. Other factors that may have entered into the downfall of these Reptilia were diseases and the appearance of more intelligent, warm-blooded, rodentlike mammals which may have destroyed their nests and young.

Class Aves (*avis*—bird). Birds differ from all other animals in having **feathers.** The forelimbs are usually adapted for flying. The heart has two completely separated auricles and two completely separated ventricles. Thus there can be no mixture of venous and arterial blood. They are warm-blooded animals. Modern birds are toothless.

There is strong reason for thinking that birds are descendants of the Reptilia. Some of the strongest evidence for the theory is furnished by *Archaeopteryx,* an ancient bird about the size of a crow, whose fossil remains were found in Bavaria. The jaws bore reptile-like teeth, and each wing had three free, clawed digits. The tail was long and flexible, for the vertebras were not telescoped into a little bony mound as in modern birds. On either side of the long tail were rows of feathers. This "missing link," together with the reptilian features found in modern birds, such as one occipital condyle on the base

FIG. 234. Restoration of extinct reptiles. The dinosaurs were huge reptiles that were very numerous in the Cretaceous period and are now extinct. In the foreground of the reconstructed picture is shown a struggle between a large herbivorous dinosaur, *Triceratops*, and the carnivorous dinosaur, *Tyrannosaurus rex*. *Photograph furnished by the Buffalo Museum of Science.*

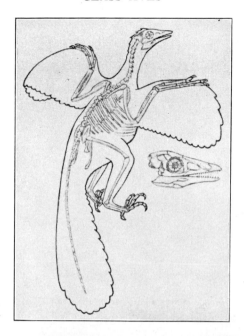

FIG. 235. *Archaeornis,* a primitive extinct bird. *Upper,* the fossil skeleton; *lower,* restoration. Note the long bony tail, the well-developed claws on the digits, and the teeth. *Photographs furnished by the Chicago Natural History Museum.*

of the skull, reptilian scales on the legs, and feathers closely resembling reptilian scales, certainly indicate that birds are first cousins of the reptiles (Fig. 235).

In modern birds the feathers are grouped in definite regions or tracts and are of three kinds: **contour feathers, down feathers (plum-**

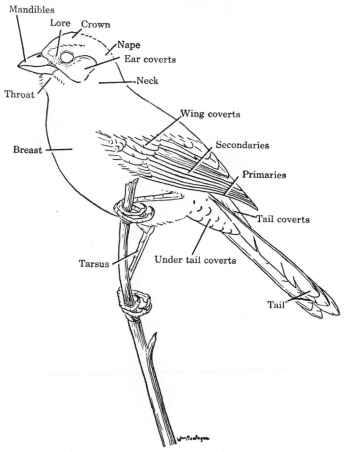

FIG. 236. External features of a bird.

ulae), and **hair feathers (filoplumes)** (Fig. 237). The contour feather is supported by a stiff axial rod, which in the feather proper is called the **rachis.** On each side of the rachis is a row of parallel filaments called **barbs,** branching from which are **barbules** held together by **hooklets.** The broad part of the feather is known as the **vane.** Down feathers have a soft shaft and no vane. Filoplumes have a slender, hairlike shaft. Feathers form a light, efficient insulator which enables the bird, as a warm-blooded animal, to conserve heat. Birds shed their feathers or molt at fairly regular intervals, just as snakes shed their skins. Quite often the color pattern of a bird changes with the coming of the new feathers.

Flying has involved more changes in birds than the mere working over of the forelimbs into wings. The bones in flying birds are made as light as possible by means of air spaces. Some of the bones are even hollow. Often the sternum has a well-developed keel or edge down the center, which affords additional surface for the attachment

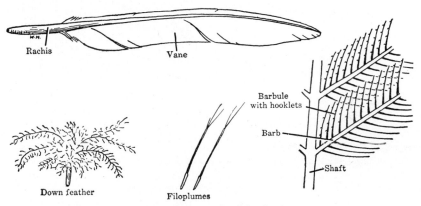

Rachis   Vane

Barbule with hooklets

Barb

Shaft

Down feather   Filoplumes

Fig. 237. Types of feathers.

of muscles that move the wings in flying. For its size the humming-bird has a remarkably large keel, whereas ostriches, cassowaries, and other running birds have no keel on the sternum (Fig. 238). It has been estimated that the wings of a hummingbird make between 600 and 1,000 strokes per minute.

Since the bird depends almost entirely on flight for protection it may have many partial and interrupted meals. However, in many birds the esophagus may be dilated for food storage, and in the fowls and pigeons a further differentiation of the esophagus is the saccular **crop,** a storage organ. The toothless beak as well as rapid gorging allow for little tearing and grinding of the food. However, this function is performed by the stomach, which is modified to form the **gizzard,** a highly muscular grinding organ with a tough lining. Usually there are fine pebbles in the gizzard that assist in the grinding (Plate II).

Birds lay eggs which closely resemble those of reptiles. Birds' eggs have a hard shell of calcium carbonate. The egg containing a supply of yolk is fertilized soon after it leaves the ovary. As it passes down the oviduct there is added first the albumen or white, and finally, just before the egg is laid, there is added the shell derived from secretions of the shell glands. The young embryo, as mentioned previously, floats in the amniotic fluid in the amnion and gives off wastes into the allantois (Plate XI). Young birds when hatched are in a

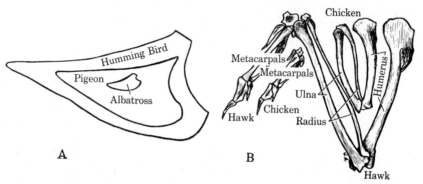

Fɪɢ. 238. Relation between flight (function) and structure in birds. *A*, comparison of the sternums of different birds, assuming that all have the same weight. It should be noted that the flight muscles are attached to the sternum. The albatross is a soaring bird; on the other hand, the wings of the hummingbird beat so rapidly that they become almost invisible. *B*, comparison of the wing of a chicken with that of a hawk. Note the relative length of the bones that determine the area of wing spread. *A, modified from Lucas.*

relatively advanced stage of development, and, with helpful parental care, many of them reach the adult stage.

The Australian bush-turkey, behaving somewhat like the alligator, lays her eggs in a heap of decaying leaves and rubbish which furnishes the heat for incubation. The nighthawk and whippoorwill lay their eggs on the bare ground. Most birds build nests woven of grasses, small twigs, and other materials. They often line their nests. The American robin lines its nest with soft grasses and roots. One of the swifts of northern Borneo makes a nest which is more or less a gelatinous network composed of the secretion of its salivary glands. These nests are considered quite a delicacy and are collected and sold, the price depending on the purity of the materials in the nest. The nests are made into soups, jellies, and other dishes.

Birds are highly specialized animals. In fact their specialization has reached such a degree that they are considered racially old. Thus we find sharp-hooked beaks and curving grasping talons on the birds of prey. Swimming birds have webs between the toes. The wading birds have long slender legs and toes which enable them to walk on soft muck. Their beaks may be long and slender, thus facilitating search through the mud for larvas and other food. The hummingbird has a beak specially adapted for gathering nectar. One of the most generalized birds is the English sparrow. It eats probably all types of food and lives in any environment. Generalization in

FIG. 239. Birds. Class Aves. *Above,* ruffed grouse; *below,* pheasants. *Photographs furnished by the Chicago Natural History Museum.*

structure has enabled it to survive and adapt itself to many varied conditions. In adaptability the European starling is a close second to the English sparrow.

Specialization of structure also occurs in the nervous system of birds. We find a very highly developed cerebellum, which, it will be remembered, is the center of muscular correlation and reflex action. Since the cerebrum or thinking organ does not appear to be so well developed, it is doubtful that birds rank very high in intelligence. Many of the bird's responses seem to be of the reflex type. Birds have a poor sense of smell but make up for it by their keen vision, their eyes being capable of remarkable adjustments for near and far sight. Thus the vulture does not smell his meal but detects the dead animal by its position and lack of motion.

The largest modern bird is the ostrich. An ostrich may reach a height of eight feet and weigh more than three hundred pounds. Ostriches do not fly but depend on running and blows of their long legs for protection. Contrary to popular belief, they do not hide their heads in the sand. Because the plumes are valuable to man, ostrich farming is a large industry. The industry is especially large in Africa, and there are some farms in the United States. It is estimated that there are 500,000 tame ostriches on the African ostrich farms. These birds are worth between $700 and $1,000 a pair. Each bird produces annually about $15 or $20 worth of plumes. Other flightless birds, not related to the ostrich, are the emus, cassowaries, and penguins. Penguins have short paddle-shaped wings adapted for swimming. They spend the greater part of their lives in the ocean and are graceful swimmers, but on land they walk awkwardly erect or slide along on their bellies.

Several penguins may form a partnership for incubating their young. The eggs are laid during the long antarctic night, only one to a female. After an egg is laid, it is rolled on top of the bird's foot, and a flap of loose skin folds over it to protect it and incubate it. When the bird is tired of carrying the egg thus, it rolls it off the foot, and immediately a number of others rush up to gain possession of it. Both males and females participate in this transference of eggs, and when finally hatching occurs the egg is as likely to be in the custody of a male as of a female.

The various kinds of ducks and geese with their webbed feet, flattened bills, and aquatic habits are grouped into one order called the Anseriformes (gooselike birds). They are very useful as food and are hunted quite extensively.

Birds of prey, such as hawks and eagles, are related and have a bad name as killers of other animals valuable to man. But the vultures are valuable as scavengers, and not all hawks are our enemies (Fig. 240). The little sparrow hawk kills very few birds but feeds mostly on mice and insects. Often owls are placed among the birds of prey. Owls come in for much abuse, especially from the so-called sportsmen, who blame them for killing other birds and young game which they wish to kill for sport but which wild animals have to kill in order to live. With the exception of the great-horned owl, owls feed extensively

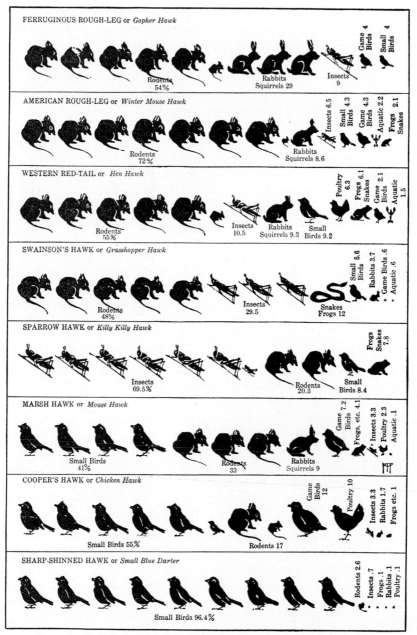

FIG. 240. Chart showing the food of various hawks. Note that insects and rodents furnish the bulk of the diet of most of the hawks. *Chart furnished by the National Association of Audubon Societies.*

on rodents. We have no better friend than the little screech owl, and the monkey-faced owl or barn owl is extremely useful as a rodent destroyer. Surprisingly enough, the near relatives of the owls are kingfishers, hummingbirds, and woodpeckers. The woodpeckers deserve honorable mention, for they search out and destroy various insect larvas and beetles hiding under and in the bark of trees. They cling to the tree by their long claws, propping themselves by their stiff tail feathers, and drill with their drill-like beaks for the insects hidden beneath. The insect or grub is impaled on the tongue and eaten.

The birds most familiar to us—sparrows, thrushes, warblers, and crows—are called passerine birds (Passeriformes) or sparrowlike birds. They are mostly of medium size and have feet adapted for perching. Almost all the birds of this group feed on insects or weed seeds and thus are of inestimable value to man. They should be protected and encouraged in every way.

We cannot exaggerate the importance of birds to man. They serve for food and are the guardians of our food supply. They are our allies in our war with the insects. A hawk or an owl may steal an occasional chicken or rabbit, the robins and blackbirds may pick a few cherries, but, in comparison, the help they give makes such depredations a very minor matter.

Class Mammalia (*mamma*—breast). Mammals are distinct from other vertebrates in that they are covered with **hair** at some period in their life, have **mammary** or milk **glands,** and suckle their young. Mammals are **warm blooded** and have hearts made up of two auricles and two ventricles. The chambers on the right side of the heart are completely separated from those on the left. The red corpuscles are round and non-nucleated.

Most mammals are viviparous, but a few primitive ones lay eggs. Most mammals have small, almost microscopic eggs containing very little yolk. The young develop within the uterus, with which they are in more or less intimate contact by the **placenta,** which is characteristic of mammals only. An amnion and an allantois are present, but the allantois is sometimes rudimentary. The egg-laying habits of the primitive mammals as well as certain of their anatomical characters seem to indicate that mammals are descendants of reptilian ancestors. Man, of course, is a mammal. There are many orders in the class, but we shall consider only the most important and interesting of them.

Order Monotremata (*monos*—one; *trema*—hole). These are primitive, egg-laying mammals of the Australian Archipelago. Besides the egg-laying habit, they have other reptilian characters such as a cloaca

Fig. 241. Mammals (Class Mammalia): *a*, Canadian porcupine; *b*, little brown bat; *c*, armadillo; *d*, spider monkey; *e*, hippopotamus. *Photographs: a, furnished by the Fish and Wildlife Service (Spencer); b, R. L. Fricke, Carnegie Museum; c and e, National Zoological Park; d, New York Zoological Society.*

into which empty the two oviducts, the intestine, and the urethra. In other mammals the genito-urinary opening is separate from the intestinal opening. These and other reptilian characters have led some zoologists to dub the monotremes the "missing link" between reptiles and mammals. The very primitive mammary glands pour their secretions on the hair of the abdomen, from which it is licked by the young animal. The duckbill and the spiny anteater are monotremes. The duckbill not only lays eggs but also has a toothless, flattened bill and webbed feet.

Order Marsupialia (*marsupium*—a pouch). The marsupials are mammals which carry their young in a ventral abdominal pouch. Included in this group are the opossums of North America and the kangaroos, pouched moles, and other animals found in Australia. The young of these animals are born in a very immature condition and are placed within the pouch where they are anchored to the teats by their mouths. The flesh of kangaroos and opossums is edible, and the hide of the kangaroo makes very good leather.

Order Insectivora (insect; *vorare*—to devour). This group of small moles and micelike shrews feeds almost exclusively on insects, insect larvas, and earthworms. The common mole is entirely subterranean in its habits. It often excavates its long tunnels just under the surface of the ground, and the rounded roof sticks up above the general surface. This does not look well on a smooth lawn, but we must remember that the mole is seeking insect pests and their larvas. The mole shows interesting adaptations to its mode of life. The eyes, useless underground, are very rudimentary and have almost disappeared, and the front feet have developed into broad, handlike structures which enable a mole to burrow through the ground at a rapid rate. Except as insect destroyers moles have little value, although they have been eaten as food.

Order Chiroptera (*cheiro*—hand; *pteron*). Chiroptera are bats, the only true flying mammals. The fingers and arm bones of bats are exceedingly long, and between them, and to the tail and hind legs, extends a membrane forming a wing. Bats vary in size from a wing spread of only a few inches to one of five feet in the tropical forms. Bats, as is well known, sleep during the day and work at night. Usually a number of them occupy the same roost. These nocturnal animals amaze us by their ability to avoid objects in their swift flying through the darkness. They seem to have a very keen sense which enables them to detect their approach to an object by the perception of supersonic waves which they have initiated. A bat whose eyes had been blinded flew about in a darkened room

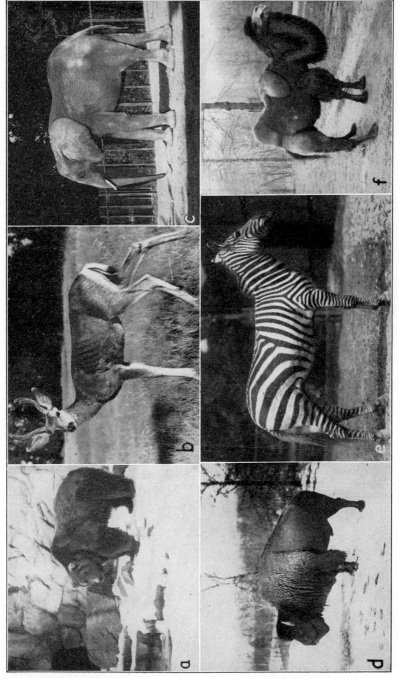

Fig. 242. Mammals (Class Mammalia): *a*, grizzly bear; *b*, Virginia or white-tailed deer; *c*, African elephant, *d*, bison, *e*, zebra; *f*, camel. *Photographs a, c, d, e, f furnished by the National Zoological Park; b, furnished by R. L. Fricke, Carnegie Museum.*

through which a number of strings had been stretched and did not hit any of them.

Our bats here in America carry on the work of insect destruction at night and the birds continue the job during the day. They are our benefactors and friends. They do not carry bedbugs and do not get tangled in women's hair! In the Orient and the tropics there are large fruit-eating bats. The vampire bats of South America attack domestic and other animals and suck their blood. A few isolated attacks on man have been reported.

Order Carnivora (*caro*—flesh; *vorare*). Most Carnivora are flesh eaters, but, as usual, there are some exceptions. The Carnivora have small, weak incisor teeth and sharp, curved canines, or eyeteeth, with which they grasp and tear their prey; the cutting premolars and grinding molars complete the job.

This is an interesting and important order numbering among its members lions, tigers, bears, dogs, and wolves, as well as many valuable fur-bearing animals such as minks, martens, skunks, otters, seals, and foxes. In 1943, Alaska yielded 117,164 fur-seal skins. At two public auctions in St. Louis, 38,655 fur-seal skins were sold for a gross sum of $1,738,002.35. Many people are engaged in fox farming, and skunks, minks, and similar animals are raised on farms.

Some of the Carnivora are very destructive to livestock and the bigger game animals. On the western ranges, in one year the livestock destroyed by wolves, coyotes, and other predatory animals were valued at $20,000,000. Nor should we fail to mention the house cat as a predatory carnivore. It is estimated that a cat kills ten to fifty birds in a year. If cats should average only ten birds per year, the estimated kill for Massachusetts alone would total about 700,000 birds!

Order Rodentia (*rodo*—I gnaw). Rodentia comprise a group of familiar animals including rats, mice, beavers, muskrats, ground hogs, squirrels, rabbits, and others. They do the chiseling and gnawing with their sharp, chisel-like incisor teeth, which continue to grow as the cutting end is worn away. The canine teeth are missing. The rodents are the most typical of all mammals, very prolific, and readily adaptable.

Beavers and porcupines are very interesting rodents. Beavers live along streams. They fell large trees and make dams which often cause considerable areas to be flooded, and at the same time such flooded areas afford a sufficient water level to cover and protect the entrances to their burrows. Porcupines are interesting because of

FIG. 243. Mammals (Class Mammalia): *above,* water buffalo; *middle,* Alaskan caribou; *below,* American elk. *Photographs furnished by the Chicago Natural History Museum.*

their defense mechanism of sharp, penetrating quills which prick the attacker when he comes in contact with them.

The "personal" habits of and the losses inflicted by rats and mice are well known. The United States Biological Survey estimates that in one year rats alone may cause losses amounting to $200,000,000. Mice are household pests, and field mice do enormous damage to growing crops. In Nevada, from 1906 to 1908, meadow mice ruined the alfalfa crop on 18,000 acres. Rabbits and mice will girdle fruit trees and thus ruin orchards. Rabbits, squirrels, and ground hogs are eaten quite extensively, and rabbit skins are tanned and used in the preparation of furs. One of the most important fur-producing animals in America is the muskrat.

Order Artiodactyla (*artios*—even; *daktylos*—toe). Animals of this order are cattle, pigs, deer, camels, hippopotamuses, giraffes, and others. They are even-toed, hoofed animals having two functional toes with well-developed toenails or hoofs. Thus a cow or a pig actually walks around on the toenails of two toes on each foot! Two splints of other toes are often present but are not used by the modern representatives. Many of the Artiodactyla such as cattle and deer are known as ruminants or cud-chewers. In the wild state the cud-chewers depend mostly on speed for protection, so they crop their meal of grass or herbage in haste and send it down to the first two stomach compartments for storage. This material is later returned to the mouth, chewed thoroughly, and then swallowed to pass into the last two stomach chambers—there are four in all—where digestion continues. Digestion is finally completed in the intestine.

The food value of most of the species of this group is very well known. Reindeer have been domesticated for a long time in Lapland and were introduced into Alaska about 1892. The animals, distributed among specially trained Eskimos, number about 712,000. Reindeer furnish food and leather and are useful in transportation. In one year, almost half a million pounds of reindeer meat were exported from Alaska to the United States.

Camels have been domesticated since the earliest times. They are useful as beasts of burden, their hair is woven into cloth, and camel milk is used as food. Camels are well fitted for desert traveling; their feet are soft padded, and their nostrils can be closed against the sand. Moreover, they can provide nourishment and water during long journeys, for they are able to store food in the humps on their backs and fifteen or twenty quarts of reserve water in small saccular compartments of the stomach. Each compartment is closed off by a muscle. "One celebrated traveler mentions the case of a camel that

Fig. 244. Mammals (Class Mammalia): *a*, northern wart-hog; *b*, Malay tapir; *c*, young bull fur-seal; *d*, yak; *e*, moose; *f*, chimpanzee. *Photographs a, b, d, e, f furnished by the National Zoological Park; c, furnished by Fish and Wildlife Service, U. S. Department of the Interior (Carr).*

had been dead for ten days and yet had no less than three pints of not unpleasant water remaining in his stomach."

Order Perissodactyla (*perissos*—odd; *daktylos*). Perissodactyla are odd-toed, hoofed animals such as horses, zebras, tapirs, and rhinoc-

FIG. 245. Mammals (Class Mammalia): *a*, giraffes; *b*, Rocky Mountain goats. *Photograph a furnished by Publicity Department, South African Railways and Nature Magazine; b furnished by the National Zoological Park.*

eroses. Horses gallop and prance about on the toenail (hoof) of the sole remaining toe on each foot. The present horses are apparently descendants of Asiatic ancestors. The wild horses of the western plains are not native but are descendants of horses brought here by the early Spanish explorers.

Order Proboscidea (*pro*—before; *bosco*—feed). Elephants live in Asia and Africa. The elongated trunk is the nose, and the tusks are the modified and greatly elongated incisor teeth of the upper jaw. The Asiatic elephant, being more intelligent and better tempered, is seen most often with circuses and is the beast of burden in many countries.

Order Primates (*primus*—first) include lemurs, monkeys, gorillas, apes, and man. With the exception of man, primates are most plentiful in the warmer parts of the world. Man is found in all regions. Primates have nails instead of hoofs and claws. Usually only one offspring is born at birth. As far as the skeleton is concerned they are not so highly differentiated, but in intelligence they lead all animals.

The lemurs have rather long tails. They are arboreal and resemble squirrels as they flit through the tree tops in Madagascar. Apes and monkeys are also tree-living forms. The new-world monkeys have widely separated nostrils, but the old-world monkeys and apes have nostrils rather close together and directed downward. The tail of the old-world monkeys and apes is very small and sometimes even rudimentary. The highest primates are the gibbon, orangutan, gorilla, chimpanzee, and man. Gibbons have arms so long that they can touch the ground even when standing erect. The orangutan builds a nest in the trees and is somewhat retiring. The gorillas and the chimpanzees are mostly fruit and vegetable feeders and live in herds. It may be interesting to know that in intelligence the chimpanzee is more closely related to man than is the gorilla, whereas from the anatomical standpoint the gorilla is the more closely related.

Order Cetacea (*ketos*—whale). There are various types of whales, dolphins, porpoises, and narwhals. Like some of the reptiles, these mammals apparently were originally land forms which have taken to the water. The fore limbs have been modified into flippers, and the pelvic appendages have practically disappeared. Some of the cetaceans are the largest mammals—in fact, they are the largest animals of which we have record. One species reaches a length of a hundred feet and may weigh as much as 300,000 pounds. The old whaler's cry of "thar she blows" is heard when a whale is seen spouting a cloud of spray and vapor from its nostrils as it comes to the surface after a dive. Some of the whales have well-developed teeth, but the upper jaws of the whalebone whales are equipped with numerous frayed horny strips which, collectively, are known as baleen or whalebone. The strips of whalebone may be ten or twelve feet in length. When feeding, the whale gulps a large mouthful of water and then strains it out between the horny strips. Naturally, most of the living organisms in the water are retained in the mouth and swallowed.

Whales are hunted to obtain not only the whalebone or baleen but also whale oil. One whale will yield as much as 3,000 pounds of baleen, worth from five to six dollars a pound, and about 300 barrels of oil. Ambergris, secreted by the intestine, is a solid comparable perhaps to gallstones of other animals. It sells for about five to ten

Fig. 246. Mammals (Class Mammalia): *upper,* giant panda; *lower,* anteater. *Photographs furnished by Chicago Natural History Museum.*

dollars per ounce. It has been used in making perfumery and also in medicine.

Other Orders of Mammalia. We have tried to present the most interesting and important orders of Mammalia. There are other orders in this class which can be studied in detail in various books of zoology and natural history.

23

Animals and
Their Environment
Ecology

All living organisms whether bacteria, trees, amebas, men, or whales in order to exist must adjust themselves to their environment in the particular portion of the world in which they live. Thus we find fish in the sea, earthworms in the soil, and tapeworms in the bodies of other animals. Such adjustments involve certain modifications of structure and certain types of physiological reactions as induced by the physical and biological factors in the environment. The interrelationships among living organisms and between them and their surroundings make up the subject matter of **ecology** (*oikos*—house; *logos* —discourse). If we were to make a hasty review of the many phases of animal behavior discussed in the previous chapters, we would reach the conclusion that ecology is a broad, complex, and inclusive subject, and that any brief presentation will be somewhat inadequate.

Importance of plant life to animals. Since the energy required by animals is derived from the sun through the photosynthetic action of green plants, consideration must be given also to those environmental factors which influence the growth and activities of plants. It is common knowledge that the kinds and abundance of plants in a given area depend on such factors as the daily and seasonal temperature cycle, the nature of the soil, the relative amount of moisture in the air and the soil, and other factors that influence plant growth.

At the very outset, it should be emphasized that the various factors of any environment are so closely interrelated that it is frequently difficult and sometimes impossible to ascertain the exact influence of any one factor acting independently of the others. It will be impossible to undertake a detailed study of the role and interactions of all these factors, but first we shall consider briefly the influence of substrate, light, temperature, and water on animal life.

435

Substrate. The medium on or in which animals live is an important ecological physical factor. The lower reaches of the atmosphere are frequently a supporting medium in transportation for animals such as birds and certain insects. However, no animal as yet has been able to pass its entire life history "floating through the air." Animals must spend some period of their lives either on or in the substrates of water or land. Parenthetically, certain animals exist on living (biological) substrates. The parasitic worms, such as tapeworms live within the host. In some instances animals may live attached to the surface of others. For example, mollusks and barnacles are found attached to the shell of horseshoe crabs.

The surface of the water is an important substrate for water birds which float or swim on it. Many small animals are supported by this denser upper layer of water. Water striders are quite at home on the surface. Hydra may attach themselves to this surface film and hang suspended from it, and certain species of snails may cling to it. Just under this surface may float such animals as frogs, alligators, and even hippopotamuses. Other animals such as fishes and whales may use the underlying water areas as a substrate.

The nature of the bottom of a stream, lake, or sea affects the type of animal life found living there. Hard rocks afford secure places for attachment for echinoderms, sponges, and sea anemones. Sand and mud offer more advantages for burrowing. A sandy substrate usually maintains the most sparse population, but when mud is mixed with sand, there is a greater population of bottom-dwelling and burrowing aquatic animals, such as certain clams and annelids.

Exposed soils, that is, those not covered by water, present varied conditions that influence the distribution of animal life. The temperature in exposed soils varies. Dark exposed soils absorb heat more readily than light-colored soils such as sand and clay. Moreover, the temperature at the soil surface fluctuates more than that of the air just above or the soil below. This is in contrast to the fairly stable temperature conditions found in large bodies of water.

The amount of moisture in the soil is an important factor. Where there is poor drainage, as in a low meadow, many animals may be unable to adjust and so may be forced to leave this habitat, either for a season or, perhaps, permanently.

The animal population is also affected by the type of chemicals found in the soil. The chemical condition is related to some extent to the amount of moisture present in the soil, since many substances go into solution. The variety and the amount of chemicals depend on the character of the soil through which the water percolates. For example, soils in limestone regions are rich in calcium, which affords favorable life conditions for animals such as snails. It has also been found that the bones of mammals in limestone regions tend to be heavier than those of animals living where there is a predominance of igneous rock. On the other hand, the fire salamander of Germany avoids soils abundant in calcium. Sheep suffer from a cobalt-deficiency disease when the cobalt concentration in the soil drops below a certain level. It has already been pointed out that a lack of iodine in the soil affects the function of the thyroid gland. Soils rich in salts—the so-called "alkaline soils"—such as are found near the Great Salt Lake and around the Dead Sea are almost devoid of animal life.

In a rocky terrain there are found few terrestrial animals which actually bore into the rock. A certain bee of Colorado may excavate a cavity, but most rock dwellers burrow among the stones or live in crevices in the rock. Living in rocky habitats are certain arthropods, snails, small mammals, and some reptiles.

In the more open country of the prairies, the savannas, and other grasslands may be found burrowing snakes, turtles, and lizards. In these soils are found various moles and rodents such as prairie dogs and ground hogs. Burrowing owls may also be found living in this substrate. The sand dunes and deserts furnish a much-burrowed substrate. Here are found various spiders, wasps, and the very interesting ant lion.

There are other soil factors such as acidity, or pH, and the physical texture of the soil that also play a part in animal distribution.

Light. Light affects animals either indirectly by determining their food supply or directly by altering their physiological processes and their behavior, as well as certain structural features. Relative length of days and nights appears to be an important factor in the complex ecology of periodical migration. Apparently the migration of certain birds northward is initiated by longer days. Reproductive activities in some animals undergo various modifications in response to changes in the duration and intensity of light. The onset of the breeding period of many birds, mammals, and fishes is brought about by adding more hours of light by artificial means. Many animals such as deer and trout mate in the autumn when the days become shorter. Poultrymen increase the egg production of hens by exposing them to longer light periods.

There is good evidence that light rather than temperature is responsible for the change in the pelage and plumage of certain animals and birds. In the varying hare, the fur is brown in summer, but, with the coming of winter, it changes to white as a result of the change in length of day, regardless of temperature. Experiments have shown that "change from white to brown can be brought about in January by a sudden increase of eighteen hours of illumination every day." Despite high temperature, prime winter pelts can be produced in weasels in the summer time. Birds such as the scarlet tanager and bobolink can be made to break out into their spring songs in mid-winter if they are gradually for a week or two brought into the light for longer periods and meal worms are added to their diet.

Fig. 247. Plumage changes of the artic ptarmigan. *Left,* winter plumage; *right,* summer plumage. *Photographs furnished by the Chicago Natural History Museum.*

Apparently, life in direct sunlight is made possible only by some protective adaptations. For example, the salamander *Proteus,* when exposed to continuous light, first becomes brown and then black. The human skin develops more pigment (tans) which protects it from injury caused by the rays of the sun.

In their habits organisms become adjusted to light. Among animals there are the nocturnal forms, such as the cockroach, bat, owl, and flying squirrel, and the more extreme example of termites which live in dark tunnels in wood through which no light can pass. The caterpillar feeds in the sunlight but avoids light when it pupates.

Photoreceptors, such as pigment spots and eyes, have developed as an adaptation to light, thus enabling the animal to explore better its environment, to procure its food, or to evade its enemies. The photoreceptors probably play a part in the recognition of mates during the breeding season. They also function in the formation of color patterns. For example, the mottled pattern of the flounder not only changes its shades of color but may even take on the same mottled appearance as the sand or gravel on which the fish is resting (Fig. 248). Similar changes in color pattern occur in the skin of the frog and chameleon. These changes, taking place instantaneously or quite slowly, are brought about by the spreading or concentration of the pigment in certain parts of the pigment cells.

FIG. 248. Protective resemblance. Note the pattern of the flounder resting on two different backgrounds. *Photographs furnished by the Fish and Wildlife Service, U. S. Department of the Interior.*

An important effect of light is seen in the development of vitamin D through exposure to sunlight. Children supplied with an abundance of sunlight seldom suffer from rickets. When spotted cattle exposed to direct sunlight are fed on buckwheat, a rash develops on the skin of the white spots. As the disease progresses, the affected skin scales off, a fever develops, and the animal dies. White mice kept on a buckwheat diet thrive in a dark room, but in bright light they quickly die. Evidently buckwheat contains materials that render protoplasm sensitive to intense sunlight.

Temperature. For every organism there is a range of favorable temperatures within which life processes go on smoothly. Below the lower limit of this range, or minimum temperature, and above the upper limit, or maximum temperature, the activities of the organism cease. The optimum temperature is that at which the organism thrives best. Minimum, maximum, and optimum temperatures vary with different organisms, but the minimum must generally be slightly above 0°C., since water freezes at this point, and the maximum usually falls in the neighborhood of 60°C. In certain organisms the range may extend beyond these limits. Animals work most efficiently at temperatures near maximum toleration.

Adjustments to temperature involve modifications of both structure and behavior. Animals may adjust to winter's cold by **hibernation,** by **migration,** or by special seasonal development of fat, fur, or feathers, or a combination of all three. In the Arctic regions, animals such as the arctic fox, seal, and polar bear are well protected by heavy pelage and also by thick layers of fat.

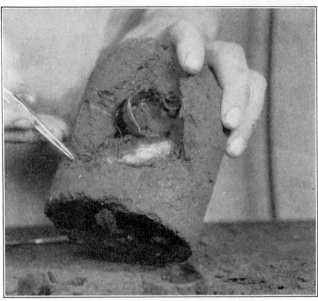

FIG. 249. Estivation of the African lung fish (*Protopterus*). Note the lung fish in the mucus-lined cocoon in the block of mud. *Photograph furnished by the General Biological Supply House.*

Many arctic and some temperate-zone animals, such as woodchucks, reptiles, insects, amphibians, and mollusks, hibernate in winter. During hibernation there is a drop in body temperature, a slowing of the heart beat and the respiratory rate. In fact, in some animals there may be times when there is a complete suspension of breathing for several minutes. The body temperature of some animals may fall as low as 1°C. The Alaskan black fish is reported to be able to live after being frozen solid! Some of the factors that are thought to induce the torpor ("sleepiness") of the hibernating animal are gradually decreasing temperatures; inadequacy of heat-regulating mechanisms; lack of food; concentration of carbon dioxide in the place of hibernation; accumulation of fat; and glandular disturbances. Most fresh-water fish are less active in the winter than in the summer. Usually the temperature of fish is about 10° higher than that of the surrounding water. Many hibernating mammals become cold blooded (poikilothermic) during hibernation. Some animals escape winter's cold and consequent scarcity of food by migration.

During the dry seasons of summer, certain of the insects, spiders, fish, snakes, the aardvarks and the lemur **estivate.** An estivating snail from the border of the African desert "came to life in the British Museum" after a period of four years! As a rule, temperate-zone and tropical animals have less heavy coats, are of a darker shade, and are often more brilliantly colored. Not only do extremely low temperatures present a problem of survival for organisms, but high temperatures likewise affect length of life. The majority of aquatic animals live at a temperature below 40°C. Likewise it has been found that animals from small ponds can withstand higher temperatures than those from streams. Some of the adaptations of terrestrial animals for heat hardiness include, among other devices, evaporation from the skin or lungs and, in the case of the social hymenoptera, evaporation from the nests. Some animals migrate when a certain region becomes too warm, others burrow into the soil, and still others become nocturnal in their habits. Generally, terrestrial insects and mammals are more resistant to heat than fishes, echinoderms, and other marine invertebrates.

Water. It has already been pointed out that water makes up a large portion of the bodies of animals and plants and has an important function in the physiology of the organisms, where it aids not only in chemical processes, but also in the regulation of body temperature, and in respiration. Aquatic animals encounter little difficulty in maintaining the proper water balance but for terrestrial animals this is a real problem. Loss of one-third of the water present often causes death. Most animals obtain water by drinking and certain others, such as frogs and toads, may absorb it from damp ground. Other animals may get water from their food. Important factors in determining the distribution of animals are the methods of securing water, the supply of liquid water available, and resistance by the animals to the drying effects of the surrounding atmosphere. Only those animals can survive in relatively dry habitats that have protective devices against "drying out," such as the chitinous covering of insects, the scales of reptiles, the feathers of birds, and the non-sweating of certain animals. Moist-skinned animals, such as amphibians, earthworms, and certain insects, are confined to moist habitats. Other devices for water conservation are the excretion of relatively dry feces and nitrogenous wastes. Most insects, reptiles, and birds deposit fairly dry

A   B

C

FIG. 250. Modification of appendages for swimming. A, note the flattened tail and the fore appendages modified as flippers in the sea cow; B, the modification of the penguin wing; C, the flattened tail of the beaver. *Photographs A and B furnished by the Chicago Natural History Museum; C by the Fish and Wildlife Service, U. S. Department of the Interior.*

feces. Unquestionably estivation serves to conserve moisture as well as to adjust to high temperatures.

Life doubtless originated in water. Animals inhabiting the water do not require skeletons as strong as those of land animals, and they are usually cold blooded and more sluggish. They range from free-swimming to floating forms. The capacity to float is made possible by the production and retention of gas bubbles, oil globules, or jelly-like substances. Gills are peculiar to aquatic animals. The sessile habit of animals has been developed only in an aquatic habitat. The moisture in the atmosphere, or atmospheric humidity in the environ-ment of land dwellers, is an extremely important ecological factor.

Among the major adaptations of the aquatic vertebrates to their mode of life are the commonly streamlined body and the modifica-tion of the organs of locomotion. In fishes these organs are the flattened tail and fins. The general pattern of a flattened tail is found in the whale, the alligator, and other aquatic reptiles. The lateral appendages of the whale and seal appear as flippers, and the wings of the penguin are modified to form swimming organs. Because of the general stability of the environment, i.e., the relatively constant temperature, the comparatively uniform concentration of dissolved gases and inorganic salts, and the unvarying food supply, the animals of the sea are less progressive and show less variation.

SOME FOOD RELATIONSHIPS OF ANIMALS

Life for all organisms is a continual struggle for survival or, one might say, a struggle for energy. Since plants get their energy from the sun, the struggle among most plants is for a place in the sun, but the struggle among animals is for the energy locked up in the bodies of plants and animals. The strong prey upon the weak, and these in turn prey upon those still less able to defend themselves. The follow-ing verse depicts this competitive interrelationship among animals quite tersely and realistically:

> Big fleas have little fleas
> Upon their backs to bite 'em;
> And little fleas have lesser fleas
> And so ad infinitum.

Food chain. The interdependence of animals on plants and each other for their food or energy requirements makes up what is known as a **food chain.** The first "link" in the chain is the green plants attached to which is the second link, the herbivorous animals which feed on the plants. The third link is the carnivorous animals which feed on the herbivorous forms. In turn there may be several links of carnivores. This first link of carnivores may be made up of rather small animals and in turn may be joined to another link of more powerful carnivorous predators. The number of links involved depends on the varying sizes of carnivores in a given community, but the last link in the chain will be the most powerful predator with respect to size and strength. To illustrate, rabbits are herbivorous and in turn they are eaten by foxes. Foxes may become the prey of wolves, and wolves, in turn, may be eaten by some of the large cats. It is obvious that the herbivorous animals must be the most abundant and form the base of the pyramid which rests on the green plants. The "top" carnivores will be fewest in number. There cannot be one rabbit per fox but there must be many rabbits; nor can there be one fox per wolf but many foxes, and so on to the top predator.

Of course, there are other factors that may alter this sequence. Mice, men and houseflies are omnivorous. Certain of the whales eat all the plants and animals that are left in the buccal cavity and pharynx after straining tons of water through the mouth. Some species have highly specialized food preferences. For example, beavers usually will eat only the inner bark of poplars and willows.

Symbiosis. In its broadest and latest interpretation symbiosis includes "the phenomena of commensalism where two animals live together without detriment to either and parasitism in which the relation is typically detrimental to the host." Since certain food relationships are involved under commensalism and parasitism, these phenomena will be discussed here. In a sense animals may be regarded as "broadly symbiotic in their relations with the plant kingdom," provided that they devour only the surplus and thus do not threaten the existence of particular species of plants.

Parasitism. Whenever one organism lives at the expense of another and confers no benefits in return, the relationship is called **parasitism.** The organism receiving benefit is the parasite; the other is the host. There are numerous illustrations of parasitism. Plant lice, bedbugs, tapeworms, and roundworms are parasites, and many others could be mentioned. Ichneumon flies have sharp ovipositors with which they puncture the wall of a cocoon, or the skin of a larva of some other insect in which the female deposits her eggs. The eggs hatch quickly, and the ichneumon larvas attach themselves to the tissues of their host and devour it. When they have finished their meal the larvas emerge from the host and spin their cocoons. One may frequently see a caterpillar thickly studded with little ichneumon cocoons that will soon release a new crop of parasitic flies (Fig. 251).

One of the most interesting and helpful parasites is the *Megarhyssa* fly that parasitizes the larvas of the common wood-borer. The female pigeon horntail (*Tremex columba*) has a strong, sharp ovipositor by means of which she deposits her eggs at the depth of a half an inch in the solid wood of a tree trunk. The eggs hatch and grow into *Tremex* larvas—white, soft-bodied grubs that bore

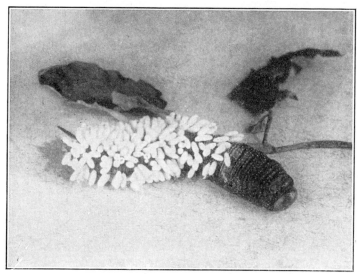

FIG. 251. Tomato worm covered with cocoons of a small Hymenopteran (*Braconid*) whose larvas are parasitic on the caterpillar. *Photograph furnished by the General Biological Supply House.*

deeply into the trunk of the tree, forming extensive tunnels. A female *Megarhyssa*, finding one of these infested trees, guided by what mechanism no one knows, selects a spot directly over a *Tremex* tunnel and elevates her long, slender, flexible ovipositor over her back with its tip resting against the bark. Then, using her body as a derrick, she starts to drill a hole into the tree. When her ovipositor penetrates the *Tremex* tunnel, she deposits an egg in it. Presently the egg hatches and the *Megarhyssa* larva creeps through the tunnel until it reaches its victim. It attaches itself to the *Tremex* larva, sucks its juices, and destroys it. When full grown, the *Megarhyssa* larva pupates in the burrow of its host and, when the adult form has developed, it gnaws its way out through the bark unless it is successful in following the *Tremex* tunnel to the outside.

The oft-described *Sacculina,* a parasitic barnacle that lives attached to the abdomen of a crab, represents the ultimate of dependence (Fig. 252). Its body looks like a swollen sac. It takes its nourishment from its host by means of threadlike structures that invade the tissues of the crab. It has reached the extreme limit of degeneracy, having lost its eyes, mouth parts, thoracic appendages, the segmented structure, and practically all semblance of a typical barnacle.

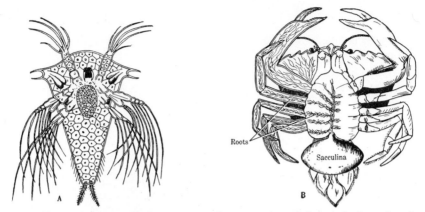

FIG. 252. *A*, crustacean parasite, *Sacculina*. *B*, the adult attached to the abdomen of a crab, and feeding on its host by means of "roots" which grow through the body. *Redrawn from Hegner, "Invertebrate Zoology." (After Leuckart.) By permission of the publisher, the Macmillan Co.*

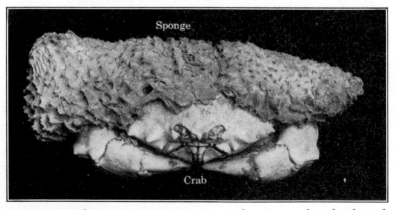

FIG. 253. Mutualism. Sponge growing on crab. Sponge benefits from fragments of food left by the crab, and the crab in turn benefits from the concealment furnished by the growing sponge. *Photograph furnished by the American Museum of Natural History.*

Commensalism (*com*—together; *mensa*—table). According to Van Beneden a commensal organism is a messmate that "requires from his neighbor a simple place on board his vessel, and does not partake of his provisions. The messmate does not live at the expense of his host; all he desires is a home or his friends' superfluities." Here the host is a passive partner. Among animals there are many examples of commensal relationships. The remoras, commensal fishes, attach themselves to sharks and other large marine animals. Barnacles are found attached to the shells of marine mollusks and turtles. Certain small

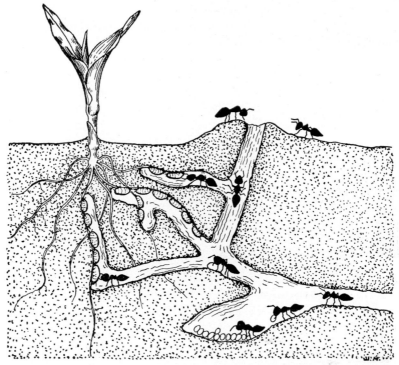

Fig. 254. Mutualism of ants and aphids. The aphids are kept in the nests of the ants where they are cared for throughout the winter. In the spring the ants carry them through tunnels to the roots of corn plants, where they feed on the plant sap. In return the aphids give off a secretion that is relished greatly by the ants. *From Curtis and Guthrie, "Textbook of General Zoology." (After J. J. Davis, Farmers' Bulletin.)*

fishes may live among the tentacles, or even in the stomach cavity of sea anemones and corals.

Mutualism. Often the host and the uninvited guest derive mutual benefit from living together. Such relationships are now summarized under the concept of mutualism (formerly symbiosis). There are numerous instances of this relationship between animals and plants. Certain algae (zooxanthellae) grow in intimate association with coral polyps. Presumably the plants furnish oxygen to the polyp, and in return the algae receive carbon dioxide released by the polyp in its metabolic activity.   Certain termites establish chambers in which a fungus grows on which they feed.   However, the food of the fungus, termite excrement, is furnished by the insect.

Mutualistic relations also exist between animals.   A classic example is furnished by the hermit crab and the hydroid colony.   The crab lives in an old mollusk shell on which a colony of hydroids is growing. The body of the crab fills the shell, its head and large claws protruding from the opening.   When the crab has dined the hydroids have the advantage of eating the leftovers.   The transportation also is furnished by the crab.   On the other hand, the crab probably benefits from the protection afforded by the stinging cells of the hydroid.

Another illustration of mutualism often described is that of the ants and the aphids or plant lice.   Certain species of ants carry aphids from one plant to another or even into their subterranean chambers, where they place them on the roots of plants.   The aphids live on the juices of plants and so the ant has been of service in transporting them and keeping them where they will be well supplied with food.   The aphids excrete a sweet liquid, often called "honeydew," of which the ants are very fond.   They approach the aphids and, stroking them with their antennas, excite and cause them to excrete the honeydew.   The ants eat these droplets of sweet liquid and are thus repaid for their service to the aphids, often spoken of as the ants' "cows" (Fig. 254).

PLANT AND ANIMAL LIFE

The type of vegetation growing in a given geographical region is a reflection of the interaction of the physical factors of light, moisture, and temperature just mentioned.   Another important physical factor is the quality of the soil.   Some soils are alkaline in their reaction, whereas others are acid.   Thus plants, such as rhododendron and laurel thrive on an acid soil.   The texture of the soil is important.   Dry sandy soils of certain regions have a characteristic flora of cactus and mesquite; in a moist swampy soil there may be found such plants as cypress, cattails, and rushes.   The moisture- and heat-retaining qualities of the soil must also be considered.

Widely separated areas having similar physical conditions will support in general, the same or comparable types of plant growth.   Thus the plants and animals living in deserts, in prairies, and in forests will in each case have many similar structural and physiological adaptations.   But even within these larger areas there may be smaller divisions, each supporting its own characteristic kinds of plants and animals.   For example, in a forest, there is the marginal area, and there may be some small open grassy glades scattered through it, rock outcrops, stream margins, or swampy tracts. On the higher ground, there will be a preponderance of oaks and hickories, whereas in some other part, where the drainage is poor, there will be gums, elms, swamp maples, and willows. Such a smaller area having a fairly uniform population is called a **niche.** In each plant community there exists a rather characteristic animal population or niche, which persists year after year. The nature of the vegetation in a given community affects the food supply, shelter, and breeding habits of the animals living there. In the environment of an animal the sum total of the factors that influence it in any way constitute its **habitat.**

Climatic formations. According to their temperature requirements, plants and animals are distributed in great regional groups, each of which is restricted to a geographic zone. Thus there are arctic, temperate, and tropical floras and faunas. Within these regional areas and also determined by climatic influence, there are characteristic communities. Thus in the arctic zone we find the tundra; in the temperate zone, the prairies and the northeastern deciduous forest; and in the tropics, the tropical rain forest.

These are **climatic formations.** In North America nine climatic formations are recognized, each of which comprises a number of different kinds of communities or groups. Such classifications are based on the present distribution of animals and plants, but how these organisms came to be best adapted to some particular set of conditions is another story. Within the larger regional and climatic groups are more restricted groupings or communities characteristic of the various habitats involved. Each such habitat has a characteristic group of plants and animals that do not represent "chance assemblages" but are to be regrded as "more or less closely interwoven communities." Just as each plant and animal is a balanced physiological system within the community, so is each community a balanced system of plants and animals that tends to maintain a balanced relationship within itself and with its environment.

Plant and animal associations. Plants that can thrive together and adjust themselves continuously and successfully to the same general environment form what is known as a **plant association.** Animals often make use of plants and plant communities as breeding places and for shelter. This together with the fact that animals depend either directly or indirectly on plants for their food, some requiring one kind of food and some another, would naturally lead to the inference that particular kinds of animals will be found in a particular plant community. Even a superficial study of the animal and plant life of any region will reveal the correctness of this inference.

When we study animal communities, we find two main categories based on the type of habitat: the **terrestrial** and the **aquatic.** These main groups, in turn, may be divided into smaller communities each within its own peculiar habitat. For example, on the temperate grassland regions of North America we find such animals as the pronghorn antelope, the coyote, the jack rabbit, and the prairie chicken, and, before man disrupted the faunal life, herds of buffalo.

Zonation. Around a pond or lake, zonation of plant associations may be seen (Fig. 255). In the shallow water may be a pond lily

FIG. 255. Zonation. In the foreground back of the water's edge is a zone of rushes and sedges. Back of this is a belt of shrubs, and back of the shrubs is the tree zone. *Photograph by W. E. Rumsey.*

zone; back of this is a cattail zone; next a sedge zone; and last a zone of grasses. Or, in a wooded area, the sedge zone may be followed by a shrub zone, and this in turn by a tree zone. Each zone supports its characteristic population of animals.

In ascending the slope of a high mountain, one can observe a zonation comparable to that which one would find in passing from the equator toward the poles. Since changes in altitude, direction of slope, and distance from the equator involve changes in temperature, light, moisture, and other factors, it is evident that the type of life found in these different situations will vary accordingly. If one ascends a mountain located in the tropical region, one will find tropical vegetation and animal life at the base and lower levels of the mountain slope. Higher up, there is a temperate-zone flora with deciduous trees sheltering a temperate-zone fauna. Still higher, trees do not grow, and here the plants are herbs, low shrubs, grasses, and sedges—an association somewhat resembling that of the arctic tundras. In this high montane region there is also a characteristic alpine fauna. In different regions this fauna is represented by such forms as the mountain sheep, ibex, chamois, yak, and condor.

We also find that characteristic animal life is associated with each of the different plant layer societies—the high treetops, lower trees,

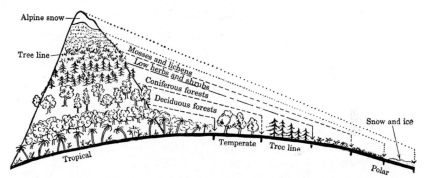

FIG. 256. Diagram showing distribution of plants as influenced by altitude and latitude. *Redrawn from Storer, "General Zoology," by permission of the author and the publisher, McGraw-Hill Book Co.*

the shrub layer, and the forest floor. This has been pointed out by Allee in the case of the tropical rain forest. The highest tree-top level is the abode of certain insects, birds, and other animals. Successive lower levels have their characteristic animals until we finally come to the forest floor, where the animal community is made up of ground dwellers—turtles, snakes, salamanders, and many other animals including such larger forms as the wild hog or peccary, and the tapir. Thus both animals and plants become organized into layer societies, and each of these communities contains its own peculiar group of organisms.

Animal distribution. With plants and animals alike, the distribution found today cannot be explained entirely on the basis of existing conditions. Geology teaches that in the history of the earth there have been elevations and subsidences of different regions of the earth's crust, floods, glaciation, and great shifts of the climatic zones. All these changes have left an impress on the distribution of living organisms over the surface of the earth. Fossil evidence shows that, during late Cretaceous time, great dinosaurs ranged northward into

Alberta and Mongolia, and such tropical and subtropical species as figs, breadfruits, cinnamons, and tree ferns flourished in Greenland. Such facts furnish indisputable evidence that the climate of that period was more mild and equable over most of the land surface of the earth than it is at the present time.

Each species has originated in some specific place and, from this center of origin, has migrated in all directions as far as environmental conditions permitted. The more favorable habitats have served as convenient highways along which the migration has taken place most rapidly. The unfavorable regions such as high mountain ridges and large bodies of water have been barriers to the spread of the species. The migration of species into a new territory brings about an increase in competition which, as we have seen, is a very important factor in determining the distribution of organisms. Therefore, the problem of explaining the distribution of both plants and animals is a difficult one, involving conditions and experiences of the past as well as those of the present.

When man interferes with the natural distribution of plants and animals, new relationships are set up that often bring far-reaching consequences. The introduction of a new fruit or a new grain may mean the bringing in of a new fungus or insect parasite. Sowing a new kind of grass seed may introduce new weeds that may multiply and replace the grass. The weeds may furnish food for some insect that is injurious to some other species. Such changed relationships may involve a whole chain of coactions whose ultimate results cannot be predicted. A species living in a certain region often has its natural enemies to hold it in check. However, if this species is moved into another region where its enemies do not exist, it may become a serious pest. Examples are seen in the multiplication of the English sparrow and the starling when introduced into this country from England and in the plague of rabbits in Australia when these animals were introduced. Whenever there is any thought of introducing any species from one country into another, the possible consequences should be carefully considered. The chestnut-blight fungus has long been known in Japan, where it does little damage to the native chestnut trees. In 1904, the disease was introduced into this country, perhaps through the importation of some goods from the Orient; and in about twenty-five years the native chestnut trees were practically wiped out.

ECOLOGICAL SUCCESSION

In the development of the community many complex changes take place in the animal and plant life. Whether changes take place in a pond or on an area as large as North America, the principles are the same. Suppose there is an area of barren ground. This is first invaded by plant life such as lichens or some other simple plants.

If conditions are favorable, these plants become established. By the death and decay of some of these plants, organic matter is introduced into the soil, more moisture is accumulated, and thus the habitat is improved. Spores of mosses and ferns, and ultimately seeds of higher plants, carried by wind, birds, or water, are introduced, and,

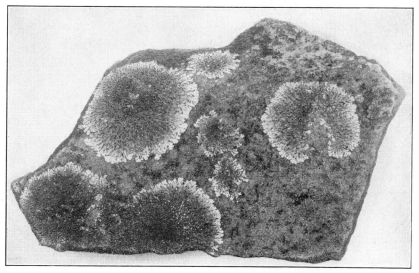

FIG. 257. Crustose and foliose lichens on a rock; a source of humus. *Photograph by courtesy of the New York Botanical Garden.*

under the changed conditions of the habitat, a higher form of plant life takes root and becomes established.

If conditions are not too unfavorable, other higher plants may appear as the result of seeds being carried there by wind, birds, or water. If conditions are favorable, they grow. As these plants grow, it is apparent that the young community is altering the conditions of the habitat. There is increasingly more shade and consequently less evaporation. The root systems are changing the physical structure of the soil, and other influences are setting up new conditions. As these reactions continue, the habitat will become increasingly more favorable for other species that will eventually replace the older ones. In time, a new plant community will appear. Thus, as vegetation develops, continuous change is taking place so that any given area will be occupied by a succession of different plant communities. This change is known as plant succession, but we shall see that animals are also involved, and, therefore, we may speak of ecological succession, a broader term covering both kingdoms. So long as the reactions cause a disturbance in the equilibrium between the organisms and the environment, succession will be continued, until the reactions maintain a relative equilibrium with the environment, when further succession ceases. The terminal phase of the succession is called the **climax stage.**

If we trace the development of vegetation on some barren area from its very beginning, we can form some picture of the dynamic struggle involved in the establishment and maintenance of a plant and animal population. In 1883 half of the island of Krakatau in the East Indies was blown away in a violent volcanic eruption. Three years later a botanist found algae, bacteria, and some mosses and ferns growing on the island. Very few seed plants were found. Ten years later the island was covered with such plants as grasses, ferns, flowers, shrubs, and a few trees. In 1906 a tropical jungle was growing there. Animals had also arrived. There were present mosquitoes, ants, lizards, birds, and bats. Here we have evidence of ecological succession.

In the filling in of a pond we may observe an interesting succession of animal and plant life. When first found, the bottom of the pond was practically barren. Then there appeared simple plants such as algae. Bacteria and Protozoa were present and some crustaceans and other invertebrate aquatic animals (Fig. 258).

The water in the young pond is comparatively free from stagnation, and bass and pickerel thrive there. But, as time goes on, the residue of the decayed bodies of animals and plants accumulates on the bottom, forming a layer of humus. Soon such plants as cattails and bulrushes invade the margins of the pond, and the pond itself is being rapidly filled with algae.

As the filling in continues, the bass and pickerel are gradually replaced by carp, bullheads, and perch. The pond likewise becomes a breeding place for aquatic insects such as dragonflies and mosquitoes. Eventually the pond is succeeded by a swamp and all fishes have vanished. The aquatic fauna is now made up mostly of amphibians, such as frogs, salamanders, and certain species of snakes. Mosquitoes continue to breed in the open pools. With the final filling in and complete elimination of the swamp, the meadow or swamp forest develops in which we find the animals of the meadow or forest floor, such as meadow mice, moles, rabbits, skunks, and various non-aquatic insects.

However, with respect to succession, there is one very fundamental difference between plants and animals—the plant is sessile and the animal is mobile. If conditions become unfavorable, the plant dies,

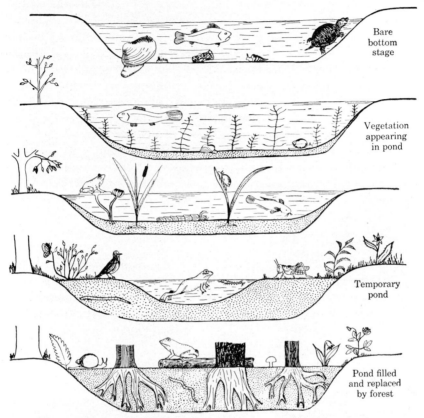

FIG. 258. Possible plant and animal succession in a pond. Note that, as the pond gradually fills with debris, the vegetation changes. Along with the change in vegetation the pond becomes less suitable for certain species of animal life and these are replaced by other species which are adapted to the changed conditions. *Redrawn, modified from Buchsbaum's "Readings in Ecology," University of Chicago Press.*

but the animal may move out and on. The migrations of the animal are limited by its capacity for adjustment, yet they are sufficient to render the animal community readily modifiable.

BIOTIC COMMUNITIES

In our study, we have learned that inorganic materials and organic materials become organized to form protoplasm, that protoplasm is organized in the formation of cells, that cells are organized in the building of tissues, that tissues are organized into organs, that organs are coordinated in systems, and that systems are organized into organisms. Now we shall learn that the principle of biological organization extends even further than this and that organisms become organized into groups or communities. In nature plants and animals do not occur as scattered individuals but rather tend to form natural groups, or communities, which are fairly independent of other adjacent groups. The animals and plants making up a community are never unrelated isolated units. On the contrary, in every community there is an interrelationship among its component organisms, i.e., there are many and varied interactions between plants and plants, between animals and animals, and between plants and animals. Communities are made up of "compatible species populations whose collective requirements of food, shelter, and reproduction are satisfied, in the last analysis, by a certain range of environment."

ANIMAL AGGREGATIONS

Among the various animal and plant communities previously described, there often occur more or less numerous collections of animals which make up a unit or units within the larger communities. They are known as animal **aggregations**. From the social standpoint they are often very loosely organized, but in the colonies of ants and bees they are closely knit into compact societies. These aggregations may be a result of reactions to some of the same factors that influence the formation of the larger communities, but here the animals themselves rather than the surrounding environment become the principal formation factors. The number of individuals which make up an aggregation varies. Some mound-building ants have as many as 10,000 individuals in the colony, whereas certain colonies of tropical termites may contain as many as 3,000,000 individuals exclusive of other animal species which may be present.

Origin of aggregations. Sometimes animal aggregations may be the result of chance. Individuals driven ashore along the ocean beaches by the wind and tides may form groups living among the driftwood and debris. However, in most instances aggregation seems to be a result of reactions to such stimuli as light, heat, food, and moisture, or it may be the result of inborn coactions of the animals to each other. Thus we find certain insects which tend to collect near lights, and certain larvas of marine worms which aggregate in the regions of the most intense light. These reactions are apparently tropistic. Among certain animals, such as sowbugs or land isopods, one animal in its aimless wanderings comes to rest on a spot where there is more moisture. Here it will stop and other isopods will find the same place, and soon quite a colony or aggregation is formed. Or one isopod finding another may stop, and this pair then forms the

FIG. 259.   Aggregation of canvasback ducks. *Photographs furnished by the Fish and Wildlife Service, U. S. Department of the Interior. Photograph by Worcester.*

nucleus of a new aggregation which increases in number as other isopods add themselves to the group.

A species of the fresh-water catfish forms a most interesting aggregation of this type. These animals, hatching from eggs in a nest, grow to form a school. Experimental studies show that they tend to move toward anything of similar form, size, and color. When two animals approach, they move their sensitive barbels toward each other and apparently receive some peculiar chemical stimulus which they recognize. Sometimes it is a touch reaction. When two catfish push against each other they remain together, but, if one of the fish happens to be of another species, it moves away. Catfish may accept into their aggregation others of the same species but from different nests, forming what is known as an **open society.**

For the most part ants and bees form **closed societies.** Membership in this kind of colony is determined by a contact-odor system. If an individual does not have the proper odor, it does not belong. When attempting to break into a new society, ants having the wrong odor are quite often killed.

Types of aggregations. Some aggregations are very loosely organized. One of these is an overwintering aggregation of snakes, in

Fig. 260. Rookery of fur seals, an aggregation. Note the large bull seals, surrounded by the smaller cows of the harem. *Photograph by the Fish and Wildlife Service, U. S. Department of the Interior. Photograph by Carr.*

which large numbers of different species assemble in places where there is greater heat. Another frequent type of aggregation occurs during the breeding season when the ordinary, solitary animals, such as frogs and toads, collect in large numbers in every available pond. This type of aggregation is formed by insects, birds, and other animals. Sometimes aggregation occurs during dry weather and helps the animals to conserve moisture.

Integration of aggregations. In most aggregations there is a certain amount of integration or group organization. In the aggregation itself some integration is brought about by contact stimuli. Thus the movement of one animal is transmitted to the next, and so on to the next, until the entire group is affected. Sometimes, instead of a touch or contact stimulus, a chemical stimulus passes from individual to individual. Sight and sound also play an important part in group integration, particularly where birds and insects are involved. Thus among crows a warning from the sentinel may set the entire flock in motion.

In a flock of chickens the "social" rank of a hen will be indicated by her reaction when another hen pecks her. Certain hens submit to pecking by other hens which apparently have the "peck right" over them. There apparently exists a "peck order" in which certain hens may peck others without being pecked in return. Rank in this "peck order" is established by fighting or by passive submission. Thus in a flock peck order may exist somewhat as follows: hen A pecks hen B; hen B pecks hen C; and so on through the flock. In a flock of hens, the cock leads the peck order!

Benefits of aggregations. It can be clearly seen that aggregation for breeding purposes has a very important role in the continuance of the race. Other effects of aggregation have been noticed. Attention has often been called to the stunted animals and the lowering of reproductive activities which result from dense aggregation. Moreover, under crowded conditions, the animals seemed to have a higher death rate. However, it has been demonstrated that, in a given habitat, a large number of animals frequently have a better chance to survive than a small number. One of the effects of crowding is a lowering of oxygen consumption. As Allee expresses it, "The group exercises some sort of soothing effect upon the members that compose it." For certain aquatic species, apparently, the water of the environment must be conditioned by the animals living in it before it presents an optimum habitat for the group. The individual evidently gives off substances that tend to neutralize toxic materials in the environment. This is true not only of animals of the same species but also of animals of different species. Thus the fresh-water mussels excrete into the water certain substances that will protect fish and other animals from various toxic substances. Indeed, many fish, particularly aquarium fish, thrive best in apparently stagnant water. Experiments have shown that fruitflies will grow to a larger size under crowded conditions than when comparatively few are present. Experiments with various Protozoa and other animals show that the rate of reproduction is increased under crowded conditions. Out of these various aggregations, with the integrating factors and protective effects for the individuals and the race, may come the beginnings of animal social organization, which culminates in man.

Social life of some insects. Honeybees, ants, termites, social wasps, and other insects lead a communal life. The termites, or "white ants," are very primitive insects anatomically but have an elaborate social organization equaling that of the true ants, bees, and other Hymenoptera. Some of the termite colonies may number hundreds of thousands of individuals living in earthen or wooden nests. The material is chewed, mixed with saliva, and built into a nest that is as hard as cement. Some of these nests may be eighteen to twenty feet high. Usually the royal chamber is in the center, with other rooms and passages surrounding it. All are carefully protected from light and heat.

In the termite society we may find as many as eight castes with both males and females in each caste (Fig. 200). They may be summarized as follows:

1. First-form adults which are usually kings and queens. The royal pair lose their wings after they have taken a dispersion flight and settle down to form the colony. The queen is well fed, and her abdomen may increase to 20,000 times the volume of that of a worker.
2. Second-form adults are the substitute kings and queens—crown princes and princesses. They may take the place of the king and queen if these die.
3. Third-form adults are substitutes also for the royal family.
4. Workers without wings and possessing a small brain.
5. Soldiers without wings and with a very small brain. The jaws are so large and specialized that this caste must be fed by the workers. There are three castes of the soldiers.

Termites feed on dead wood and vegetable matter, which they are able to digest with the assistance of commensal protozoans living in their alimentary tract, another example of coaction. Termites have developed quite an elaborate system of mutual feeding called **trophallaxis.** They may feed each other on saliva, on "recalled" partially digested food, or even with fecal material. Some may even give off a fatty substance from the body which is licked off by fellow colonists. Logically, the queen gives off the most delicious and plentiful supply, and her greedy subjects often tear off pieces of the "royal hide" to increase the flow. Wheeler says that the members of the termite colony may be said to be bound together by a circulating medium of glandular secretions, fatty exudates, and partly and wholly digested food, just as the cells of the body of a higher animal are bound together as a "syntrophic" (*syn*—together; *trophein*—to nourish) whole by means of the circulating blood. Certain termites, like some of the true ants, cultivate their fungus gardens underground. They also have captive flies and beetles which give off secretions and so are carefully watched and cared for by the worker termites. A similar type of communal life is carried on by many insects in the groups mentioned, and the social organization developed is quite remarkable.

INDIVIDUAL ADAPTATIONS

The chief business of each animal is to establish and maintain the most harmonious and balanced relationship with its own peculiar habitat. When an animal *fits* into its environment, it is said to be adapted to that environment. Such adaptation is not necessarily the result of conscious effort on the part of the organism. It may be the result of heredity, or of the influence of special factors, or of the accumulated effects of past experience, or of other conditions and correlations of which we have little or no knowledge.

Adaptation is rarely perfect. Some organisms are very poorly adapted to the environment in which they are obliged to live. However, every organism is able to modify to some extent its structure or function, or both, in response to ordinary changes in its environment. Whenever a species loses the capacity to adjust, or ceases to use it, that species becomes extinct. Since all habitats are constantly changing, it follows that the organism must keep making continual adjustment and readjustment if it is to maintain any approximate equilibrium with its habitat. This means that every living organism is engaged in an active, perpetual, unceasing struggle for adjustment that can be terminated only by death. From the viewpoint of biology, *only that organism or race is successful that can maintain itself and its kind in a favorable environment* or in an environment to which it can adapt itself. Each habitat sets the limits within which adaptations of the organism may be effected and thus shapes both the structural and the dynamic or functional pattern of the animals living there.

In all organisms, regardless of how it came about, there is an inherited fitness for a particular kind of habitat; this fact in general explains why animals and plants live where they do. Thus there are marine animals and fresh-water animals; subterranean animals and aerial animals; pelagic animals, i.e., animals that live far from shore, and littoral animals, i.e., animals of the shore waters and beaches. In considering the land habitat of animals, we meet variable conditions

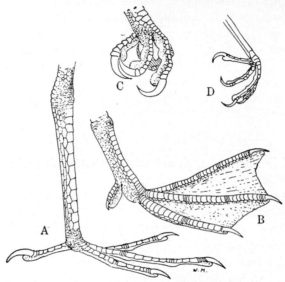

FIG. 261. Adaptations and specializations of feet of birds. A, wading bird; B, swimming; C, grasping; D, perching.

with respect to water supply, respiration, substrate for locomotion, temperature, flora, and food conditions. As has been pointed out previously, a watery habitat offers much more stable, uniform conditions than the land. We have already considered adaptations to water supply, temperature conditions, and food. Locomotion on land is effected mainly by crawling, walking, and flying, or by a combination of all these methods. Snails, slugs, and snakes crawl, whereas most vertebrates, except fish, walk or fly. The feet of various animals are modified in accordance with the type of substrate. Thus the toes of wading birds are long and slender (Fig. 261). The caribou of the north has a wide spreading hoof that functions somewhat like a snowshoe. The great cats have padded feet which enable them to move quietly through the forests and tall grass to stalk their prey.

Many land forms spend most of the time in the air and in trees, a type of life likewise involving certain modifications. Thus there are certain frogs, especially in the tropics, whose toes are equipped with suckerlike disks that enable them to climb about in the tops of the highest trees. Some mammals, such as flying squirrels and certain lizards, glide from tree to tree by means of folds of skin which extend from the fore to the hind limbs. Monkeys swing from branch to branch by means of slender, prehensile tails and grasping hands

Fig. 262. Adaptations in animals. The two-toed sloth, a tree-dwelling mammal. *Photograph by the National Zoological Park.*

and feet, whereas winged flight is practiced by most birds and insects. Both structural and physiological adaptations are so numerous that nothing like a complete list can be given in this brief discussion.

Since many organisms have similar needs with respect to one or more factors such as light, water, food, temperature, and air, there will be lively competition among them whenever they chance to develop a more or less crowded population within a limited territory. The pressure of competition and the necessity for adjustment to an ever-changing environment are met by organisms in three different ways: partial or complete adaptation may enable the organism to maintain itself successfully; the organism may migrate to a more favorable region; or, finally, the organism may fail to make an adequate adjustment, and die. Keeping in mind the enormous output of spermatozoa and ova by animals, as well as the power of regeneration and asexual reproduction, we can easily understand how the law of overproduction is operative and how intense the struggle for existence must be wherever living forms thrive under favorable conditions. It follows then that, in all these densely populated regions, the organism meets keen competition, which constitutes a very important factor in determining the distribution of, and mode of life among, living organisms everywhere.

In studying the struggle for survival we find various structural devices, form designs, and color patterns which may be of real assistance to both the hunter and the hunted, but are probably most helpful to the hunted. The turtle and armadillo are clad in a strong protective armor. The porcupine is amply protected by his quills against all comers except man. Elk, deer, moose, antelopes, cattle, bison, and rams have horns or antlers of various types; and the giraffe, deer, and antelope have sharp, knifelike hoofs. The deer, antelope, rabbit, and many other animals depend largely on fleetness of foot to escape the attacks of their enemies.

Fig. 263. Adaptation of the polar bear to life in the Arctic. *Photograph by the Chicago Natural History Museum.*

Protective coloration. It is a well-known fact that certain animals elude their foraging enemies by reason of their resemblance to immediate surroundings, or to other, more noxious or ferocious animals. There are birds whose plumage blends so closely with the background that we may pass within a few feet of them without seeing them. The arctic ptarmigan changes its plumage, and the varying hares change their pelage to match their surroundings. Their brown coats of summer are changed to white in winter so that they match well the snowy landscape. However, it must be observed that this same protective device may likewise help the snowy owl to capture the varying hares. The stripes of the zebra of Africa, browsing in the tall grass, may make it less conspicuous to its enemies, but a similar arrangement of stripes may assist the Asiatic tiger in stalking its prey. The chameleon and the flounder can readily change their own color pattern to match closely that of the substratum upon which they chance to be resting. All such color patterns and color changes as have been mentioned are generally considered forms of protective coloration.

Special resemblance. In form, or by reason of some peculiar behavior or position, some animals may closely resemble certain inani-

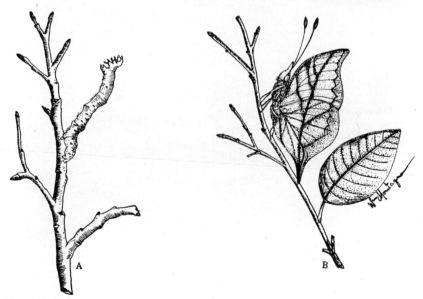

Fig. 264. Protective resemblance. *A,* resemblance between a geometrid larva and a twig. *B,* resemblance of the folded wings of the Indian butterfly, *Kallima,* to the leaves of a plant. *Redrawn from Heath, Jordan, and Kellogg, "Animal Studies." By permission of the publisher, D. Appleton-Century Co.*

mate objects in their environment. Thus the walking-stick looks like
a dead twig. Some of the leaf hoppers resemble buds and young
leaves. The classic example of this type of protection is the dead-
leaf butterfly (*Kallima*) of India, whose folded wings closely resemble the leaves of the twig on which it may be resting (Fig. 264).

Mimicry. Another feature supposed to be of protective value is
mimicry. In color and pattern, certain non-poisonous or less noxious
insects may resemble poisonous or less palatable insects and thus
escape capture. In this way the inedible monarch butterfly (*Anosia
plexippus*) may be mimicked by the edible viceroy (*Basilarchia
archippus*). The poisonous coral snake is closely mimicked by the
harmless scarlet king snake. Other interesting examples of supposed
mimicry might be cited.

Other special survival adjustments. Some animals, such as the
musk turtle, certain insects, and the much-maligned skunk, may emit

Fig. 265. Opossum—death feigning ("playing possum"). *Photograph furnished
by the Fish and Wildlife Service, U. S. Department of the Interior. Photograph
by McColm.*

disagreeable odors. Death-feigning is practiced by certain animals,
the opossum for example (Fig. 265). The harmless puff adder does a
good job of bluffing with its hissing and ferocious demeanor, or fail-
ing in this it, too, may "play dead." Some animals are said to possess

warning colors. Thus the white tail feathers shown by the meadow lark, junco, and other birds may serve as an alarm signal to others of their kind. This same function has been attributed to the "cottontail" of the rabbit and the white tails of certain species of deer. Some poisonous snakes and stinging insects are rather brilliantly colored—supposedly a warning that they should be left alone and undisturbed.

MIGRATION

We have already spoken of the migration of animals in relation to changes in plant communities, but there are other migrations, more

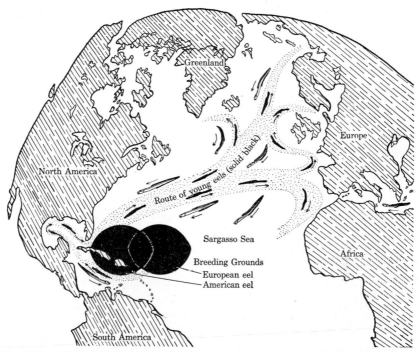

FIG. 266. The adult European and American eels migrate to the breeding places in the Caribbean. Here they spawn, and later the young eels of each group return to the regions inhabited by their parents. Young eels are shown in solid black; adult animals in outline.

or less rhythmical in nature. Some of them are rather erratic, some are seasonal, and others take place only once or twice during the life of the individual. Although several theories have been proposed to explain the cause of such migrations and how the habit began, the question still remains unanswered. Salmon live from two to seven years in the ocean and then, fasting and living on stored fat, they migrate up the rivers in great numbers, struggling through rapids and leaping water falls, until they come to the headwaters, where they spawn. As a result of their journey, the fish become flabby and frail and many soon die. After remaining in the fresh water six to eighteen months, the young fish move down to the ocean. Eels, on the other hand, live in the fresh water for a number of years until they become sexually mature. Then they migrate down the streams to the ocean where the eggs are laid, after which the old eels apparently die. After living for a time in the ocean, the young eels migrate into the fresh water of the rivers.

The annual migration of birds is one of the most puzzling problems of animal ecology. The practice of bird banding has taught us many facts concerning the phenomenon. For example, it is now known that many birds after making a long migratory flight will return the next season to the same place whence they started.

Dr. Allen tells a story about three tree sparrows which he trapped and banded in January. In March, they left for their nesting grounds in the north. In January of the following year, three tree sparrows visited his feeding shelf, and when they were trapped he found they were wearing the bands which he had placed on them the preceding January. A similar experiment has demonstrated that a chimney swift, after spending the winter in the southern part of North America, returned the following spring to the same chimney it had occupied the year before.

What guides these birds back to their old homes after making such long journeys to distant places? Numerous suggestions have been made in answer to this puzzling question. It has been suggested that the migrating birds are guided by visual landmarks, but certainly over-water routes lasting for hundreds of miles would apparently negate this hypothesis. Others think that wind direction is a guiding cue, but winds are decidedly changeable. Some are of the opinion that the sun may serve as a guide. Some biologists think that birds possess the equivalent of a magnetic compass and that they are thus guided by their reaction to the earth's magnetic power. A recent theory has been advanced that the birds orient themselves by means of magnetic forces arising from the earth's rotations. Another recent suggestion has been made that "birds find their way home by exploration"; in other words, visual landmarks may play a part in the homing ability of certain birds. But again certain objections have been raised. Moreover, this theory might hold for the migration of adult birds but it does not seem to explain the behavior of the young birds migrating for the first time. Such juvenile birds may be guided by older birds that chance to be in the same migrating flock. Physiological adjustments at one time might cause the bird to move in the direction of warmer latitudes and at another time toward cooler regions. Further investigations are needed to give more definite and accurate information concerning all phases of this most interesting problem.

The eastern golden plover summers on the shores of the Arctic Ocean and spends winters in South America. Every autumn the Pacific golden plover flies from Alaska to the Hawaiian Islands, and since his route lies over the Pacific Ocean he is compelled to travel the distance of 2,000 miles in one single non-stop flight. But, as far as long-distance flying is concerned, the "ace" of all birds is the Arctic tern. This bird may celebrate the Fourth of July in Greenland or Labrador but always enjoys Christmas somewhere south of the Antarctic Circle, requiring a tour of 11,000 miles. If this bird returns to the north the next season, the total distance covered in a single year will be not less than 22,000 miles.

As a usual thing, birds migrate mostly at night and advance rather leisurely during the day. The robin averages about 13 miles a day in going from Louisiana to Minnesota, increasing its speed with increasing latitude, until it covers 31 miles a day in southern Canada and 52 miles a day in central Canada. By the time it reaches Alaska it advances 70 miles a day. The speed of flight of the different birds varies considerably. The homing pigeon during a period of 4 hours averaged 55 miles per hour. The speed of the blue heron is about 35 miles per hour; migrating geese approximate 44 miles per hour. Studies reported by the U. S. Fish and Wildlife Service show that the duck hawk can travel from 165 to 180 miles per hour. Among wild ducks, the canvasback is about the fastest—72 miles per hour. Smaller birds fly at a somewhat lower rate of speed, varying from 20 to 35 miles per hour.

In addition to these more or less regular rhythmical migrations, there are others of a sporadic nature, such as the flights of butterflies, locusts, dragonflies, and other insects. They have been explained as irregular, dispersal movements. At times, similar dispersal movements of other animals occur, such as the spreading of lemmings and squirrels. Thorough studies have been made of the periodical migrations of the lemmings, which are small ratlike rodents of northern latitudes. At times they reproduce in prodigious numbers and then great hordes of them migrate, chiefly at night, into the lowland regions. They move steadily forward, swimming streams, climbing walls, and overcoming all obstacles, although many are killed every day. The march continues until they reach the sea, into which they plunge and continue on their course until they are drowned. Early settlers in South Africa tell of periodic southern migrations of hundreds of thousands of springbok, continuing day after day for some time. It is estimated that one of these great migrating hordes was 15 miles wide and 42 miles long—630 square miles of animals! The

Soil conservation.   Since all animal life depends on plant life, and plant life, in turn, depends on the soil, the first and basic need is the conservation of the soil.   Fertile soil is a very complex organization of mineral substances, air, water, and living organisms.   The

FIG. 269. Conservation. *Above,* conservation of top soil by strip cropping; *below,* water conservation by terracing. *Photographs furnished by the Soil Conservation Service.*

building of such a soil requires long periods of time, but it can be disorganized or removed by erosive action in a comparatively short time. The best way to conserve the soil is to maintain a vegetational covering. In cultivated fields various conservation methods are employed, depending on the slope, nature of the soil, rainfall intensity, and other factors. Contour plowing and strip planting are necessary on relatively steep slopes (Fig. 269). Where active erosion must be checked, terraces are built usually in combination with spillways, check dams, floodways, reservoirs, and the like. If erosion can be checked sufficiently to permit the development of a close plant cover, stabilization will occur, and normal succession can be maintained.

Wildlife conservation. The forest has always been known as a natural home of wildlife. Here we find moose, elk, and deer; bear,

FIG. 270. The passenger pigeon—a now-vanished species of bird, once very abundant. *Photograph furnished by the Chicago Natural History Museum.*

bobcat, wolf, and mountain lion; wild turkey, ruffed grouse, and mountain quail; beaver, raccoon, marten, and wolverine; and many smaller forms including both birds and mammals. The destruction of the forest has changed the picture. After the removal of its natural cover and deprived of its natural food supply, much of our wild

Fig. 271.   Wildlife refuges.   *Photographs furnished by the Fish and Wildlife Service, U. S. Department of the Interior.   Upper photograph by Van Huizen; lower by Greenwalt.*

animal life has vanished. The passenger pigeon is extinct, and the wild turkey has become rare in most sections of the country. Killing by the hunter has been a factor in the reduction of wildlife, but undoubtedly the disturbance of natural conditions has been a more influential agency. A lively popular interest has developed in wildlife conservation. One of the most-publicized examples of this interest has been the program of conserving deer. Originally, it was believed that, if refuges were established, the deer would multiply and establish themselves securely. The experience with deer in Pennsylvania and the Kaibab herd taught the conservationists that under protection and provided with favorable conditions deer will multiply until overpopulation results and starvation ensues. On the Kaibab National Forest the deer population became so large that the territory was severely overgrazed. Many of the better browse plants were actually killed, and with the resultant food shortage the continued existence of the entire herd was imperiled. Many other examples could be cited, but this will serve to illustrate the need of wildlife management, a modern conservation measure that attempts to make use of available ecological and biological information in the solution of urgent wildlife problems.

One of the many problems confronting the wildlife manager is the control of predators. The numerous so-called vermin campaigns being waged in all parts of the country give evidence of the wide popular interest in this problem. The subject is one of great complexity, the ramifications including matters of economic welfare as well as the natural balance of animal populations and the interests of sportsmen. Many of the control measures now in vogue are based on too much positive opinion unsupported by sufficient knowledge. Many of the vermin campaigns, as one author says, "are a waste not only of time and effort but also of an element of the native fauna." Wise measures of predator control demand intensive study of each particular problem in each separate community, for, in each instance, coactions are involved whose ultimate influence cannot be ascertained by mere guessing.

24

Life
Its Nature and Origin

Organic and inorganic matter. Although the sugars, fats, and many other chemical compounds obtained from animals and plants had long been known, it remained for Lavoisier (1743–1794) to show that nearly all plant substances are made up of carbon, hydrogen, and oxygen. He also showed that, in addition to the three elements just mentioned, animal substances always contain nitrogen and sometimes sulphur and phosphorus. Today we know that additional elements enter into the composition of protoplasm.

The peculiar composition of these compounds and the fact that they were more combustible than the so-called inorganic substances, like lead, iron, and salt, led to the belief that carbohydrates, fats, and proteins were made under the influence of some peculiar vital force. It was thought that they could be produced only by the living organism and that they reacted differently from the "mineral substances." This distinction between organic and inorganic material received its death blow in 1828, when Wöhler succeeded in synthesizing urea, an animal excretion, from ammonium cyanate, which is an inorganic compound. This synthesis showed that the influence of a living organism is not necessary for the production of the "organic substance" urea.

Since the time of Wöhler chemists have made many organic substances from inorganic materials. We have synthetic orange, vanilla, and other fruit flavors which never came from the actual fruit; synthetic perfumes; and synthetic drugs and gland extracts (thyroxin, adrenalin). Thus the supposed difference between vitalized and non-vitalized compounds apparently has disappeared.

Yet there is a difference between compounds and elements united and combined in a living organism and those same compounds uncombined, unintegrated, and non-related. Whether matter is alive or not depends on the peculiar, intricate combinations of atoms and compounds, such as the proteins, carbohydrates, fats, salts, and the like, of which it is composed. It will be readily understood that living protoplasm is constantly changing, taking in materials from the environment, working them over, using them, and finally discarding them as wastes. Yet, in the process of material change, the living protoplasm, usually in the form of an organism, maintains its individuality until death. The living organism is like a whirlpool in a stream. It retains its identity even though its constituents are constantly shifting and changing.

This living protoplasm is irritable and adaptable, carries on metabolism, grows, is capable of spontaneous movement, and, finally, gives to organisms the ability to produce new individuals like themselves. This is life—an adjustment of internal relations to external conditions.

Origin of life. In the light of the conclusion that there is no sharp boundary between the organic and the inorganic world, and that all matter has the same general plan of structure and obeys the same general physical and chemical laws, it is of interest to consider how life began. One theory originally offered to explain the origin of life was the theory of **spontaneous generation** or **abiogenesis** (*a*—not; *bios*—life; *genesis*—birth). The adherents of this theory held that living things could form spontaneously from lifeless and inorganic matter. "Is there, in the inorganic world, a happy concourse of atoms that become chained together through the action of the sun's rays and other natural forces, so that a molecule of living matter is constructed in Nature's laboratory without contact or close association with living substance?" * Does life come only from pre-existing life, or can it come directly from inorganic matter?

From the time of Aristotle (325 B.C.) to A.D. 1668, the theory of spontaneous generation was accepted by practically everyone. It was erroneously alleged yet firmly believed that under the influence of the sun's rays the mud and slime of ponds and streams transformed into frogs, toads, and eels. Dewdrops transformed into grasshoppers, bees, and ants. The recipe for the production of mice was to place some cheese and old cloth in a vessel and in due time they would be transformed into mice. In Egypt mice supposedly had their origin in the mud of the river Nile. Sir Thomas Browne, who was inclined to doubt some of these acts of creation, was flayed for his disbelief by Alexander Ross, in these words:

So may we doubt whether in cheese and timber worms are generated, or if beetles and wasps in cow-dung, or if butterflies, locusts, shell-fish, snails, eels,

* William A. Locy, *Biology and Its Makers*, Henry Holt and Company, New York, p. 227.

and such life be procreated of putrefied matter, which is to receive the form of that creature to which it is by formative power disposed? To question this is to question reason, sense, and experience. Or if he doubts this let him go to Egypt, and there he will find the fields swarming with mice begot of Nylus to the great calamity of the inhabitants.

One of the reasons for this belief in what, to our minds, is pure foolishness was the fact that no one subjected the theory to experimental tests, i.e., scientific analysis. However, in 1668, an Italian, Redi, decided to test scientifically the theory that meat would transform into worms. This experiment was done in a simple and homely fashion by placing meat in flasks. Some of the flasks he covered with paper, others with a kind of gauze, and others he left uncovered. The flies, attracted by the odor of the decaying meat in the jars, came and laid their eggs in the exposed meat in the uncovered jars and on the gauze covering other jars. In time the eggs hatched, and the meat in the uncovered flask became a crawling mass of maggots. No maggots appeared in the meat in the covered jars, but the eggs laid on the gauze hatched into maggots. Thus Redi demonstrated that the maggots came from the insect eggs and not from meat. Redi made other important and interesting experiments, but it is recorded of him that **"with acute scientific analysis he never allowed his conclusions to run ahead of his observations."**

The investigation begun by Redi was carried on by later experimenters. A scientist named Leeuwenhoek had improved the microscope, and in 1687 he discovered a new world of minute animals and plants, including the bacteria. These minute living organisms appearing in apparently pure water, in fruit juices, and in sterile foodstuffs were now thought to be the first organisms produced whenever inorganic material was changed through natural agencies into organized living things. Spallanzani (1777) found that, if meat broth was boiled for about an hour and then sealed in a vessel, no life appeared in the broth.

In 1864, Pasteur, a French chemist, showed conclusively that boiled or sterilized fruit juices and other food materials would remain unchanged if kept free from contamination by germ-laden air. He made a special flask with two necks, one of which had a double curve and a small opening. After an infusion had been poured into the flask the larger opening was sealed. The infusion in the flask was then boiled to kill all living things that might be in either the infusion or the flask. No dust particles carrying germs could get into the flask because of the curved neck provided with a liquid seal. Regardless of how long these infusions were kept under these conditions, no

microscopic organisms could be found in them.   When his critics
objected that boiling had so changed the infusions that they could
no longer support life, Pasteur broke open some of the flasks containing the previously boiled and sterilized infusions, thus admitting air.

FIG. 272. Louis Pasteur (1822–1895). *From the Fisher Collection of Alchemical
and Historical Pictures. Fisher Scientific Company, Pittsburgh, Pa.*

Very shortly these solutions swarmed with living organisms.   This
result was Pasteur's reply to his critics, for it proved that the boiled
infusions could support life.   This experiment clearly showed that
living organisms could not arise spontaneously but that they entered
with the air only when the flasks were broken.   Tyndall, an English
physicist, also produced scientific evidence disproving the theory of
spontaneous generation.

Thus the theory of spontaneous generation or abiogenesis, namely, that living things or life can come from inorganic or lifeless material, was succeeded by the theory of **biogenesis,** which maintains that all life must come from some pre-existing life—*omne vivum e vivo.*

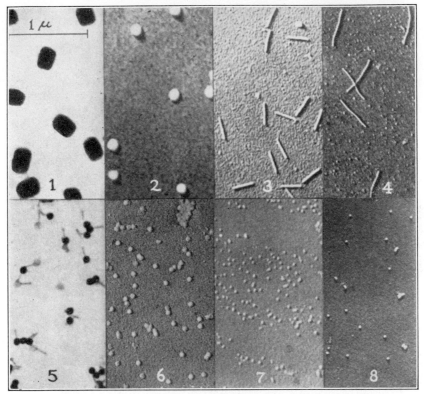

Fig. 273. Photographs of viruses made with an electron microscope. 1, Vaccinia; 2, influenza; 3, tobacco mosaic; 4, potato mosaic; 5, bacteriophages; 6, Shope papilloma; 7, bean mosaic; 8, tomato bushy stunt. *Photographs furnished by Dr. C. A. Knight.*

However, many scientists think that there may have been and still is some sort of spontaneous generation which connects the inorganic with the organic world.

In considering the origin of life we must think of a living organism which would be too simple and primitive to be classed either as an animal or a plant, probably merely an undifferentiated blob of ultramicroscopic protoplasm. Today the virus seems to be the simplest thing which may be considered living. Viruses were first discovered in 1892 by a Russian botanist, Iwanowski, while he was studying a disease of the tobacco plant known as "tobacco mosaic." In the continuing study of viruses through the years it has been demonstrated that they can live and multiply only in living bodies; they cannot be cultured in the absence of living host tissue, and consequently some living organism must have preceded the present viruses as we know them.

So far as is known, viruses do not possess cell membranes or any of the morphological features characteristic of living cells. However, as Stanley points out, there are at least some viruses which are complex proteins possessing the power of reproduction and showing evidence of heredity. Further, they may be destroyed by the same agents that destroy living cells. Biochemists have succeeded in crystallizing certain viruses which would indicate that they are chemically pure substances. However, to date it has been impossible to demonstrate that viruses do carry on metabolism. Because of these two developments many are inclined to believe that viruses are non-living. Nevertheless one well-known biochemist has suggested that "if these units are proteins, the gap between the living and the non-living has been almost bridged."

By what process then was a virus produced? The very improbable guess would be that random chemical and physical reactions taking place among billions of molecules might have brought about a fortuitous combination which would have resulted in a self-reproducing protein. If such a reaction could have taken place, life could be said to have originated by spontaneous generation. At the present level of our knowledge of biology, our conception of the origin of life is very largely hypothetical and doubtless it will remain so until we ascertain much more definitely the intrinsic nature of protoplasm itself.

25

The Theory of Evolution

From the very earliest times men have been interested in the origin of living things and in how they came to be what they are. The idea of evolution is not so recent as many people think. The early Grecian philosophers thought about evolution and discussed it but failed to gather objective data. Anaximander (600 B.C.) was of the opinion that in the beginning there was a fluid earth which gradually dried up to give some patches of land onto which man, in fishlike form, crawled and gradually acquired limbs. Then came Empedocles (approximately 490–430 B.C.), who advanced a doctrine of strange creatures with mixed parts and wrong appendages, all of which later found their proper places to produce the modern forms of plants and animals. Aristotle (384–322 B.C.) later came much closer to modern ideas of creation, for he arranged the animals and plants in consecutive series, with the higher forms following the lower. Aristotle was a scientist. He based his conclusions on observations made on living plants and animals. Most of us are familiar with the interpretation of the account of creation in Genesis, how all species of plants and animals were created in the beginning, with the forms they now have. This explanation, called **special creation**, served as a satisfactory interpretation until about 1880. Even today, it satisfies those who have never troubled themselves to study the question objectively and scientifically. St. Augustine (?–604) and St. Thomas Aquinas (1125–?), leaders of the church, had thought that our present living forms came from a more primitive ancestry. However, it was not until the middle or latter part of the eighteenth century that man began to speculate once more concerning the mode of creation. About this time the French biologist Buffon, who was much interested in comparative anatomy, pointed out structural likenesses in animals and concluded that there must be blood relationship among them. He did not believe that the pig was a special creation, because he found two useless or vestigial toes in addition to the two functional ones on each foot, and he concluded that some ancestral hog had used all four toes. But in later years he gave up the problem of origins as being impossible of solution.

Lamarck pointed out that animals and plants vary with changing environmental conditions and that, as they adjust themselves to new conditions, they apparently change their form. He thought that this change within the organism was brought about by some inner drive toward a certain necessary adaptation. It was Lamarck's idea that organs *used* tend to develop and those *not used* tend to atrophy. The changes made or acquired by one generation could be passed on to the next. In other words, acquired characteristics could be inherited, a problem which we have previously discussed. Lamarck and his ideas as well as the whole general theory of evolution were opposed by Cuvier. There were others who held evolutionary ideas, but it remained for Charles Darwin, an Englishman, to present to the world the modern theory of evolution.

CHARLES DARWIN

Today the mere mention of the theory of organic evolution at once suggests the name of Charles Darwin (Fig. 274). Darwin's father and grandfather were

Fig. 274. Charles Darwin (1809–1882). *Photograph from Bradford "Darwin."* *Reproduced by the permission of the author and the publisher, Houghton Mifflin* *Company.*

physicians. His maternal grandfather was Josiah Wedgwood, a careful, painstaking man who manufactured pottery which is famous even today. Thus we see that from the standpoint of both heredity and environment Darwin had a scientific background which may have strongly influenced his career. Darwin was a rather delicate boy and not a particularly good student. He first tried the study of medicine, but sickened at the sight of operations. While at Cambridge he became acquainted with Henslow, a botany professor, and Sedgwick, a professor of geology, with whom he made many field trips. It was the influence of these men that initiated and helped to shape the future career of young Darwin.

Shortly after Darwin's graduation in 1831, Henslow arranged for his appointment as naturalist on the British ship *Beagle* which was soon to set sail on a mapping journey around the world.

Now among Darwin's reading material was Lyell's *Elements of Geology* a new work just off the press, which Henslow, the donor, told him to read but not to believe. In his book Lyell advanced the thought that present-day geologic forces, such as earthquakes, volcanoes, and rain, could account for the earth's history and that the present geologic facts are the result of these forces operating in the past. Lyell concluded that this orderly geologic development was brought about by natural causes, but he thought that such factors did not operate in the organic world.

In South America, Darwin was astonished at the multitude of plants and animals and was particularly interested in the sloths and armadillos. On some of his explorations ashore he found fossil skeletons of megatheriums and glyptodons which closely resembled living sloths and armadillos. He got the idea, therefore, that these fossils may have been the ancestors of the present-day sloths and armadillos. While studying the terracelike plateaus of Patagonia he found a series of marine shells resembling those of modern shellfish living in the sea. Later, while sailing along the west coast, he found the same geologic formation there as he had seen on the east coast, which suggested the possibility that both coasts of South America had been elevated from the bed of the ocean.

His ship made another stop at the Galapagos Islands. Here he found more similarities among the animals and plants of adjacent islands than among those of more widely separated islands. However, all the island forms resembled one another even more closely than they did those of the mainland. Therefore it seemed evident that the island forms were descendants of those of the mainland; but, widely separated from the homeland, they had gone slightly different ways. Darwin continued to study. He was interested in corals and studied coral island formation. He collected barnacles, in fact all kinds of animals and plants, which, with assistance, he later classified. He worked at the task of classification for eight years. Meantime he had written a narrative of the voyage and published a number of papers so that he had gained the respect of the world. However, the more he pored over his notes and the more he studied his material, the more thoroughly he was convinced that present-day forms are the descendants of former animals. Of this he was fairly certain, but how and why it happened he could not quite see. He once had read a book by Malthus on human populations, which pointed out that men would multiply more rapidly than the available food supply, if all of them lived. Moreover, Darwin had been impressed with the enormous overproduction of animals and plants. For example, if an annual plant produced only two seeds, and all the seeds were to grow, there would be 16,777,216 in the twenty-fourth generation. It is estimated that the conger eel lays approximately 15,000,000 eggs in one season. Other plants and animals could be cited which are just as prodigious in their reproductive rates (page 199). It was quite clear that only a small percentage of animals and plants survived. Presumably, those that survived must have differed or varied somewhat, and in favorable ways, from those that perished. This last is natural selection, or the survival of the fittest, which we shall discuss in greater detail later.

Darwin finally wrote a full exposition of his ideas but when about ready to publish he received from Alfred Russel Wallace a manuscript presenting practically the same conclusions. Wallace asked Darwin to arrange for the publication of this paper, which Darwin generously decided to do rather than to publish his own, but finally both papers or essays were presented together. At once the conflict between science and theology became bitter and intense. The publication of Darwin's *Origin of Species* in 1859 served to fan the flames. Darwin won followers not only at home in England, but also in Germany and other countries, and today the idea of organic evolution is firmly fixed not only in the thinking of the scientist but also in that of the layman.

Although Darwin wrote many other scientific treatises besides his *Origin of Species,* he deserves special credit for collecting and presenting to the world such an accumulation of observations and data in support of the theory of organic evolution that it became widely accepted and still endures. In 1882, after a life of real service, Darwin died and was buried in Westminster Abbey where kings, statesmen, clergymen, artists, and other great men of England are entombed.

Darwin was in a peculiarly favorable situation to accumulate data and to formulate his theory of evolution. He had five years free from other distractions to study the flora and fauna of the world. Moreover, though his mind may have worked cautiously, he had wonderful perseverance and patience in the use of his remarkable powers of discrimination. It is to these characteristics of the man that we owe the first convincing statement of, and evidence for, the theory of evolution.

THE THEORY OF EVOLUTION

The theory of evolution holds that animals and plants, throughout the ages, have changed and transformed into new and different species. Indeed, such changes are responsible for the various present-day species of animals and plants, for the process of transformation is continually going on all about us like respiration, metabolism, and other physiological activities. However, it is moving so slowly that we cannot perceive it in the span of a lifetime. For instance, we cannot expect to see a cat develop batlike wings and fly. The keynote of this doctrine of evolution is the word *change*—a change in form from those organisms of the past to those of the present and a change from those of the present to those of the future. Nor do the changes necessarily imply development of "better" organisms, for some plants and animals may degenerate whereas others increase in complexity.

It can readily be seen that the theory of organic evolution is vastly more dynamic in its concept than the older theory of special creation. Cuvier introduced a variation into the theory of special creation which he called **catastrophism**. According to Cuvier, great worldwide cataclysms occurred which completely wiped out the then existing plants and animals, after which new ones were created. For him, this explained the presence of the fossils very nicely.

Today, there is practically unanimous agreement as to the validity of the theory of organic evolution as a mode of creation. However, there is some diversity of opinion with respect to the mechanism of the process. Later in the chapter we shall see that Darwin had ideas concerning the mechanism, and collectively these ideas are today generally known as **Darwinism.**

Evidence for Organic Evolution

In the very beginning of this part of our discussion the reader is warned that a complete demonstration of the theory of evolution, such as we find in problems of geometry or chemistry, is impossible. Many difficulties and unsolved problems remain. Much of the evidence is indirect, and, though pointing to strong probabilities, it does not quite reach absolute certainty. The many varied and complex aspects of the problem, together with the slowness of the process and the countless millions of years involved, make the unveiling of the evidence very difficult. However, the fact that the lines of evidence seem to converge and lead to one common conclusion adds strength and probability to the proof of the theory.

Classification. We have already discussed Linnaeus and his system of classification of animals and plants. The fundamental unit or concept of this system was the **species.** According to Linnaeus, who believed in the doctrine of **Special Creation,** each species represented a separate act of creation and showed clear, distinct characteristics which separated it from other species. Moreover, each species had been here since the creation of the earth and was immutable. During his time and afterwards, the main task of the biologist was to ferret out the different species, give them names, and place them properly in the classification scheme. In hunting down the "species," certain animals and plants were found that could be placed in their respective genera, but they differed so slightly from each other that one species graded into the next. Controversies arose as to what constituted a species in these groups. For example, originally there was recognized only one species of giraffe, but today the one species is broken up into eleven subspecies. This intergradation between species is what we would expect according to the evolution theory which postulates gradual change on the part of the organism, but it certainly does not fit into a theory which assumes the creation of separate, unchanging entities. If we accept the evolutionary explanation for the creation of species, the relationships made evident by the groupings of animals and plants in the system of classification become more logical and natural to us and take on new significance. In fact, there is no known way to account for these similarities except on the principle of a common heritage.

Evidence from comparative anatomy. When we study and compare the structures found in various animals, several different plans of structure may be observed which may characterize certain great groups of animals. Thus we have already seen that vertebrates and invertebrates are more widely separated than fishes and birds, or than annelids and arthropods. Invertebrates possess a much greater variety of structural plan, and at first sight the structures found in the invertebrates of the various Linnaean categories may not seem to be related. On the ventral side of the abdomen the crayfish has appendages called swimmerets, each made up of a basal piece joined to which are two other divisions. This is a **biramous** (two-branched) appendage which, with considerable variation, serves as a model for the walking legs, the claws, and most of the mouth parts of the crayfish (Fig. 179). Theoretically, the ancestor of the Crustacea may have been equipped with similar biramous appendages which became modified to serve various functions. Continuing the study of comparative invertebrate anatomy, we need only to call attention once more to the mouth parts of insects which have been modified to form chewing organs, long tubular structures for sucking as in the Lepidoptera, and the biting-sucking types found in mosquitoes (Fig. 186). Nor should we forget that the mantle of the mollusks may be modified as an organ to secrete a protective exoskeleton in the clam, to act as a breathing organ in certain snails, and as a locomotive structure in the squid.

If we select and compare certain structures, for example, the foreleg of the horse or cow, and the human hand, we cannot fail to note some similarity in general structural pattern. We have already seen that these structures are homologous, for they have the same embryological origin and general structure. Study of the muscles and nerves shows other marked resemblances. The human hand is a grasping organ with five nail-tipped digits, and it rotates on a flexible wrist with eight bones. The ulna and radius, as may be recalled, are two separate bones articulated with the humerus which fits onto the shoulder blade in a ball-and-socket joint. The human forearm and hand serve a multitude of purposes, whereas the horse uses the homologous structures for one purpose only—locomotion—which requires only a forward and backward movement in one plane. So in the horse we find only one big digit with its nail enlarged to form a hoof. Two other digits are present as rudimentary vestigial structures. The metacarpals are fused, and there are only seven wrist bones. The ulna and radius are fused into a single bone, and the

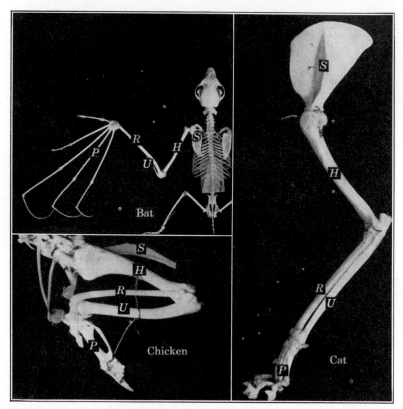

Fig. 275. Evidences for evolution from comparative anatomy. Comparisons of the pectoral girdle and forelimbs of the bat, chicken, and cat. *H*, humerus; *P*, metacarpals; *R*, radius; *S*, scapula; *U*, ulna. *Photograph of skeleton of bat furnished by the Chicago Natural History Museum. Photographs of the forelimbs of the chicken and cat by Dana M. Garner.*

joint arrangement is almost solely of the hinged type. Yet, in spite of these differences, we readily recognize the same fundamental plan of structure. If we compare the bat's wing to the organs just mentioned, we find the same pentadactyl plan of structure, except that here the bones are much elongated, especially the phalanges, and connected with one another by the wing membrane, which is attached also to the legs and the short tail (Fig. 275). The digit corresponding to our thumb is free and tipped with a claw. In birds we find a great fusion of digits, carpals, and metacarpals, as well as some elongation of bones, particularly in the soaring birds. Here the function of the membrane of the bat's wing is taken over by feathers. Thus we might go on pointing out such similarities of structure in the vertebrates as variations and modifications adapted for burrowing, climbing, and swimming.

The testimony of comparative anatomy has been questioned because it does not connect such diverse animal types as crayfish and bony fish, oysters and amphibians. It is hard to see much similarity between a starfish and an oyster. However, we can find evidences of evolution among the shellfish themselves, and among the various echinoderms. And it is quite possible that thousands of intermediate forms may have lived and become extinct, of which we have no record at all.

Additional anatomical evidence is offered by what are known as vestigial organs, that is, structures which apparently are useless to an organism and not necessary for its existence. This phase of the discussion is well illustrated by the following analogy of Lydekker. If a screw-driven steamer has some of the machinery such as paddle boxes, paddle posts, and the like, all of which are used on a side-wheel paddle boat, two conclusions are possible—either the designer was crazy or the boat had been converted from the paddle type to the propeller or screw-driven type. Clearly the second conclusion is the only reasonable one. So, in the organic world, vestigial organs must be considered remnants of structures which were functional in ancestral animals.

The python has two claws, one on each side of the anus, and they are supported by slender bones. The claws are considered vestiges of hindlegs (Fig. 276). Further, many snakes have only one functional lung, the other lung being represented by a small budlike growth only. In many cave fishes and moles the eyes, although present, are not functional. Whales have developed enormous tail flukes to drive them through the water, and, although the posterior limbs have apparently vanished, under the skin there are vestigial pelvic bones and other limb elements. A few more examples must suffice for this phase of our discussion. It has already been pointed out that in the foot of the horse there are two rudimentary bones which correspond in position to the second and fourth digits of the human hand. Perhaps the most interesting vestigial remnants in man are the groups of functionless ear muscles which correspond to those that serve to move the ears of horses and dogs. The vermiform appendix is another vestigial organ. Then there are the Diptera, whose hind wings have disappeared except for the knobbed hairlike balancers. In some of the annelid worms, the larvas develop in cocoons from which they emerge as completely formed crawling "worms." Yet, in the close confinement of the cocoon, larval organs have been formed which would be useful only if the larvas were swimming in the water.

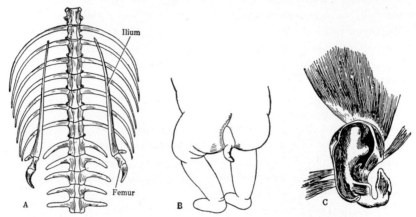

Fɪɢ. 276. Vestigial structures. A, vestigial hind limbs of the snake, *Python.* B, rudimentary tail on a newborn infant. C, vestigial and useless muscles for moving the human ear. *A and C redrawn from Romanes, "Darwin and After Darwin." By permission of the publisher, Open Court Publishing Co. B, redrawn from Arey, "Developmental Anatomy." By permission of the publisher, W. B. Saunders Co.*

These are but a few examples of an imposing list of vestigial structures. Certainly it does not seem reasonable that these vestigial and often detrimental structures would have been developed if animals had had their origin by special creation. On the other hand, this is exactly what would be expected in an evolutionary process where the old is either constantly being worked over into something new or discarded altogether.

Evidence from embryology. We have already seen that embryology is the study of the origin and development of the individual from the egg to the adult. The different phases in the development of the individual organism are called collectively its **ontogeny** (*on*—being or individual; *genos*—descent). The study of the history of the development of the species or race is called **phylogeny** (*phylon*—race; *genos*). From the standpoint of evolution we are interested only in embryology as it throws light on the possible ancestry of the organism.

In the early part of the nineteenth century, many biologists, particularly students of embryology, placed much confidence in the theory that higher animals, in their embryological development, pass through stages that correspond to, or are very similar to, the embryonic stages of lower animals which, in the light of the theory of evolution, would be their ancestors. In ontogeny the human embryo, for example, resembles the embryos of fish, amphibians, and reptiles but develops additional structures since the young mammal develops within the uterus rather than in an egg shell. These later differentiations may blur and distort the original characteristics common to the lower animals. Thus theoretically we may see, in a way, a moving picture of the history or the evolution of an organ or a system. True, the reel is old, with gaps here and there, with sequence mixed in places, and even with much unrelated material. Haeckel stated that "Ontogeny is a short recapitulation of phylogeny," which is known as the **theory of recapitulation.** Thus every animal, as it developed from the egg to the adult, was supposed "to climb its own ancestral tree." Psychologists seized upon the theory to explain types of human behavior, and the sociologist made use of it to explain his problems.

We shall first examine the evidence of recapitulation supporting the theory of evolution and afterward we shall consider some objections to the **theory of recapitulation.** The early embryologists held the theory of **preformation** (page 221), but this was succeeded by the theory of **epigenesis** (page 222), which maintained that the relatively unorganized zygote gives rise to new tissues, new organs, and new systems, forming a new individual. So we have been interested to observe that all the vertebrates with their varied structures and habits have a very similar embryonic history or ontogeny. In tracing the embryonic history, some compare the zygote to the protozoon, and the two-layered gastrula to the coelenterate structure. Restricting our comparisons, we find that at certain stages the embryonic mammal has pharyngeal pouches and gill arches (Fig. 277). Through the gill arches the blood flows, in a fishlike arrangement of blood vessels, from a fishlike heart. We still possess one of these fishy heirlooms, the Eustachian tube, which we believe represents what in our ancestors was a gill slit. Embryological evidence seems to indicate that lungs may have had their primitive forerunners in the swim bladder of fishes, as in the lungs of the lung fishes. The very primitive chordates have a rather simple type of kidney called a pronephros which functions throughout life. Fishes and Amphibia in their embryonic stages have a pronephros that is replaced later by a more complex kidney known as the mesonephros, which persists in the adult. As far as the kidneys are concerned, reptiles, birds, and mammals, during the embryonic stages, theoretically recapitulate their early

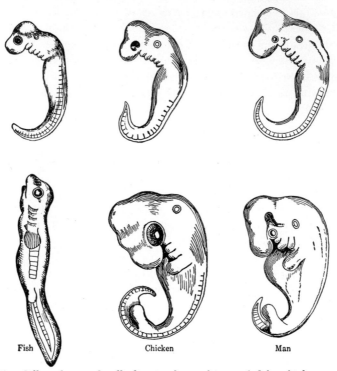

Fish   Chicken   Man

FIG. 277.   Gill arches and gill slits in the embryos of fish, chicken and man.
After Haeckel.

chordate days with a pronephros; their fish and amphibian days are lived through again with a mesonephros, which, in turn, is partially discarded for the metanephros or most complex type of kidney in the adult.

By somewhat similar comparisons of the embryos, we find the Annelida and Mollusca related by their very similar larvas, called **trochophores** (Fig. 292). Often there are countless numbers of trochophores in the ocean, and it is almost impossible for the average person to distinguish between those of the mollusks and those of the worms. If space permitted additional striking similarities among other invertebrate animals could be presented.

What are the objections to the theory of recapitulation? First of all, we must not overlook the fact that many of the structures seen in embryonic or larval stages are adaptations to environmental conditions encountered by the young animals. These adaptive structures may have developed irrespective of ancestry. Such larval adaptations or structures Haeckel called **coenogenetic;** the true ancestral structures he called **palingenetic.** The coenogenetic structures are of recent origin and so can have no ancestral significance, for only the palingenetic characters are ancestral. It was a difficult task to assign the embryonic structures to the proper groups. Many controversies arose, and a marked diversity of opinion was held as to what are coenogenetic and what are palingenetic structures. Consequently there were about as many phylogenetic trees as there were students of embryological evolution. Some of the trees were very poorly rooted. Many biologists became disgusted and were inclined to scrap the entire theory, but today most of them agree that the fundamental truth of the theory—that many ancestral features are repeated in the development of the individual—is still sound and worthy of consideration.

Also, we are forced to admit that the ancestral history is greatly abbreviated. For example, theoretically, the chick, in the short period of three weeks, lives through an ancestral history covering millions of years. Now the only reasonable view to hold is that much of the history has been omitted and that the remainder is very much abbreviated.

Evolution and paleontology. Paleontology is the study of the fossil remains of animals and plants which are found in the rocks of the earth. Fossils for the most part are not organic structures of the original organism but are imprints or mineralized replacements (Fig. 278). The original organic materials have completely disintegrated. Someone has pointed out that this branch of science should present the most convincing testimony for evolution since it deals entirely with ancestral organisms. However, one of the difficulties encountered is that the fleshy structures of many animals and plants do not preserve well. Tissues with a high water content such as we find, for example, in the jellyfishes and many plants, likewise decay without leaving traces. Consequently many fossils are known only from the partial skeletons which have been found, and many types or links needed to complete the chain of the various groups are missing.

Darwin described the situation very well in the following words:

I look at the geological record as a history of the world imperfectly kept and written in a changing dialect; of this history we possess the last volume alone, relating only to two or three countries. Of this volume only here and there a short chapter has been preserved; and of each page only here and there a few lines. Each word of the slowly changing language, more or less different in the successive chapters, may represent the forms of life which are entombed in our successive formations and which falsely appear to us to have been abruptly introduced.

FIG. 278.   Fossils.   *Left,* a fossil trilobite, an extinct arthropod.   *Right,* imprint of a leaf.   *Photograph on the right furnished by A. K. Miller; on the left, by H. Lee Dean.*

Now it is an obvious commonplace to everyone who sees a brick or stone wall that the layers put down first are at the bottom and that the most recent layers or the ones laid last will be found at the top. So it is with the rock layers or strata. If we examine the series of strata often uncovered along roads or exposed by nature, as in the Grand Canyon, we find those formed first, or the oldest from the standpoint of time, at the bottom, and at the top are the youngest or the ones formed last. The geologist has studied exposed rock layers with their contained fossils on various continents and has been able to detect a rather definite chronological succession of these rocks. Beginning at the bottom he has marked off the oldest rocks as those that were formed in the Pre-Cambrian era. On top of the Pre-Cambrian, in order of succession, rest the rocks of the Paleozoic, the Mesozoic, and the Cenozoic eras. The eras show certain peculiar fossil rock formations which furnish a basis for subdividing them further into a chronological succession (Fig. 279).

According to our concept of evolution, viz., that living things are changing and have changed from the simple to the complex, we would expect to find the simplest and most primitive animals and plants in the oldest rocks, and the most complex in the most recent formations. This is what the paleontologists find, except in the oldest rocks where the life record is not too clear. These oldest rocks would contain the fossil remains of the early protozoans and coelenterates, animals with little or no skeletal structures. The soft bodies would not be readily preserved. Moreover, since the oldest rocks would be at the bottom they would be subjected to great stresses because of the pressure of the overlying strata.

Almost all the animal fossils of the Paleozoic are marine invertebrates, such as mollusks and echinoderms. There is also a profusion of trilobites, a very primitive group of arthropods (Fig. 278). The rocks near the top of the Paleozoic contain some fossil fishes and a few primitive insects. No mammals or birds are there. In the Mesozoic appeared primitive birds and mammals, but the vertebrate life was represented by the highest development of the reptiles. Some twenty orders of Reptilia existed, whose members ranged in size from small birds to the huge dinosaurs already mentioned. The bony fishes became more highly developed and more varied. Most of the invertebrates were very similar to modern forms.

Finally, when we come to the Cenozoic rocks, which more nearly approach the present in time, we find fossils which closely resemble modern plants and animals. We find the mammals and birds well developed, but only five orders of reptiles are found instead of the twenty that existed in the preceding Mesozoic era. Of the numerous invertebrates of this period we call attention to the higher orders of insects such as the Coleoptera, Hymenoptera, and Lepidoptera. Other arthropods and also mollusks and echinoderms are present in abundance. This rather hasty survey shows that, the farther back we study the history of life, the more differences do we see between those early forms found as fossils in the oldest rocks and those of the present. Moreover, we see no haphazard conglomeration of life forms, but a logical sequence from an evolutionary standpoint. As Scott puts it, "The history of life, both animal and vegetable, is a story of progress and differentiation, of advance continued through millions of years to modern conditions from far-off beginnings, which were of radically different character."

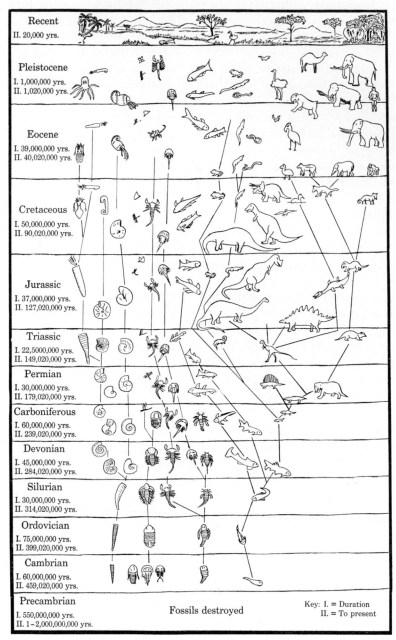

Recent	
II. 20,000 yrs.	
Pleistocene	
I. 1,000,000 yrs.	
II. 1,020,000 yrs.	
Eocene	
I. 39,000,000 yrs.	
II. 40,020,000 yrs.	
Cretaceous	
I. 50,000,000 yrs.	
II. 90,020,000 yrs.	
Jurassic	
I. 37,000,000 yrs.	
II. 127,020,000 yrs.	
Triassic	
I. 22,5000,000 yrs.	
II. 149,020,000 yrs.	
Permian	
I. 30,000,000 yrs.	
II. 179,020,000 yrs.	
Carboniferous	
I. 60,000,000 yrs.	
II. 239,020,000 yrs.	
Devonian	
I. 45,000,000 yrs.	
II. 284,020,000 yrs.	
Silurian	
I. 30,000,000 yrs.	
II. 314,020,000 yrs.	
Ordovician	
I. 75,000,000 yrs.	
II. 399,020,000 yrs.	
Cambrian	
I. 60,000,000 yrs.	
II. 459,020,000 yrs.	
Precambrian	Fossils destroyed
I. 550,000,000 yrs.	
II. 1–2,000,000,000 yrs.	

Key: I. = Duration
II. = To present

FIG. 279.   Chronological succession of rocks and type fossils.

Critics point out that both the fossil and living animal and plant forms which are necessary as connecting links for this gradual transition from one group of organisms to another are sometimes missing. There may suddenly appear new groups of animals or plants which are more highly developed and radically different from the other contemporary forms. A possible explanation for this is that new

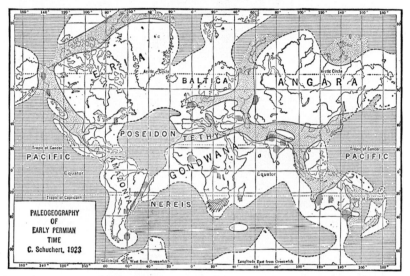

FIG. 280. Ancient land bridges. A study of the map indicates that our present continents were interconnected by areas of lands known as land bridges. Other studies show that North America was connected with Asia in the region of Bering Strait. *From Schuchert and Dunbar, "Textbook of Geology, Part II." By permission of Charles Schuchert and of the publisher, John Wiley & Sons.*

groups have migrated into new regions, for the geological evidence indicates that at various times in the past the continents were connected by land bridges. Thus the elephants appeared suddenly in Europe at one period and in North America at another. The explanation is that they came from Africa over land bridges which have since vanished (Fig. 280).

We shall describe briefly but two of the many ancestral histories preserved in rocks. To describe all of them would require several volumes. About 1870, Rowe, an English doctor, spent his leisure time collecting from the chalk formations of England fossil specimens of a sea urchin called *Micraster*. He carefully recorded the level at which he found each specimen in the chalk, and found a variation of the sea urchins increasing progressively from the lowest to the

FIG. 281.   Restoration of primitive horses.   A, *Neohipparion*; B, *Mesohippus*;
C, *Eohippus*.   *Photographs furnished by the American Museum of Natural History.*

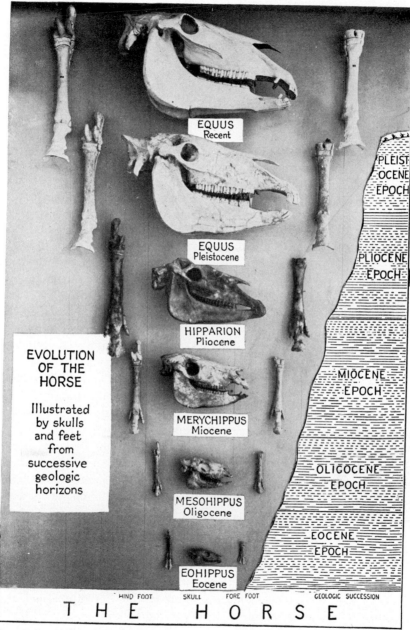

FIG. 282. The evolution of the horse. *Photograph furnished by the American Museum of Natural History, New York.*

uppermost levels. He found four principal lines of descent, and these in turn showed variations among themselves.

One of the most interesting and complete genealogies is that of the horses of North America (Figs. 281 and 282). The earliest known fossil horses were found in Eocene rocks. These little animals were about the size of a well-grown cat and had short necks and legs. They had four functional toes on each front foot and three on each hind foot, together with the vestigial splintlike remains of the first and fifth digits of each foot. As we trace the history of the horse through the rocks to the present, we find that in the Oligocene the horses were about the size of sheep. The ulna and fibula, which are missing in modern horses, were already becoming smaller. The neck was somewhat elongated. The teeth were low crowned. Coming to the lower Pliocene and upper Miocene rocks, we find horses which were about the size of deer, and, although the feet were three toed, the second and fourth toes barely touched the ground and the fifth toe was very rudimentary. The third toe was now coming to bear the brunt of the burden. The teeth began to have a complicated pattern and were longer. Then, reaching modern horses, we find animals with only the third toe functional, with the ulna fused to the radius, and the fibula fused to the tibia. The teeth are high crowned, persistently growing, and equipped with a complicated grinding surface of dentine and enamel which, wearing away irregularly, leaves a characteristic pattern on the teeth. Both the neck and the face have elongated. Many intermediate stages or connecting links might be mentioned, but this description serves to ilustrate the use of paleontology in indicating evolutionary descent.

In addition to the fossil series of the sea urchin and the horse, described above, equally good series of fossils have been found of the elephants and the camels. Many interesting, somewhat isolated specimens have been found which throw some light on the descent of other modern forms. Among them we have already mentioned *Archaeopteryx*, which very definitely furnishes evidence of the linkage of the birds with the Reptilia (page 415).

Evidence from distribution. The distribution and relative abundance of animals and plants throughout the world have always interested men, who, recognizing the value of these creatures and also impelled by their own curiosity, have catalogued and numbered them. We know that certain animals and plants are abundant in some regions and missing in others. Everyone knows that polar bears are found in the arctic regions and that lions and tigers live in the tropics.

rum of the other animal, forming
In this reaction, the closer the
animals, the greater will be the
of dogs and that of wolves shows
tion, thus indicating close relation-
y that animals may resemble each
similar in their chemical constitu-
es it, "The blood of an animal is a
l composition." Bird's blood tested
ecipitate denser than that produced
y other reptile or mammal. As may
comparative anatomy, paleontology,
believed that the birds are related to
w that pigs and cows are related to
lationship which had been previously
ence similar to those just mentioned

of relationship is furnished by the
s from the hemoglobin of vertebrate
different species vary, but those from
to the same genus seem to have certain
eover, hormones from different verte-
ommon effects. For example, the hor-
s of cattle may be used to compensate
Many digestive enzymes from animals
seem to produce similar effects.
cience, the carefully controlled objective
lts that can be accurately measured is
for any hypothesis, theory, or law. This
esirable for substantiating the theory of
f human life makes a long series of ex-
, and therefore it is extremely difficult to
have said that evolution has been occur-
rs, yet the opponents of the evolutionary
charge that no one has ever seen evolution
vertheless, a number of instances are re-
ly do see the appearance of new species.
ed animals and plants are the result of
ild-type ancestor. In the course of breed-
d plants have been so profoundly changed
te to recognize the derived forms as new
s the different varieties of pigeons are de-

This distribution might be explained as the result of the influence of climate alone, but on examination, we find various regions with the same climate inhabited by different types of plants and animals. The climate of Australia is very similar to that of Africa, yet the animals and plants of the two regions are very different. Moreover, when various species are introduced into new regions they often flourish in greater abundance than in their original habitat. Here in America we have proof of this statement in the rapid multiplication of the English sparrow and the European starling.

According to the theory of special creation, all this could be explained on the assumption that animals and plants remained where they had been created and placed, for each organism was peculiarly fitted for each environment. But the explanation fails when we find fossil remains of animals whose present forms are found on another continent and when, as has been pointed out, climate does not seem to be the limiting factor. According to the theory of evolution, life, since its first appearance on the earth, has developed gradually and in orderly sequence. Consequently the distribution of the animals and plants, present and past, will find an explanation in the geologic changes of the former eras, representing the earth's evolution.

Modern geology points out that the face of the earth is constantly changing and has undergone continuous change in the past. In certain regions of the world the land is gradually rising, whereas in other places it is sinking. New land emerges at one place, and the sea invades the land at others. Ocean currents shift their courses. Climate changes. At one time, as indicated by fossil plant remains, the arctic region enjoyed a mild and temperate climate. The existence of ancient seas is indicated by the fossil remains of marine animals and plants found in the rocks of the hills and mountains which were formerly at the bottom of the seas. Ancient land connections are shown by soundings taken in various parts of the ocean, also by the present and past distribution of closely related groups of animals and plants. Briefly, these methods indicate rather clearly that North America and Asia were once connected in the area which is now the Bering Sea; that North and South America were once separated by a sea which covered the isthmus of Panama and Central America. Evidence of the former existence of such a sea is shown also by the similarity of fishes in the Atlantic and the Pacific Oceans now separated by the isthmus. Other land connections also have been indicated, such as the connection between North America and Europe by way of Greenland and Scandinavia, and between South America and Africa (Fig. 280).

Now if we find rather similar animals in two different separated regions, it would be logical to infer that the two regions were once connected. Since we find true camels in Asia, and the llamas, guanacos, and other camel-like animals in South America, we must conclude that it was possible for camels to get from one continent to the other. According to geologic evidence, camels first appeared in North America. Later, according to their fossil remains, the true camels appeared in India and the llamas migrated southward to Argentina. Then for some reason—perhaps climatic changes or epidemics—the camels vanished from North America. Knowing of the climatic changes which have occurred in the arctic regions, and that North America and Asia were once connected by a land bridge in the region of the Bering Sea, we can readily understand the mode of distribution.

The converse of the situation just described might be stated as follows: the more distinct and peculiar the flora and fauna of a given region, the more certain it is that such a region has been isolated for a long time by natural geographic barriers. Such barriers are mountains, rivers, deserts, seas, and climatic differences. Later we shall discuss physiological barriers. In Australia and adjacent islands there are very peculiar animals and plants, unlike any found elsewhere in the world (Fig. 283). Here we find a great development of the primitive marsupials—kangaroos, wombats, and even a peculiar marsupial "bear." Geology shows that this region has been isolated from the other great continents for a long time. When we study island life, this theory of isolation is proved in an even more striking manner. Continental islands, such as the British Isles, Sumatra, and Java, are separated from the adjoining continents by a relatively shallow sea and so must have been part of the continents in past ages. The large continental islands usually have a flora and a fauna closely resembling those of the adjacent continent. The oceanic islands, being of volcanic origin and having been built up from the ocean bottom, have never had any connection with the continent. They have a rather limited variety of living forms. According to the evolution theory, oceanic islands should have a limited number of species, since they have to depend for their animal and plant life on wind, current-borne seeds, animals adrift on floating wood, and seeds carried by birds.

Further, with respect to island life, and more particularly the oceanic island type, the animals and plants which do reach these islands are isolated from their relatives, and so each group may vary to give rise to new varieties and perhaps species. Islands were intensely interest-

combine with the protein of the se
a precipitate of insoluble protein.
relationship between two different
precipitation. A test of the blood
almost the same degree of precipit
ship. This would indicate not on
other structurally but that they ar
tion as well. As Newman express
sort of quintessence of its chemica
with crocodile's blood gives a pr
when tested with the blood of an
be recalled from the evidence of
and embryology, biologists have
the reptiles. Precipitin tests sho
whales and dolphins—another re
worked out along lines of evid
for birds.

Other physiological evidence
examination of hematin crysta
blood. Crystals of the blood o
the blood of animals belonging
common characteristics. Mor
brate animals seem to have c
mone from the thyroid gland
for thyroid deficiency in man.
belonging to different groups

Genetics. In all fields of s
experiment which yields res
the most desirable evidence
kind of evidence is highly
evolution, but the brevity
periments almost impossible
obtain such evidence. We
ring through millions of ye
theory have often made the
actually taking place. Ne
corded where we apparen

Most of our domestica
careful breeding of some
ing, the original animals a
that we would not hesita
species (Fig. 284). Thu

This distribution might be explained as the result of the influence of climate alone, but on examination, we find various regions with the same climate inhabited by different types of plants and animals. The climate of Australia is very similar to that of Africa, yet the animals and plants of the two regions are very different. Moreover, when various species are introduced into new regions they often flourish in greater abundance than in their original habitat. Here in America we have proof of this statement in the rapid multiplication of the English sparrow and the European starling.

According to the theory of special creation, all this could be explained on the assumption that animals and plants remained where they had been created and placed, for each organism was peculiarly fitted for each environment. But the explanation fails when we find fossil remains of animals whose present forms are found on another continent and when, as has been pointed out, climate does not seem to be the limiting factor. According to the theory of evolution, life, since its first appearance on the earth, has developed gradually and in orderly sequence. Consequently the distribution of the animals and plants, present and past, will find an explanation in the geologic changes of the former eras, representing the earth's evolution.

Modern geology points out that the face of the earth is constantly changing and has undergone continuous change in the past. In certain regions of the world the land is gradually rising, whereas in other places it is sinking. New land emerges at one place, and the sea invades the land at others. Ocean currents shift their courses. Climate changes. At one time, as indicated by fossil plant remains, the arctic region enjoyed a mild and temperate climate. The existence of ancient seas is indicated by the fossil remains of marine animals and plants found in the rocks of the hills and mountains which were formerly at the bottom of the seas. Ancient land connections are shown by soundings taken in various parts of the ocean, also by the present and past distribution of closely related groups of animals and plants. Briefly, these methods indicate rather clearly that North America and Asia were once connected in the area which is now the Bering Sea; that North and South America were once separated by a sea which covered the isthmus of Panama and Central America. Evidence of the former existence of such a sea is shown also by the similarity of fishes in the Atlantic and the Pacific Oceans now separated by the isthmus. Other land connections also have been indicated, such as the connection between North America and Europe by way of Greenland and Scandinavia, and between South America and Africa (Fig. 280).

Now if we find rather similar animals in two different separated regions, it would be logical to infer that the two regions were once connected. Since we find true camels in Asia, and the llamas, guanacos, and other camel-like animals in South America, we must conclude that it was possible for camels to get from one continent to the other. According to geologic evidence, camels first appeared in North America. Later, according to their fossil remains, the true camels appeared in India and the llamas migrated southward to Argentina. Then for some reason—perhaps climatic changes or epidemics—the camels vanished from North America. Knowing of the climatic changes which have occurred in the arctic regions, and that North America and Asia were once connected by a land bridge in the region of the Bering Sea, we can readily understand the mode of distribution.

The converse of the situation just described might be stated as follows: the more distinct and peculiar the flora and fauna of a given region, the more certain it is that such a region has been isolated for a long time by natural geographic barriers. Such barriers are mountains, rivers, deserts, seas, and climatic differences. Later we shall discuss physiological barriers. In Australia and adjacent islands there are very peculiar animals and plants, unlike any found elsewhere in the world (Fig. 283). Here we find a great development of the primitive marsupials—kangaroos, wombats, and even a peculiar marsupial "bear." Geology shows that this region has been isolated from the other great continents for a long time. When we study island life, this theory of isolation is proved in an even more striking manner. Continental islands, such as the British Isles, Sumatra, and Java, are separated from the adjoining continents by a relatively shallow sea and so must have been part of the continents in past ages. The large continental islands usually have a flora and a fauna closely resembling those of the adjacent continent. The oceanic islands, being of volcanic origin and having been built up from the ocean bottom, have never had any connection with the continent. They have a rather limited variety of living forms. According to the evolution theory, oceanic islands should have a limited number of species, since they have to depend for their animal and plant life on wind, current-borne seeds, animals adrift on floating wood, and seeds carried by birds.

Further, with respect to island life, and more particularly the oceanic island type, the animals and plants which do reach these islands are isolated from their relatives, and so each group may vary to give rise to new varieties and perhaps species. Islands were intensely interesting to Darwin, who studied the Galapagos Islands, and to Wallace, who studied the Malay Islands.

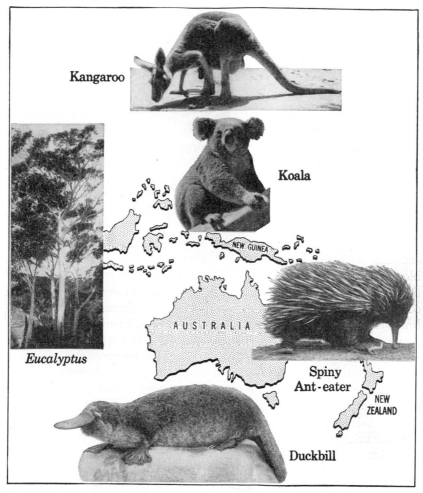

Fig. 283. Map of Australia and neighboring islands. These land masses have been separated from contiguous land for a long period of time, with the result that Australia has a large number of animals and plants peculiar to that region. *Photographs of animals furnished by the New York Zoological Society; photograph of* Eucalyptus *furnished by the New York Museum of Natural History.*

Physiology. We have heard much about blood relationship, but certain experiments and discoveries of the century have added new significance to the term. We have already discussed the preparation and reaction of precipitins. The serum from the injected animal will combine with the protein of the serum of the other animal, forming a precipitate of insoluble protein. In this reaction, the closer the relationship between two different animals, the greater will be the precipitation. A test of the blood of dogs and that of wolves shows almost the same degree of precipitation, thus indicating close relationship. This would indicate not only that animals may resemble each other structurally but that they are similar in their chemical constitution as well. As Newman expresses it, "The blood of an animal is a sort of quintessence of its chemical composition." Bird's blood tested with crocodile's blood gives a precipitate denser than that produced when tested with the blood of any other reptile or mammal. As may be recalled from the evidence of comparative anatomy, paleontology, and embryology, biologists have believed that the birds are related to the reptiles. Precipitin tests show that pigs and cows are related to whales and dolphins—another relationship which had been previously worked out along lines of evidence similar to those just mentioned for birds.

Other physiological evidence of relationship is furnished by the examination of hematin crystals from the hemoglobin of vertebrate blood. Crystals of the blood of different species vary, but those from the blood of animals belonging to the same genus seem to have certain common characteristics. Moreover, hormones from different vertebrate animals seem to have common effects. For example, the hormone from the thyroid glands of cattle may be used to compensate for thyroid deficiency in man. Many digestive enzymes from animals belonging to different groups seem to produce similar effects.

Genetics. In all fields of science, the carefully controlled objective experiment which yields results that can be accurately measured is the most desirable evidence for any hypothesis, theory, or law. This kind of evidence is highly desirable for substantiating the theory of evolution, but the brevity of human life makes a long series of experiments almost impossible, and therefore it is extremely difficult to obtain such evidence. We have said that evolution has been occurring through millions of years, yet the opponents of the evolutionary theory have often made the charge that no one has ever seen evolution actually taking place. Nevertheless, a number of instances are recorded where we apparently do see the appearance of new species.

Most of our domesticated animals and plants are the result of careful breeding of some wild-type ancestor. In the course of breeding, the original animals and plants have been so profoundly changed that we would not hesitate to recognize the derived forms as new species (Fig. 284). Thus the different varieties of pigeons are de-

Fig. 284. Various breeds of chickens produced through breeding. *a,* Black Sumatra (male); *b,* Light Brahma (male); *c,* single-combed White Leghorn (male); *d,* White-laced Red Cornish (male); *e,* White Cochin Bantam (male); *f,* jungle fowl (male); *g,* non-bearded White Polish Bantam (male). *Photographs furnished by the U. S. Department of Agriculture.*

rived from the breeding of a bluish bird called the rock dove. Dogs are the carefully bred, domesticated descendants of wolves, and the various breeds of chickens have been derived from jungle fowl.

To trace fully the development of evolution in the animal kingdom would lead us far afield and away beyond the scope of our present study. However, the brief sketch shows that animals are constantly changing, even though we may not be able to detect the changes taking place. As a result of the changes, through the medium of the mechanism of inheritance, new forms are evolving. We have seen something of the evidence that compels us to believe that such changes, taking place through the ages, are responsible for the animals of today. Therefore, we are led to conclude that evolution is the process of creation.

THE WORKING OF EVOLUTION

We have previously said that the difference of opinion existing among scientists today is not concerned with the fact of evolution, but rather with the mechanism by which it is accomplished. Even before Darwin's time, Lamarck had suggested an explanation of the changes in organic patterns. Then came Darwin, who, as we have seen, apparently established the fact of evolution and advanced a theory to account for the process. During Darwin's lifetime and up to the present day, men have been striving to find the causative factors which account for evolutionary changes.

Lamarckianism. Lamarck (1744–1829) was a noted French biologist, the youngest of eleven children of a very poor family (Fig. 285). Much against his will, he was educated for the priesthood in a Jesuit College. After the death of his father, he turned to the study of medicine. Later he reorganized the botanical garden and the royal museum in Paris. At the age of fifty he was made professor in invertebrate zoology, a field about which he, like all the others of his day, knew little. Working vigorously and intensively at this new task, he soon became one of the leading authorities in the field. While trying to organize and classify animals he saw how inadequate the theory of fixed permanent species really was. He became convinced that living forms had, in the course of time, been changed into different forms.

Briefly, this was his explanation: The more frequently and continuously an animal used an organ, the more it was strengthened, developed, and enlarged. On the other hand, if it was not used, it gradually, by imperceptible degrees, weakened and finally disappeared. These effects of use and disuse on an organ were inherited. That is, those organs or structures modified by use or disuse in one generation appeared modified in the next. In other words, according to Lamarck, acquired characters *could* be inherited. When, within the organism, a pressing continuous need for some structure arouses and maintains a new activity to supply that need, the new structure or organ can be produced.

Prominent biologists and philosophers like Darwin and Spencer accepted Lamarck's theory, but, as was pointed out in our discussion of the inheritance of acquired characters, Weismann and others were very skeptical about it. The present school of Lamarck's followers, called Neo-Lamarckians, hold that, although the inheritance of the effects of use and disuse have not been proved, it has not been shown that the possibility is not there. Living things do respond to changes in the environment. They are plastic and adaptive. Further, environmental factors, e.g. X-rays, affect the heredity of an animal or individual because they affect the germplasm.

FIG. 285. Jean Baptiste Lamarck (1744–1829). *By permission of Charles Schuchert.*

Weismann and De Vries. Weismann's theory of the evolutionary mechanism is really an outgrowth of his theory of heredity based on the continuity of the germplasm. According to this theory, all changes in animals or plants arise from the union of various lines of germplasm which takes place at fertilization. The new genic combinations resulting from these matings bring about changes in the organism. Thus there appear new combinations of characteristics which have always been present in the germplasm. Natural selection then determines which new characteristics resulting from the new combinations will survive.

De Vries (Fig. 286) explained evolution by his mutations theory, which claimed that sudden wide variations or abrupt changes called mutations occur in the germplasm. These changes in the germplasm bring about somatic changes which breed true. Natural selection again determines which of the modified forms will survive and be improved through further mutations in later years. New species thus arise in a single step or by jumps. Doubtless, species do arise through abrupt mutations, but there is some evidence to show that species may be created by the gradual accumulation of slight mutations.

FIG. 286. Hugo de Vries (1848–1935). *Photograph furnished by Henry Holt and Co.*

Darwinism. Darwin not only established the theory of evolution on a firm basis but also suggested a theory to explain how evolution takes place. His theory of the working of evolution was based on three premises: **variation, heredity,** and **natural selection** or **survival of the fittest.**

Variation. In most respects all organisms may resemble their parents, although they may vary from them in a greater or less degree. No child is the exact image of its parents.

Today, two types of variations are recognized, **somatic** and **germinal.** Somatic variations are acquired and, as has been previously pointed out, may be caused by undernourishment, diet deficiencies, prenatal injuries, hormone unbalance, and the like. A few biologists think that these changes can be transmitted to the next generation. Gene mutations or other chromosomal changes affect the germplasm.

We have already seen how the mechanism of heredity functions to transmit these mutations and changes. Of course, in Darwin's day no distinction was made between these two types of variations. To Darwin the perplexing and important question was how organisms with relatively favorable variations, irrespective of origin, were selected. In his opinion only those that could meet the rigorous demands of life conditions would survive. The unfit would be weeded out by a process of natural selection because only those animals and plants will survive that are so constructed as to be able to adjust themselves to their environment. The next generation would possess the new structural modifications.

Let us see how evolution would operate according to Darwinism. We have already pointed out that many animals lay thousands or even millions of eggs, most of which never produce an adult individual. Many of the eggs never hatch, and many of the young perish before becoming adults. Some fish eggs, for example, are destroyed by burial in the mud, some never develop, and others are eaten by various animals. Moreover, large numbers of the young fry never become adults since they are eaten by such enemies as water birds, water snakes, and other fishes. Some of them are even devoured by their own parents. Some finally reach maturity, but still the struggle continues. Droughts may change streams of pure water into polluted reservoirs lacking normal food supply and low in oxygen. Other factors might be listed that make up this agency of natural selection. It can readily be seen that any fish that can survive under such conditions, in all probability, differs somewhat from the others. It should be emphasized that natural selection does not mean that only those organisms more ideally perfect or most complex structurally survive. It means that only those survive that are better adapted to a certain environment. Thus we find that some animals become adapted to a parasitic life and, in so doing, lose many of their structures. The tapeworm, for example, living in a sea of food, has lost its digestive tract.

In the next place, animals bearing new characters or variations will have a better chance to develop into new species if they are not swamped by mating with the large number of non-variants. So it has been suggested that the factor of **isolation** must be added to that of natural selection for the effective creation of new species. It has been shown that new types of organisms are developed more rapidly where they are isolated by natural barriers and must interbreed among themselves.

There are objections to Darwin's theory of natural selection. Some biologists point out that many of the variations are so slight that they

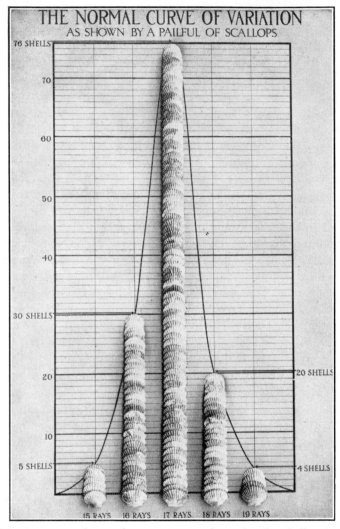

THE NORMAL CURVE OF VARIATION
AS SHOWN BY A PAILFUL OF SCALLOPS

15 RAYS   16 RAYS   17 RAYS   18 RAYS   19 RAYS

FIG. 287. Variation of animals in nature as shown by the shells of a scallop (*Pecten*, a mollusk). The photograph shows the variations in a number of shells collected at random. *Photograph furnished by the American Museum of Natural History, New York.*

could have no value to any organism in the struggle for existence. Moreover, many apparently useless structures have continued to develop by variation instead of being discarded. Darwin also believed that variations tending toward protective coloration and protective resemblance assisted in preservation, and the work of Isely confirms this belief.

Modern conception of the mechanism of evolution. For a number of years, Darwin's suggestion concerning the nature of the mechanism of evolution was severely criticized, and it lost favor. Some of the criticism was directed against his partial acceptance of the theory of the inheritance of acquired characteristics as well as against the way natural selection could operate to preserve small variations. Modern genetics has demonstrated that new species of animals and plants can arise by changes in the chromosomes. Today, as has already been pointed out, we know that loss of parts of a chromosome, interchange of chromosomal parts by inversion, breaking of chromosomes, and duplication of chromosomes may affect the characteristics of offspring. In addition there are changes in the genes themselves which properly are called mutations.

We shall examine an animal whose evolutionary and hereditary background is well known and changes in which have been carefully observed and recorded. Let us see whether an accumulation of mutations and duplications, or other changes in the chromosomes, can produce a new individual which might be called a new species. Perhaps the most-studied animal has been the fruit fly *Drosophila*. Since the geneticists began the study with the wild-type fly, thousands of mutations have been discovered.

The factor that prevents free and random mating is **isolation,** of which there are two types, **geographical** and **physiological.** Darwin stressed the influence of geographical barriers such as oceans, mountains, and deserts which made communication among animal groups very difficult if not impossible. Geographical isolation has already been discussed in connection with animal distribution.

Geographical isolation may account for the differences in species living in different regions but cannot account very well for those different species living in the same geographical location. Physiological isolation furnishes the answer here. Some of the physiological isolating mechanisms are as follows: two or more species may reach sexual maturity at different seasons or may have their breeding periods at different times of the year; there may be a lack of sexual attraction between the opposite sexes of two different species on account of differences in scents, courtship behavior, and the like; differences in the structure of the sexual apparatus may make coition impossible; hybrids may be sterile. The agencies of both geographical isolation and physiological isolation may tend to preserve the new characters appearing in animals which differentiate them into new species.

From what has been said it is clear that the race that will evolve most rapidly is the one with the shortest reproductive span. For example, a new generation of *Drosophila* can appear in twelve to fourteen days, whereas an elephant has a gestation period of about twenty months and at one time can produce only one offspring which reaches sexual maturity only after ten years.

A second factor that influences evolution is the mutation rate of the species. Some genes are exceedingly stable but others mutate rather frequently. In *Drosophila,* the fruit fly, one gene "would ordinarily undergo only one mutation while being transmitted through a 1,000,000 generations of individuals." According to Haldane the rate of mutation for the gene of hemophilia in man is about one in 100,000.

When we compare the studies made by Darwin, Weismann, and De Vries we find that all have made some contribution to the modern conception of how evolution works. Weismann showed the supreme importance of the germplasm as compared to the somatoplasm. De Vries clarified the variation concept by developing the mutation theory, and Darwin, by his idea of natural selection or survival of the fittest, showed how it is possible for only certain types of mutations to persist and lay the foundation upon which other changes may take place. His principle of natural selection is now more firmly established than ever as one of the factors of evolution.

26

The Course of Evolution

We have previously pointed out that the theory of evolution means descent with modifications. According to fairly good evidence, new species of animals appeared at intervals in the past and are appearing today. The fields of comparative anatomy, paleontology, embryology, physiology, and genetics lend support to these conclusions. Much of the proof cited for evolution in the previous discussion centered around the vertebrate animals, and very little attention was paid to the great realm of the invertebrates.

ANIMAL RELATIONSHIP. PHYLOGENY

If evolution has taken place and is taking place in all living organisms, then there should be evidence for it among the invertebrates. Further, the collected observations on invertebrates in the fields already mentioned should serve to establish the relationships that exist between the different animal groups. All of us are interested in tracing our particular family trees back as far as possible, but few of us have delved backward beyond the limit of one or two hundred years. Suppose we dig a little deeper into remote ancestry and ancestral relationships. If we are to start with the most remote animal ancestry, not only of man but of other animals, we would certainly begin with the Protozoa. The various theories that have been put forth to explain the origin of life have already been discussed (Chapter 24). We can safely assume that the primitive ancestral protozoans and the coelenterates were rather simple animals like the present forms. We should hope and expect to find the remains of the ancestors of the members of these phyla in the oldest rocks, that is, those at the bottom of the heap. Judging from the present living representatives of these two phyla, their ancestors must have had soft bodies and very little skeletal support, and thus, even under the best conditions, no very satisfactory fossilization could take place. Moreover, the old rocks in which we should expect to find the ancestral fossils of the Protozoa

513

and Coelentrata were subjected to the great pressure of the overlying rocks. This would result in stresses and pressure which would crush beyond recognition any fossils that may have been present. The oldest, best-preserved fossils appear in the Cambrian rocks, where all the important invertebrate phyla are represented.

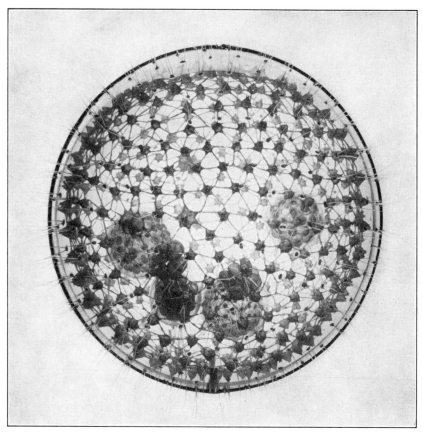

FIG. 288.   The colonial flagellate *Volvox* (Phylum Protozoa). *Photograph furnished by the American Museum of Natural History, New York.*

Of course, paleontology is not the sole source of evidence for animal relationship. Comparative anatomy and embryology also offer good leads. Doubtless you recall the theory of recapitulation presented in the preceding chapter (Chapter 25). This theory states that "every animal, in its individual development from egg to adult passes through a series of stages which correspond to stages in the long evolutionary history of its group." This theory has certain limitations which have

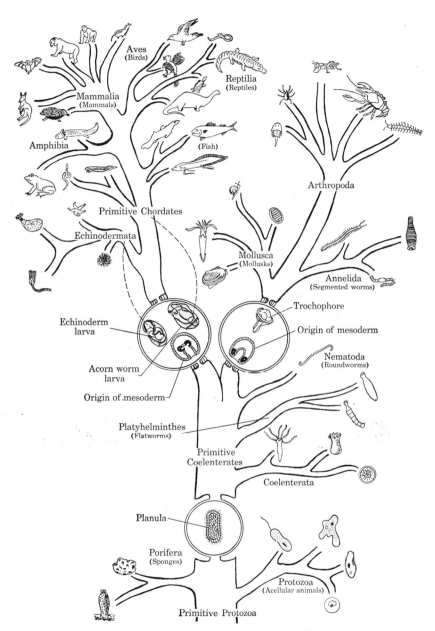

Aves
(Birds)

Reptilia
(Reptiles)

Mammalia
(Mammals)

Amphibia

(Fish)

Arthropoda

Primitive Chordates

Echinodermata

Mollusca
(Mollusks)

Annelida
(Segmented worms)

Trochophore

Echinoderm
larva

Origin of mesoderm

Acorn worm
larva

Nematoda
(Roundworms)

Origin of mesoderm

Platyhelminthes
(Flatworms)

Primitive
Coelenterates

Coelenterata

Planula

Porifera
(Sponges)

Protozoa
(Acellular animals)

Primitive Protozoa

FIG. 289.   Diagram of animal relationships.

already been discussed. In accordance with this theory, the zygote has been compared to the protozoan stage in our life history. The blastula is very reminiscent of the colonial protozoan *Volvox* (Fig. 288). The embryonic gastrula made up of the inner layer of entoderm and the outer layer of ectoderm resembles certain adult coelenterates quite closely.

After carefully reviewing the various lines of evidence that seem to indicate the degree of relationship among various animals, biologists have built up "animal trees." Incidentally, the "invertebrate tree," as

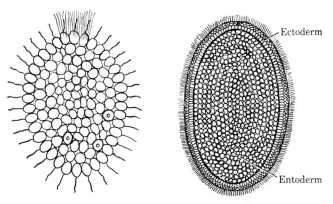

Fig. 290. Planula: *a*, hypothetical planulalike ancestor of the Metazoa; *b*, planula larva of hydroid. *Redrawn from Hyman "The Invertebrates, Protozoa through Ctenophora." By permission of the publisher, McGraw-Hill Book Company.*

may be expected because of the lack of primitive fossils and the great diversities found among invertebrates, must be considered highly speculative. The "vertebrate tree" is much better established. It should be understood that in the light of new evidence these "trees" may have to be trimmed regularly and may need to have new branches grafted on. Certainly at the base of the tree we should place the ancestral protozoan from which there developed not only the multicellular organisms such as the sponges (Porifera), but also the present-day protozoans, which have a long evolutionary history back of them (Fig. 289). Someone has observed that in existing animals we see only the ends of the branches of the "tree," for time has covered up the trunk and the bases of the main branches. Branching off from the protozoans, probably by way of the flagellates, are the sponges, which have poorly developed tissues and a very primitive body organization. The sponges have no direct relationship to animals other than the Protozoa. The two-layered "gastrula-like" Coelenterata also evolved from the Protozoa. The hypothetical two-layered ancestors of modern coelenterates probably resembled the ciliated, radially symmetrical **planula** larva of some of the present-day coelenterates (Fig. 290). There are indications that bilateral symmetry began to appear in the primitive coelenterates.

All the higher invertebrates and all the chordates are made up of three germ layers, ectoderm, entoderm, and mesoderm. The mesoderm makes possible the formation of more definite organs and organ systems with consequent increase in animal complexity. Mesoderm has two principal modes of origin. In flatworms, nemertean worms,

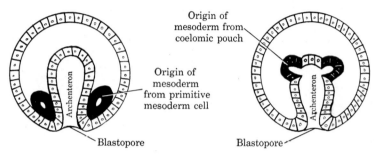

Origin of mesoderm from coelomic pouch

Origin of mesoderm from primitive mesoderm cell

Blastopore

Blastopore

FIG. 291. Origin of the mesoderm. *Left,* the embryo of a mollusk (Arthropod line), shows mesoderm-forming cells budding off from the entoderm. *Right,* the larva of an echinoderm (Chordate line) shows the mesoderm forming from pouches budding off the entodermal sides of the primitive archenteron. *Redrawn, modified from Buchsbaum's "Animals Without Backbones," University of Chicago Press.*

mollusks, annelids, and arthropods, the mesoderm develops usually from two special "primitive mesoderm cells" which are found in the early gastrula (Fig. 291). But in the Echinodermata (starfishes, sea urchins, and others) and the Chordata, the phylum that includes fish, frogs, snakes, and man, the mesoderm arises from outpocketings of the entoderm (Fig. 291). At this point, on the basis of mesoderm formation, the ancestral tree divides into two great branches, the **arthropod branch** and the **chordate branch.** It can be seen, according to this tree, that man and other chordates and the echinoderms have a common ancestry!

How have zoologists reached these rather startling conclusions? For the most part from studies of embryological development. Mollusks appear to be closely related to annelids because the early embryos of both phyla are "almost identical cell for cell." The mesoderm in both groups has a similar origin, and their free swimming larvas, called **trochophores,** resemble each other very closely (Fig. 292). The trochophore type of larva, with an equatorial band of cilia, is characteristic of a number of other invertebrate phyla. Larvas of flatworms and nemertean worms resemble the trochophore type. The

arthropods have no trochophore type, but have many adult characteristics, such as segmentation and a double ventral median nerve cord,
resembling that of the annelids, which do have a trochophore larval
stage.

The chordate branch includes only phylum Chordata and phylum
Echinodermata. It has been mentioned that the embryonic mesoderm
of both these phyla arises from pouches which pinch off from the

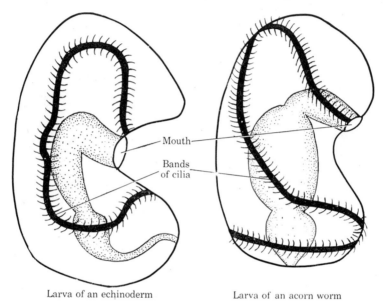

Larva of an echinoderm   Larva of an acorn worm

FIG. 292. Types of larvas of echinoderms and the acorn worm (a chordate).

archenteron. The cavities of the pouches form the coelom. In the
arthropod branch, primitive mesoderm cells form the layers of mesoderm which later split to form the coelom. The free-swimming larvas
of all echinoderms are quite different from those of the arthropod
line. It is thought that the larval stage (Fig. 292) of the echinoderms
probably resembled the adults of the ancestral stock from which the
modern forms are descended.

But what evidence bridges the gap between echinoderms and chordates? The clues are furnished by a lowly chordate, the acorn worm
(Saccoglossus), which belongs to subphylum Hemichordata (hemi—
half; chordos) of phylum Chordata (Fig. 221). The larval stages of
the acorn worm and that of the echinoderms resemble each other so
closely that a specialist on echinoderms once identified a larva of the
acorn worm as that of an echinoderm! (Fig. 292.) Further the origin

of the mesoderm and coelom of the chordates is similar to that of the echinoderms. It is thought that the segmentation of the chordates must have originated after the two ancestral groups that gave rise to the chordates and echinoderms had separated. Moreover, the method of segmentation of animals in the arthropod branch and the chordate branch is different. On the basis of these facts and others that would take us too far afield, zoologists have constructed the invertebrate phylogenetic tree as shown in Fig. 289.

Doubtless the chordates have more interest for the average reader than the invertebrates have. Zoologists who have studied the comparative anatomy, embryology, paleontology, and other lines of evidence for chordate ancestry are convinced that the relationship pictured in Fig. 289 exists between the various chordate classes and orders.

EVOLUTION IN MAN

Many people have been willing to admit that evolution may occur in plants and animals, but they refuse to concede that it occurs in man. Indeed, some have been unwilling to consider man an animal. In the light of what has already been said it would be absurd to question man's animal characteristics. As far as man's evolution is concerned, there is abundant evidence from embryology, comparative anatomy, and other fields to illustrate his emergence from other forms.

No evolutionist maintains that man sprang from any of our present-day apes and monkeys. On the contrary, it is thought that millions of years ago there was an apelike group of animals which gave rise to two branches. One branch included the arborcal apes, and the other was a terrestrial group, the apelike ancestors of man. By the process of evolution man emerged from this terrestrial apelike stock as a "new creation." The anthropologist (*anthropos*—man; *logos*) tells us that it seems evident that the human family had its origin in Asia or Africa and spread by migration in successive waves over the now vanished land bridges to the various parts of the world.

However, it is hard to trace early human history, for there have been comparatively few "finds." Early man, low in intelligence as he must have been, was able to avoid the pitfalls of the water hole, quicksands, and tar pools which claimed so many of the lower animals. Asia, often called the "cradle of the race," and Africa have been little explored. As we consider this very brief outline of the story of early man, we must remember that the conclusions are based on observations not of complete specimens, but rather of fragmentary, fossil, skeletal remains. Knowledge of present-day savages, comparison of the skeletons of man with those of the present-day great apes, as well as a study of the life of these living animals and the biology of modern man—all afford evidence of the origin and evolution of modern man. When compared with the age of the earth and the time span of animal and plant life since its first appearance, man has appeared so recently that he has fittingly been called a "zoological upstart."

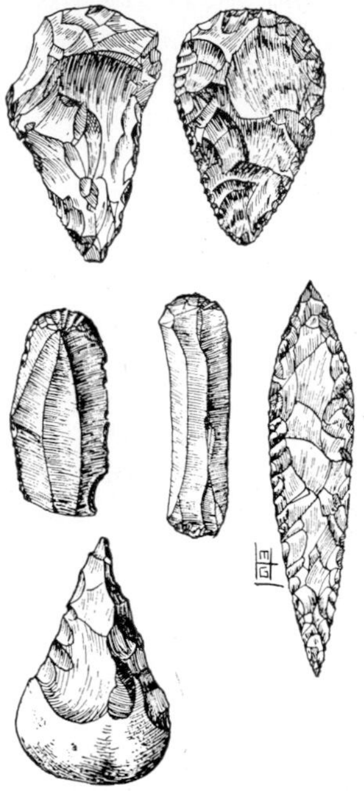

FIG. 293. Early stone flints used by primitive man.

Most of the remains of earliest man have been found in the rock formations of the Pleistocene era, which began over a million years ago. The age, as well as the food habits and social life of early man, is inferred from the fossil remains of other animals and crude utensils which are often uncovered in the same location with the remains of man himself. For example, the bones of a certain type of fossil man in Europe were associated with those of the mammoth, the rhinoceros, the saber-toothed tiger, and other animals. These animals are now extinct, but their abundant fossil remains from various locations in the world have enabled the scientist to locate definitely in the geological time table the strata in which they occur. Stone weapons sometimes made of chipped flint, polished stone axes, charred bones and wood—all suggest something of the social life of these early men (Fig. 293).

A study of the weapons and utensils of man, that is, his first culture, indicates that we are now living in the Iron Age, which began about 3,400 years ago. Previous to the Iron Age was the Bronze Age, which began approximately 4,900 years ago. Copper was used about 1,000 years before the alloy, bronze, came into use. From 6,000 years ago, back into the dim recesses of man's history, stretches the Stone Age. In the recent Stone Age, the "cultural fossil" (utensils, weapons, and the like) seems to indicate that there was some domestication of animals and cultivation of plants. Some pottery was made, and the construction of crude huts for living quarters began.

The following from Hooton * will serve to illustrate how short has been man's stay and development on the earth compared to the total geologic age of the earth.

* Hooton, *Apes, Men, and Morons*, G. P. Putnam's Sons, New York, 1937, p. 55.

"Now if we revert to Dr. Chester Reed's radio-active chart of geologic time, we find that he assigns one million years to the Pleistocene period and six million years to the Pliocene. The anthropologist is wholly incompetent to judge of the validity of such scales, but the present writer prefers to be a radio-activarian rather than a sedimentalist. Then, if we plagiarize Dr. Reed's radioactive clock, we find that the twelve-hour dial of man's culture represents no less than four million years. Each second represents 92.59 years. Accordingly, if man's culture was born at mid-Pliocene noon, he began to make Chellean fist axes at 9 P.M.; at 11.54 and 36 seconds he began to draw pictures of animals and to sculp his lady friends; and at 11.58 and 12 seconds he was beginning to try to tame animals and plants, to build huts, to live in communities, and to polish stone tools; at a little less than 37 seconds before 12 o'clock midnight he discovered the use of iron. Of course this cultural-archaeological clock is hardly accurate enough to justify the splitting of seconds."

We shall now examine some of the most important types of early man representing "missing links" which chain man in some measure to his ancestry.

Java man. In 1890–1891, Dr. Dubois, a Dutch army surgeon, found a deposit of fossil bones in Java. Among these bones of various animals, he found first a human tooth and, about a yard away, the top of a skull, and finally, the left femur and two more teeth. Dubois had set out for the East Indies to look for a missing link, and he found it. In 1936, von Koenigswald made further finds in Java, and subsequent finds have come thick and fast. The teeth are essentially human, but in some respects they resemble those of the higher apes. The femur is definitely human and by its structure and shape indicates that the owner walked erect. The skull was somewhat ape-like, with heavy brow ridges. In addition to the prominent bony ridges over the eyes, the Java man probably had a heavy, powerful jaw and a flat nose (Fig. 294). "The face was probably projecting and chinless, the nose broad and probably low bridged, but quite unlike that of an ape." Dubois called this animal *Pithecanthropus erectus,* or the erect ape man. It was estimated that the brain capacity of this early fossil man was about 940 cubic centimeters. This is considerably less than that of the modern European, whose brain capacity is approximately 1,450 cubic centimeters. However, the size and conformation of the brain far surpassed that of any known fossil ape and "was more human than simian." Since primitive stone implements have been found in the same rock strata as the ape man, it seems probable that *Pithecanthropus* was a tool user.

The Piltdown man. In 1912, an English lawyer who was interested in geology as a hobby accidentally discovered fragments of a cranium, a portion of a lower jaw with teeth in place, and some

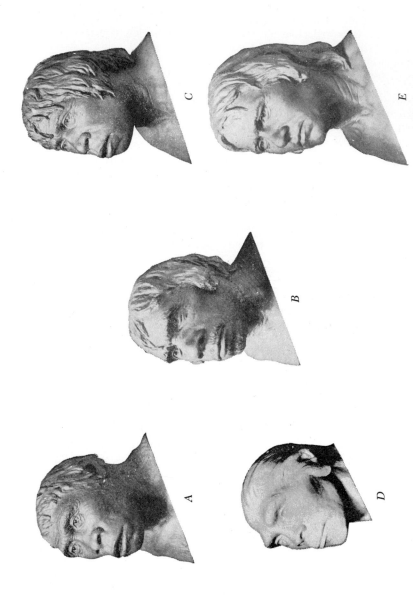

Fig. 294. Types of early man. A, Java man (*Pithecanthropus erectus*); B, Neanderthal man (*Homo neanderthalensis*); C, Piltdown man (*Eoanthropus dawsoni*); D, Peking man (*Sinanthropus pekinensis*); E, Cro-Magnon man (*Homo sapiens*). Photographs A, B, C, and E furnished by J. H. McGregor; D furnished by Science Service.

portions of the nasal bones. The fossilized fragment of the skull was part of a brown "cokernut" (cocoanut) which English workmen had uncovered. After these fragments were found, a diligent search brought to light more fragments of the skull, but apparently other fragments of the "cokernut" were removed with the gravel which went into the road building. Later other fossil remains of man were found. A reconstruction based on the remains shows a man with heavy jaws and receding chin, but with higher forehead and greater cranial capacity than the Java man (Fig. 294). This man was named *Eoanthropus,* or the "dawn man."

Peking man. Another discovery of the remains of ancient man was made near Peking, China. From the standpoint of number of specimens uncovered, this is perhaps the most complete "find" of fossil material representing men of the earliest period. Here has been uncovered a wealth of material consolidated in the debris of an old cave whose roof had collapsed. The skulls are small, narrow, and apelike, with great, bony ridges above the eyes (Fig. 294). The forehead is low, and the nose is broad. The basal parts of the skulls are missing, suggesting that they had been removed for the extraction of the brains by cannibalistic enemies. Brain casts of the inside of the skulls indicate that the brain resembled somewhat that of the chimpanzee. In addition to the skeletal remains, stone implements and ashes from ancient fires were found. The Peking man is known as *Sinanthropus.*

The three types of early man just described apparently lived at the same period in the earth's history, the Pleistocene era. The Peking man may be but slightly more advanced than the Java man, and the Piltdown man may have been further advanced than either of the other two. Both the Java man and the Peking man seem to be members of a line which led to a later group of primitive men known as the Neanderthal man.

The Rhodesian man. In the summer of 1921 there were recovered from a mine in Rhodesia, a human skull, a tibia, parts of a femur, and other fossil bony remains. There was nothing particularly remarkable about the leg bones, but, as Hooten writes, "the first glance at this skull shocks even the hardened anthropologist." There were enormous brow ridges and a bestially low forehead. The brain case is of primitive human shape, very long and relatively narrow. The skull showed a very small brain capacity but a "cast" indicates a brain much superior to that of Pithecanthropus. After studying a cast of the brain of the Rhodesian man, anthropologists concluded that he must have been "a very humble human being" somewhat higher than the apes but far below modern man.

The man-apes of South Africa. In 1925, Professor R. A. Dart of Johannesburg in South Africa studied a fossil brain cast and an incomplete fossil skull equipped with twenty-four teeth. These fossil fragments were found in a limestone fissure. He decided that these were the remains of a primate which was either a highly developed ape or a near-man which he named *Australopithecus*. Later extensive discoveries of fossil primate remains in South Africa have been made by Dr. Robert Broom. The brains of these man-apes do not resemble those of man too closely but their teeth are humanoid. They apparently possessed an apelike face and had massive jaws. They probably walked erect and lived on such food as moles, hares, and young baboons. Anthropologists who have studied these remains conclude that these man-apes were "both in a structural and a genetic sense the conservative cousins of man."

The Neanderthal man. Unlike the fossil remains just described, practically the complete skeleton of the Neanderthal man is known. Many fossil remains of this race have been found in various parts of Europe and Asia, but the earliest specimen was found in the Neanderthal gorge in Germany. Apparently, these men had large faces, enormous ridges above their eyes, and low retreating foreheads. The teeth were large, and the jaw was minus a chin projection. These men were a little over five feet in height, with a forward-thrust head and curving thigh bones (Fig. 295). Their cranial capacity was fairly large, but they were low browed and probably not too intelligent. From other remains associated with the Neanderthalers, we conclude that they were skillful workers in flints, and that they lived in caves where they gorged on choice bits of food from the woolly mammoths, the woolly rhinoceroses, and other animals. They probably wore clothing of animal pelts, and there are indications that they used torches dipped in animal fat.

Concerning the relationship between the Neanderthal man and modern man, there are two schools of thought. One group would derive modern man from the Neanderthal group, although at present no transitional types have been found. Another school holds that modern man split off from the ancestral line of the Neanderthal man and evolved separately somewhere in Africa or Asia. In other words, we are not direct descendants of this group, but may be, as Romer points out, "Neanderthal man's progressive nephew." Apparently some evidence for this last statement is afforded by discoveries in Palestine, near Mt. Carmel and the Sea of Galilee. Here fossil men

Fig. 295. Reconstruction of Neanderthal family group at Gibraltar. Photograph furnished by the Field Museum of Natural History, Chicago.

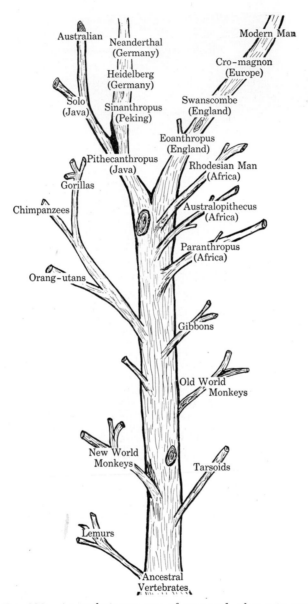

FIG. 296.   An evolutionary tree of man and other primates.

have been uncovered which resemble modern man more than the European Neanderthal. Perhaps the Neanderthal men developed in Asia and Africa and later invaded Europe, as did the other animal forms found in Europe.

There is no doubt that another race of men invaded Europe after the Neanderthals. Their remains are found in caves and layers of debris above those containing the remains of the Neanderthal occupation. It may be that this later race, the Cro-Magnon, drove out or annihilated the Neanderthal race in Europe. Apparently the Cro-Magnon race moved in from the east, that is, from Asia or Africa, and it is logically conceivable that they may have developed there to their high racial state.

Cro-Magnon man. Judging from the remains found in a grotto near Cro-Magnon in France, this was a magnificent race whose men were more than six feet tall. As indicated by the shape and size of the head they must have been quite intelligent. They had a firm, well-developed chin, shortened jaws, prominent nose, and the high forehead of modern man (Fig. 294). They evidently knew how to use a bow and arrow. On the walls of their cave dwellings there are pictures and sculptured figures of various wild animals indicating that they had some interest in art and sculpture. The collection of weapons and utensils found interred with their remains may indicate a religion and a belief in immortality.

From what has just been said, one can gather that the types of primitive man just described as well as other primitive types may be regarded as intermediate steps in the development of modern man or as offshoots from the main family tree (Fig. 296). Certainly it must be evident that these different fossils of early man do not represent one continuous line of descent. Considerations of fossil findings are interesting in that they may indicate *in a general way* some of the stages in man's development.

RACES OF MAN

In the scheme of classification used for the plant and animal kingdoms, we have seen that those forms that resemble each other most closely are grouped into species. In many instances, different species are not interfertile and so do not interbreed. Under the category of species there may be subgroups known as subspecies, and under subspecies come other groups known as races. Keeping in mind that animals of the same species were supposed to resemble each other very closely, and that subspecies were supposed to resemble each other even more closely, one can readily understand that animals or plants belonging to various races differ but little from one another. Thus it is clearly realized how difficult it is to separate members of one race from those of another. This is particularly true of man. Attempts have been made to separate races of man on the basis of common language, similarity of social and cultural traits, and, finally, differences in physical traits. It is apparent at once that language and social traits may be readily changed when one group of people adopts the language and traits or culture habits of another group. Such adoptions may be brought about by choice or by force. A good example of the adoption of a culture habit of other races is furnished by the American Indian, who replaced bow and arrow with powder and ball, from both necessity and choice, and maybe by imitation.

Of all the distinguishing features peculiar to race, the physical traits are the most dependable, but here again difficulties arise because races are interfertile and can interbreed. Thus it is difficult to find a pure race. In fact, it is doubtful that one exists. Some of the physical characteristics most used in the differentiation of race are skin color, type of hair, shape of head, stature, and often eye shape and color. Today, students of race recognize three main races, White, Negroid, and Mongoloid. These three races of men may be further divided into subraces and composite races such as the Nordic and Armenoid groups of the white race.

The Negroid race. Members of this race have dark complexions, flat noses, woolly hair, and long heads. They are found mostly in Africa south of the Sahara and in certain oceanic islands. The pygmies from various regions of the world belong to this race.

The Australoids are long headed, flat nosed, and dark complexioned. However, they differ from the Negroid in that the black hair is wavy rather than kinky, and the body is more hairy. Apparently they make up a composite group intermediate between the Negroid race and the peoples of Europe. Australoids are found in Australia, in southern India, and in the Malay region. They are almost extinct.

The White race. Included in this group are those individuals whose skin color may be white, pink, ruddy, or light brown. The hair is never "dead black" in color and is usually wavy or straight but is never woolly. There are a number of subordinate groups under this category.

The Mediterraneans are long-headed, narrow-nosed people with light and brown complexions. They have wavy hair. This subrace includes those peoples bordering the Mediterranean Sea, including Egypt, southern Italy, some sections of western France, the British

Isles, and the majority of the people of India. The members of the "Nordic race" comprize certain groups from eastern England, Scandinavia, and northern Germany. Interestingly enough, you will note that not all Germans are Nordic in characteristics.

The Alpines are the broad-headed peoples of Europe and western Asia. They have light to brown complexions and wavy hair. Asia seems to have been the seat of origin of this group, which spread into eastern and central Europe. They live in a broad belt which includes most of the east Baltic, eastern Germany, Austria, northern Italy, Switzerland, and part of France. The Slavic peoples also belong to to this group.

The Mongoloid race. People who belong to this race have straight, coarse black hair and a yellow or yellowish-brown skin. Another feature often present is the "slant eye," a characteristic brought about by the presence of a fold stretching from the upper lid which overlaps the lower at the inner corner of the eye. This race includes the Chinese, Japanese, Malays, and other groups in Asia, as well as the Eskimo and the Indian peoples of the two Americas. Geologically speaking, it is probable that the Americas were peopled very recently. It is quite possible that the original Asiatic stocks crossed into America by the long-vanished land bridge between Alaska and Asia, or ventured to cross the narrow Bering Strait by raft or boat. From this they spread southward over the Americas in successive waves.

Index and Glossary

(Illustrations occur on pages referred to in bold-face type. Colored illustrations which have no folios are referred to by the page they face.)

Agglutinins, 90, 91, **91**. Antibodies which cause clumping of bacteria or other foreign bodies in the blood.

Agglutinogen, 95. Substance acting as an antigen to stimulate formation of agglutinin.

Aggregation, 456, **457, 458**. Collection of organisms within the larger community.

benefits of, 459

integration of, 459

origin of, 456

types of, 457

Agnatha, 397. Class of Chordata (fishlike lampreys and hagfishes).

Agriculture, 3

Agronomy, 3

Albino, 260, **260**, 274. Animal lacking pigment in the eyes, skin, and hair, or plant lacking chlorophyll.

Albumin, 22.

Alimentary canal, 36. The tube in which digestion takes place in the higher animals.

Alimentary tract of man, 36, **38, 55**

Allantois, **214**, 217, **246**, 405. Embryonic sac developed by the embryo of reptiles, birds, and mammals.

Allee, 451, 459

Alleles, 230. Genes having comparable positions on homologous chromosomes, each producing a different character.

Allen, 125, 468

Alligators, **412**

All-or-none law, 141, 173. A cell always responds to the full limit of its capacity to any stimulus.

Alternation of generations, 302, 305, **307**, 308. The alternation of an asexual reproductive generation with a gamete-producing generation in the life cycle of an organism.

Alveolus, 101, **118**. The flask-shaped sac of an alveolar gland or one of the tiny pouches in which a bronchiole ends.

Ambergris, 434

Ambystoma, 253

Ameba, 286, **287**

Ameboid movement, 34. Movement by means of pseudopodia.

Amino acid, 22, **23**, 63, 64. Organic acid containing one or more amino groups (NH_2) and one or more carboxyl groups ($COOH$).

Amino groups (NH_2), 22, **23**, 64

Ammonia (NH_3), 64, 118

Amnion, 217, **246**, 405. Fluid-filled sac in which lies the developing embryo of reptiles, birds, and mammals.

Amphibia, 403, **404**. Class of Chordata (frogs, toads, and salamanders).

Amphineura, 387, **388**. Class of Mollusca (*Chiton*).

Amphioxus, 395, **395**

Ampulla, 146, 148. Small, fluid-filled sac.

of water vascular system, 389, **389, 391**

Amylase, 51. Enzyme involved in hydrolysis of starch.

Anabolism, 32. Synthesis of protoplasm.

Analogy, 215, **215**. Similarity of function.

Anaphase, 186, **187**. Stages in mitosis during which the chromosomes move toward opposite ends of the spindle.

Anatomy, 3. Study of the structure of organs and organisms.

Anaximander, 482

Ancon sheep, 247, **247**

Anemia, 84. A condition in which the red corpuscles of the blood are reduced in number or are deficient in hemoglobin.

Animal distribution, 451

Animal pole, 209, **210**. More active pole of the egg.

Annelida, 326, **327, 333, 334**. Phylum of round segmented worms (earthworms, leeches, and others).

Anopheles, 292, 368. Mosquito, the vector of the malarial parasite.

Anosia plexippus, 466

Crew, 254

Crickets, 350, **351**, 371

Crinoidea, **392**, **393**. Class of Echinodermata (sea lilies).

Crocodilia, 412, **412**. Order of Reptilia (crocodiles, alligators, gavials, and caimans).

Cro-Magnon man, **522**, **526**, 527

Crop. Dilation of esophagus in which food is stored.
of bird, 46, **54**, 419
of earthworm, 326, **326**
of honeybee, 345, **346**, **358**

Crossing over, 243, **244**. Exchange of corresponding sections of two homologous chromosomes.

Crustacea, 337. Class of phylum Arthropoda (crabs, crayfish, lobsters, pillbugs, and shrimps).
evolution in, 487

Cryptobranchus, 403. Waterdog.

Crystalloid, 18. A substance which, in solution, diffuses readily through animal membranes, lowers the freezing point of the solvent, and is capable of being crystallized.

Ctenocephalus canis, 366. Dog flea.

Culex, **293**

Cuticle, **327**. Substance secreted by, and covering the exposed surface of, epidermal cells.

Cutis laxa (loose skin), 260

Cuttle bone, 387

Cuvier, 483

Cyclopia, **219**

Cyclops, 325

Cyclosis, 34. Streaming movement of protoplasm within the cell.

Cyclostomata, *see* Agnatha

Cyst, 190, **190**, **293**. Protective envelope formed by the organism.

Cysticerci, 318, **318**. Larvas of certain species of tapeworms.

Cytology, 3. Study of cells.

Cytolysin, 90. Antibody that causes dissolution of cells.

Cytoplasm, 26, **27**. Protoplasm of the cell not included in the nucleus.

Daddy longlegs, 373

Damsel flies, 362

Daphnia, **202**, 302, 340

Dart, 524

Darwin, Charles, 249, 330, 483, **483**

Darwinism, 486, **508**. Explanation of the mechanism of evolution.

Dashiell, 175

Data, 7. Observed and recorded facts.

Davenport, 272

DDT, 371

Deafness, 149

Deamination, 59. Decomposition of amino acids with formation of urea containing the nitrogen.

de Brie, 313

Decay, 117. Decomposition of organisms brought about by the activities of other living organisms such as bacteria and fungi.

Decomposition, 17. The breaking down of compounds into simpler forms.

Deer, 427, 430

Deficiency disease, 67. Abnormal functioning, or structure, or both, caused by a lack of vitamins.

Dementia praecox, 264

Demospongiae, 301. A class of Porifera.

Dendrites, **150**, 157, **158**. Processes of the neuron that conduct impulses toward the cell body.

Dentine, 37

Dermacentor, **377**

Descartes, 128

Development, some factors modifying, 218, **219**

Devonian period, 496. The period of Palezoic time often called "The Age of Fishes."

De Vries, 224, 507, **508**

Dextrose, *see* Glucose

Diabetes, 123, **124**. Disease in which the sugar of the blood is lost in the kidneys and voided with the urine.

Diapheromera, **351**

Diaphragm, 103, **103**. Muscular partition between the abdominal cavity and the thoracic cavity.

Didinium nasutum, 296

Diencephalon, 162

Electron microscope, **30**

Element, 13. A substance made up entirely of one kind of atom.

Elephantiasis, 324, **324.** Disease caused by the roundworm, *Wuchereria.*

Elephants, **427**, 432

Elk, **429**, **430**

Elytra, 350. Horny, non-veined forewings of a beetle.

Embolus, 85. Any foreign or abnormal particle floating in the blood, such as a bubble of air or blood clot.

Embryo. Young organism in its earliest stages of development.

development of, 211

Embryology, 3, 209. Study of the development of the individual from the egg to the adult stage.

Embryonic membranes, 217

Empedocles, 482

Emulsion, 18. A dispersion consisting of small drops of one liquid suspended in another liquid.

Enamel, 37, **37**

Encystment, 190. Process of cyst formation.

Endameba gingivalis, 289

Endameba histolytica, 289

Endocrine glands, 121, **122.** Glands that secrete directly into the blood stream.

Endoderm (entoderm), 209, **210**, **214.** Inner germ layer of animal embryo.

Endolymphatic duct, **146**

Endomixis, 296. In certain protozoans the dissolution of the macronucleus and its reorganization from the micronucleus without intervention of conjugation.

Endoplasm, 286, **287**, **294.** The inner central portion of the cytoplasm in a cell.

Endoskeleton, 168, **169**, 389, **394.** The bony, cartilaginous, or other internal framework of an animal.

Endostyle, 395, 396. An organ of tunicates, situated along the ventral side of the pharynx.

Energy, 15. The capacity for doing work.

kinetic, 16

potential, 16

Enterobius, 324

Entoderm, *see* Endoderm

Entomology, 3. Study of insects.

Environment. Sum total of external and internal factors capable of inducing reactions within the organism.

and heredity, 249, 252

improvement of, 273

Environmental changes, 252, **253**

Enzyme, 47. An organic catalyst elaborated in a living cell whose activity is entirely independent of any of the life processes of the cell.

classification of, 49

naming of, 49

nature of, 49

Eoanthropus (Piltdown man), 521, **522**, **526**

Eocene, **496**, **499.** Earliest period of Tertiary time.

Eohippus, **498**, **499**

Ephemerida, 363, **365.** Order of Insecta (the mayflies).

Epidermis, 301, 302, **303**

Epididymis, **195**, **204.** Elongated mass of convoluted tubules adjacent to the testis.

Epigenesis, 222. The doctrine that the parts of the organism arise from an undifferentiated zygote.

Epiglottis, 101, **102.** Cartilaginous fold that guards the glottis.

Epilepsy, 264. A chronic nervous disease characterized by general motor convulsions and loss of consciousness.

Epinephrin (adrenalin), 128. Hormone produced by the adrenal medulla.

Epitheliomuscular cell, 28, 303

Epithelium, 40. Tissue covering or lining parts of the body.

ciliated, **41**, 42

columnar, **41**

olfactory, 144, **144**

...aeta, 326. Class of phylum An-
...la.

..., 46, **46.** Third chamber in
...e stomach of a cud-chewing animal.

Ommatidium, 153, **154.** A simple eye
of the compound eye.

Omnivorous, 62. Feeding on both
fleshy and herbaceous foods.

Ontogeny, 490. Development of an
individual.

Onychophora, 377, **378.** A class of
Arthropoda, including rather rare
soft-bodied arthropods.

Oöcytes, 227, 228. The cells that after
maturation give rise to the female
gametes.

Oögenesis, 226, **227.** Development of
ova (eggs) from the primordial
germ cells.

Oökinetes, 292. Wormlike forms which
develop from the zygotes occurring in the life cycle of the malarial parasite, *Plasmodium.*

Operculum, **398**

Ophiuroidea, 391, **392.** A class of phylum Echinodermata (brittle stars).

Opisthorchis (Clonorchis), 313, **314**

Opossum, 426, **466**

Opsonins, 90. Antibodies which increase consumption of bacteria by
white blood cells.

Optic cup, 213. Stage in the embryonic development of the eye.

Optic lobe, **162.** Evagination from the
embryonic brain: forerunner of the
eye.

Optic nerve, **151,** 152, **154, 214**

Optic stalk, 213, **214, 215**

Optic vesicle, 213, **214**

Oral arms, 307, **308**

Oral groove, **294,** 295

Orangutan, 433, 526

Order, **280,** 281. Subdivision of class.
. Taxonomic group ranking between
class and family.

Ordovician period, 496. Geologic
period following the Cambrian
and preceding the Silurian.

Organ, 29, 40. A structural unit in
which the tissues are organized
(coordinated) in the performance
of some specific function.

Organ of Corti, 148, 149. Sensitive
hair cells on the basilar membrane
which are connected with the
brain through the auditory nerve.

Organelles, 295. Small non-cellular
organlike structures.

Organic matter, 476

Organism, 1

Organismal theory, 30

Organizers, 218

Organs, building of, 212
of equilibrium, 143, 145, **146**

Oriental sore, 291, 367

Origin of life, 477

Origin of Species, 485

Oroya fever, 367

Orthoptera, 350, **351.** Order of Insecta (roaches, grasshoppers, katydids, walking sticks, and others).

Oscinidae, 367. The eye flies.

Osculum, 296, **297.** Opening of the
spongocoel of a sponge.

Osmosis, 54, **55, 56.** Passage of a substance in solution through a differentially permeable membrane.

Osmotic pressure, 54, **55**

Osteichthyes, 400. Fish possessing a
skeleton of bone.

Osteoblasts, 42. Bone-forming cells.

Ostium (pl. ostia), 87, **88, 310, 338,
374.** Any opening or entrance,
e.g., the openings that admit blood
into the heart of some invertebrate
animals such as the crayfish and
grasshopper.

Ostrich, 422

Otoliths, **146.** Concretions found in
otocysts.

Otosclerosis, 261

Otters, 428

Oval window, 149

Ovariotomy (ovariectomy) 133, 271.
Removal of the ovary or ovaries.

Ovary, 193, 195, 196, **205.** A female
reproductive organ.